Addison Wesley

Science& Technology

Authors

Kyn Barker
York Region District School Board,
Ontario

Steve Campbell
Richmond School Board,
British Columbia

Gary Greenland
Toronto District School Board,
Ontario

Douglas Hayhoe
Toronto District School Board,
Ontario

Doug Herridge
Faculty of Education,
York University, Ontario
York Region District School Board,
Ontario

Kathy Kubota-Zarivnij
Faculty of Education,
York University, Ontario
Toronto Catholic District School Board,
Ontario

Shelagh Reading
Calgary Board of Education,
Alberta

Lionel Sandner
Saanich School Board,
British Columbia

Beverley Williams
Annapolis Valley Regional
School Board, Nova Scotia

Addison
Wesley

Toronto

Managing Editor
Cecilia Chan

Project Coordinator
Jeff Siamon

Editors and Writers
Jonathan Bocknek
Julie Czerneda
Jackie Dulson
John Yip-Chuck

Production Editors
Laurel Bishop
Jane Clark
Ellen Davidson

Indexer
Dominic Ho

Research Manager
Louise MacKenzie

Researchers
Christie Hayhoe
Paulee Kestin
Keith Lennox

Design
Word & Image Design Inc.

Classroom Consultant
Lynn Short, Toronto District School Board

Acknowledgment
Addison Wesley Longman and the authors of *Addison Wesley Science & Technology Grade 8* would like to thank the teachers and consultants who reviewed and field-tested this material.

Copyright © 2000 Pearson Education Canada Inc., Toronto, Ontario

ISBN 0-201-61396-4

This book contains recycled product and is acid-free. Printed and bound in Canada.

123456 – TCP – 05 04 03 02 01 00

CONTENTS

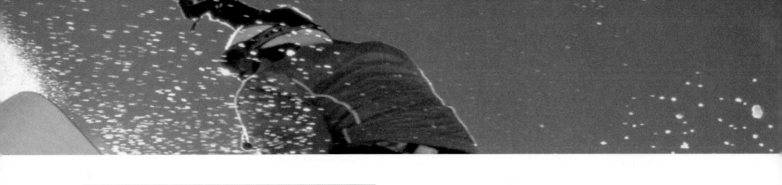

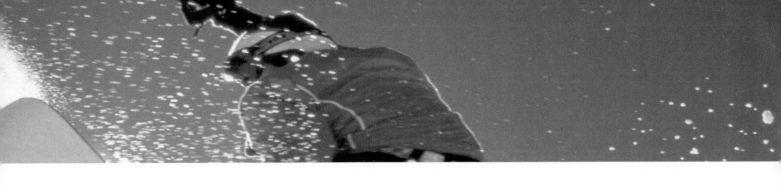

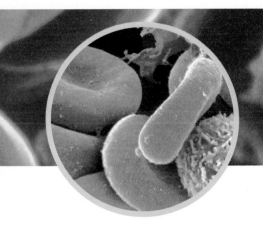

Introduction

Welcome to *Addison Wesley Science & Technology!*

You are about to begin a journey exploring Cells and Cell Systems, Fluids, Optics, Mechanical Efficiency, and Water Systems.

You'll be investigating the natural phenomena of the world around you and technological responses of our society to this world. As you do so, we help you by

- building on your own experience of scientific phenomena,
- providing you with examples of scientific achievement that people like yourself have undertaken, and
- providing you with different types of activities that suit different types of thinkers.

A Look at a Chapter of *Addison Wesley Science & Technology*

1 CHAPTER INTRODUCTION

This section of the page provides a quick overview of what you'll be doing.

The list of Big Ideas provides a road map to the learning of the chapter. The number beside the Big Idea identifies a section of the chapter, so you can use this framework to help you connect the knowledge and skills in each chapter.

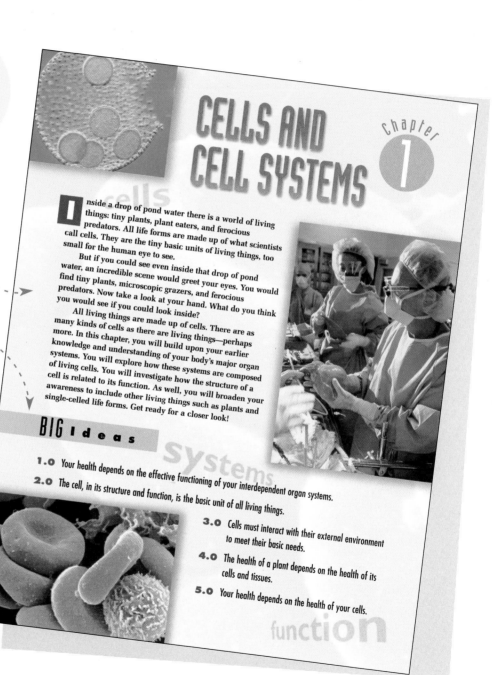

CELLS AND CELL SYSTEMS

Chapter 1

Inside a drop of pond water there is a world of living things: tiny plants, plant eaters, and ferocious predators. All life forms are made up of what scientists call cells. They are the tiny basic units of living things, too small for the human eye to see.

But if you could see even inside that drop of pond water, an incredible scene would greet your eyes. You would find tiny plants, microscopic grazers, and ferocious predators. Now take a look at your hand. What do you think you would see if you could look inside?

All living things are made up of cells. There are as many kinds of cells as there are living things—perhaps more. In this chapter, you will build upon your earlier knowledge and understanding of your body's major organ systems. You will explore how these systems are composed of living cells. You will investigate how the structure of a cell is related to its function. As well, you will broaden your awareness to include other living things such as plants and single-celled life forms. Get ready for a closer look!

BIG ideas

1.0 Your health depends on the effective functioning of your interdependent organ systems.

2.0 The cell, in its structure and function, is the basic unit of all living things.

3.0 Cells must interact with their external environment to meet their basic needs.

4.0 The health of a plant depends on the health of its cells and tissues.

5.0 Your health depends on the health of your cells.

2 INVITATION TO EXPLORE

A real-world example about the topic of the chapter will allow you to

- draw on what you already know about the topic,
- share your ideas about the topic with others,
- think about some of the implications of the topic for our society,
- ask questions before you begin the chapter of study.

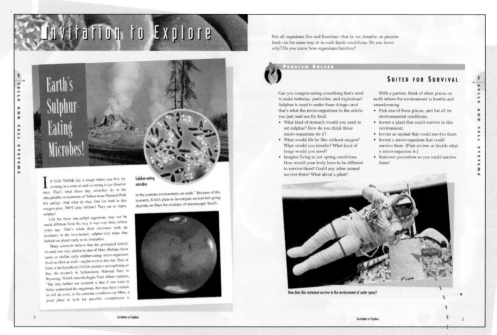

A short activity will require you to solve a particular problem and think about what you already know about similar situations.

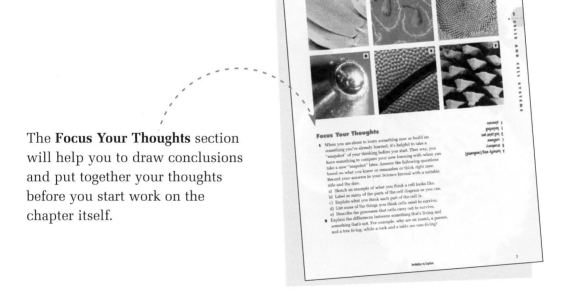

The **Focus Your Thoughts** section will help you to draw conclusions and put together your thoughts before you start work on the chapter itself.

3 CHAPTER SECTIONS

Each section has a **Big Idea** as a heading. This Big Idea is a key concept that you should remember when the chapter is done.

Each Big Idea section is broken down into smaller sections. Each small section explains an aspect of the Big Idea.

When you see the **Explore** icon, you'll be asked to draw upon what you already know before you begin the content of the small section.

When you see the **Develop** icon, you know that you will find activities that investigate a part of the Big Idea in depth.

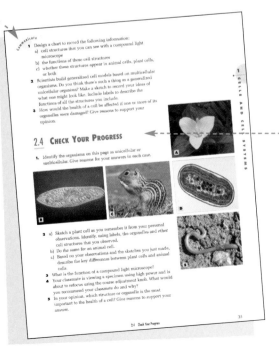

At the end of every small section, you'll see a **Communicate** icon, and know that you have a chance to test your understanding of the section and further develop your thinking.

At the end of each Big Idea section, you can check your understanding of the Big Idea.

Critical-thinking activities in *Addison Wesley Science & Technology* are of three kinds.

4 ACTIVITIES

An **Investigator** activity provides a chance for you to work in a lab setting to develop the scientific skills of observing, measuring, experimenting, and much more. Investigators encourage you to explore the material phenomena found in our world.

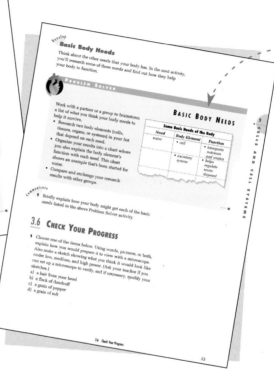

Problem Solver activities are open-ended activities with very little set-up. There is no one correct solution. With Problem Solvers, you need to be creative in your thinking.

Decision Maker activities present issues or questions related to your life. You may need to develop an opinion based on the evidence and make a decision. When you present your decision to your teacher and classmates, you may have to be persuasive.

5 PROJECT AND CHAPTER REVIEW

The **Project** at the end of each chapter presents a hands-on opportunity for you to demonstrate what you've learned. You'll work both in groups and individually. The Project requires you to apply the skills and knowledge that you've acquired to a new situation.

The **Chapter Review** presents

• a review of key terms

• questions designed to test your understanding of the concepts contained in the Big Ideas

• a chance to apply the Big Ideas to a variety of situations

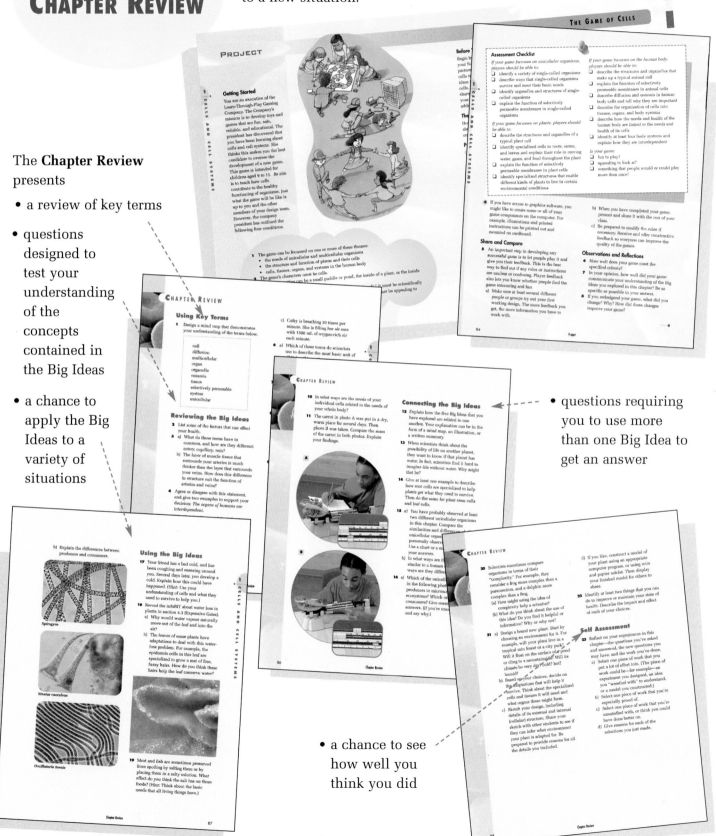

• questions requiring you to use more than one Big Idea to get an answer

• a chance to see how well you think you did

6 OTHER FEATURES

Experiment on Your Own

This is your chance to design your own experiment to check out a hypothesis or to solve a problem.

Science World

In this feature, there's an example of a real-world situation or application of the topics you're studying.

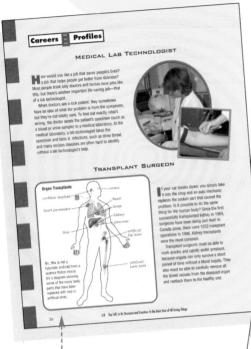

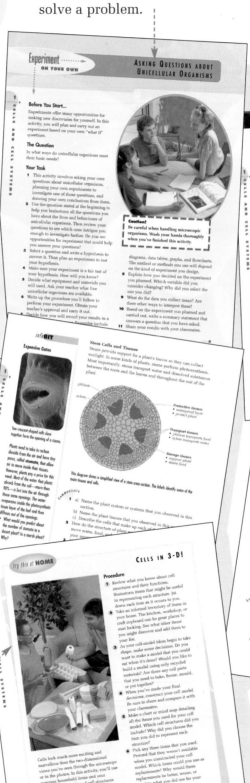

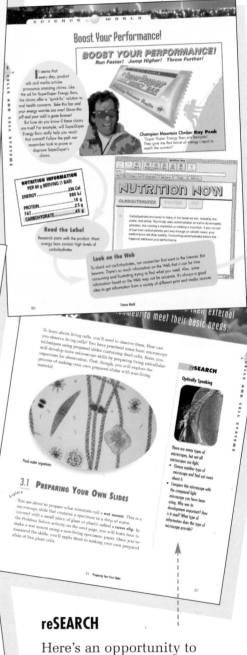

Careers and Profiles

Here you'll find profiles and interviews with people whose careers draw on the science and technology of the chapter.

infoBIT

A quick tidbit of information adds to your knowledge of the concepts of the chapter.

try this at HOME

This is an activity you can do at home on your own.

reSEARCH

Here's an opportunity to extend your thinking by investigating a particular concept.

The Big Ideas of Science and Technology

There is much to learn in the science and technology you are studying this year. The Big Ideas that organize each chapter can be used to help you develop your understanding of science and technology.

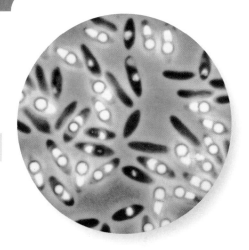

Cells and Cell Systems: Chapter 1   1

1.0   Your health depends on the effective functioning of your interdependent organ systems.

2.0   The cell, in its structure and function, is the basic unit of all living things.

3.0   Cells must interact with their external environment to meet their basic needs.

4.0   The health of a plant depends on the health of its cells and tissues.

5.0   Your health depends on the health of your cells.

Fluids: Chapter 2   89

1.0   All fluids demonstrate the property of viscosity, or the internal friction that causes a fluid to resist flowing.

2.0   Density is another important property of fluids.

3.0   Fluids exert a buoyant force on objects that allows some objects to float.

4.0   Understanding the properties of fluids helps in designing and building useful devices.

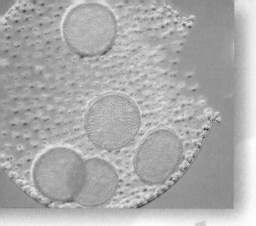

CELLS AND CELL SYSTEMS

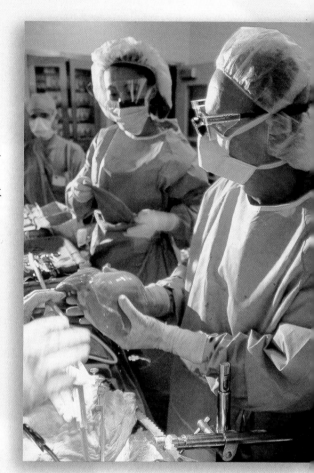

I nside a drop of pond water there is a world of living things: tiny plants, plant eaters, and ferocious predators. All life forms are made up of what scientists call cells. They are the tiny basic units of living things, too small for the human eye to see.

But if you could see even inside that drop of pond water, an incredible scene would greet your eyes. You would find tiny plants, microscopic grazers, and ferocious predators. Now take a look at your hand. What do you think you would see if you could look inside?

All living things are made up of cells. There are as many kinds of cells as there are living things—perhaps more. In this chapter, you will build upon your earlier knowledge and understanding of your body's major organ systems. You will explore how these systems are composed of living cells. You will investigate how the structure of a cell is related to its function. As well, you will broaden your awareness to include other living things such as plants and single-celled life forms. Get ready for a closer look!

BIG Ideas

1.0 Your health depends on the effective functioning of your interdependent organ systems.

2.0 The cell, in its structure and function, is the basic unit of all living things.

3.0 Cells must interact with their external environment to meet their basic needs.

4.0 The health of a plant depends on the health of its cells and tissues.

5.0 Your health depends on the health of your cells.

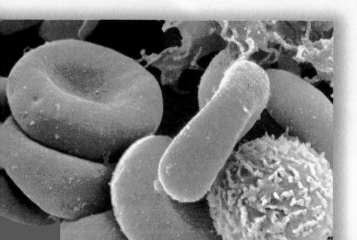

Earth's Sulphur-Eating Microbes!

Sulphur-eating microbes

I F YOU THINK life is tough where you live, try existing in a soup of acid so strong it can dissolve steel. That's what these tiny microbes do in the inhospitable environment of Yellowstone National Park hot springs. And what do they find for food in this oxygen-poor, 300°C-plus inferno? They eat or ingest sulphur!

Life for these one-celled organisms may not be much different from the way it was over three billion years ago. That's when their ancestors took up residence in the lava-heated, sulphur-rich water that bathed our planet early in its formation.

Many scientists believe that the geological history of earth was very similar to that of Mars. Perhaps these same, or similar, early sulphur-eating micro-organisms lived on Mars as well—maybe even to this day. That, at least, is the hypothesis NASA scientists are exploring as they do research in Yellowstone National Park in Wyoming. NASA microbiologist Fred Albert explains, "The idea behind our research is that if you want to better understand the organisms that may have existed, or still do exist, in the extreme conditions on Mars, a good place to look for possible comparisons is in the extreme environments on earth." Because of this research, NASA plans to investigate ancient hot spring deposits on Mars for evidence of microscopic fossils.

Not all organisms live and function—that is, eat, breathe, or process food—in the same way or in such harsh conditions. Do you know why? Do you know how organisms function?

SUITED FOR SURVIVAL

Can you imagine eating something that's used to make batteries, pesticides, and explosives? Sulphur is used to make these things—and that's what the micro-organisms in the article you just read use for food.

- What kind of stomach would you need to eat sulphur? How do you think those micro-organisms do it?
- What would life be like without oxygen? What would you breathe? What kind of lungs would you need?
- Imagine living in hot spring conditions. How would your body have to be different to survive there? Could any other animal survive there? What about a plant?

With a partner, think of other places on earth where the environment is hostile and unwelcoming.

- Pick one of these places, and list all its environmental conditions.
- Invent a plant that could survive in this environment.
- Invent an animal that could survive there.
- Invent a micro-organism that could survive there. (First review or decide what a micro-organism is.)
- Reinvent yourselves so *you* could survive there!

How does this astronaut survive in the environment of outer space?

Surviving in an Invisible World

But just what is a "microbe" or "micro-organism"? Where do they exist other than deep inside the Yellowstone hot springs? Do you have micro-organisms inside you? Have you ever seen one of these one-celled creatures?

In order to answer these questions, you will have to be able to look at objects that are invisible to the human eye. And how do you do that? You would use what's commonly called a microscope (*micro* means "very small," and *scope* means "an instrument for viewing"). A microscope magnifies objects—it makes them appear bigger. (They are *not* really bigger!) That's what the NASA scientists will use to look at the sulphur-eating microbes.

Actually, magnifying devices have been known since ancient times, but they became more widely available in the early 1600s. People were amazed with this new technology. It opened up a whole new world of wonder. They used it to observe all kinds of things—feathers, grains of sand, cork, plant parts, and even fossils. The body parts of insects were especially popular. See if you can identify the items shown in the photos on the next page. How are these views different from the views that are more familiar to you? What can you learn about these items that's different from your usual experiences of them?

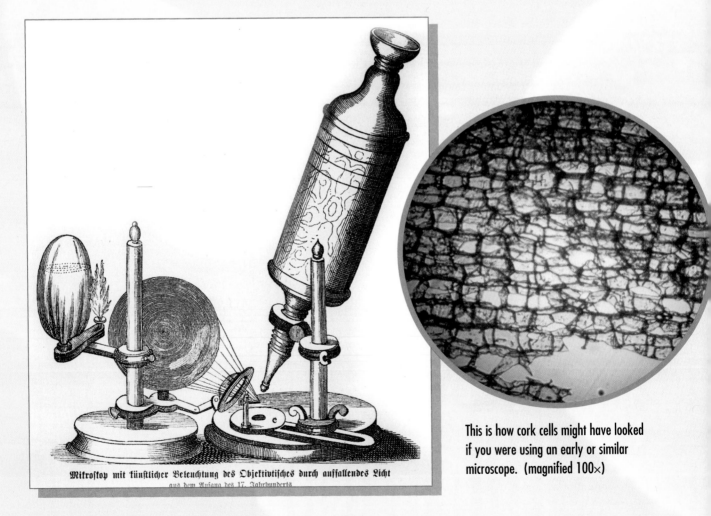

Mikroſkop mit künſtlicher Beleuchtung des Objektivtiſches durch auffallendes Licht
aus dem Anfang des 17. Jahrhunderts.

This is how cork cells might have looked if you were using an early or similar microscope. (magnified 100×)

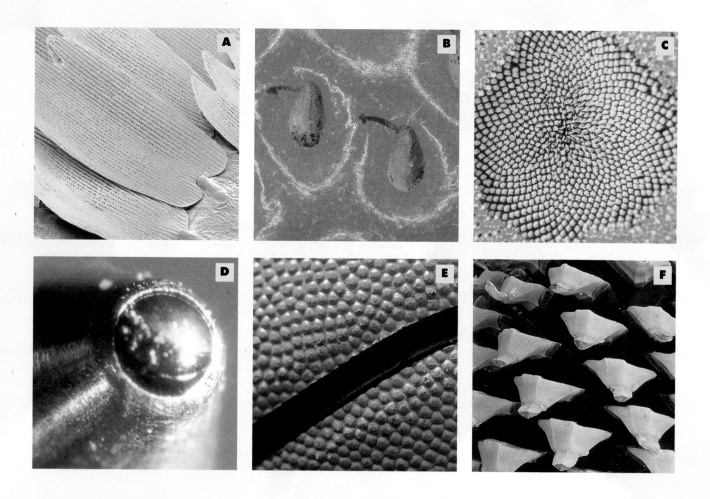

F pinecone
E basketball
D ball point pen
C sunflower
B strawberry
A butterfly wing (swallowtail)

Focus Your Thoughts

1 When you are about to learn something new or build on something you've already learned, it's helpful to take a "snapshot" of your thinking before you start. That way, you have something to compare your new learning with when you take a new "snapshot" later. Answer the following questions based on what you know or remember or think *right now*. Record your answers in your Science Journal with a suitable title and the date.

a) Sketch an example of what you think a cell looks like.

b) Label as many of the parts of the cell diagram as you can.

c) Explain what you think each part of the cell is.

d) List some of the things you think cells need to survive.

e) Describe the processes that cells carry out to survive.

2 Explain the differences between something that's living and something that's not. For example, why are an insect, a person, and a tree living, while a rock and a table are non-living?

BIG IDEA

1.0

Your health depends on the effective functioning of your interdependent organ systems.

1 CELLS AND CELL SYSTEMS

Do you think these people are experiencing stress?

If you have ever experienced any kind of stress, you would know from your natural response to it that your organ systems work together as a whole. In other words, your organ systems are interdependent. For example, one of the immediate effects of stress is your muscles become tense. This can trigger the heart, part of your circulatory system, to beat faster, so it pumps blood more quickly to the surface of the skin. As a result, you feel warmer or even flushed. Tense muscles over a period of time can also lead to aches, pains, and exhaustion.

In recent years, scientists have collected much experimental evidence that stress affects your health in many ways. Some forms of stress, such as doing something exciting or trying out a new game, can be fun and thrilling. This stress can help prepare your body to perform at its best. Other forms of stress can be unpleasant, such as being nervous in new surroundings or situations. Stress can cause nausea, stomach pain, or make you sick.

1.1 A Look Inside

Explore

How do you feel when you're tense? What about when you're relaxed? What is the effect on you and your body when you feel these ways? Try the exercises on the next page to find out.

Are these people experiencing stress?

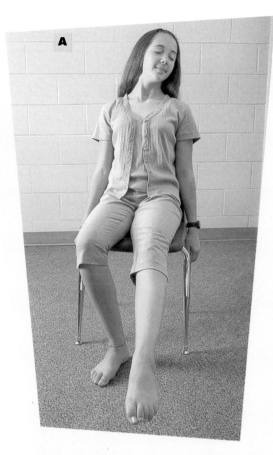

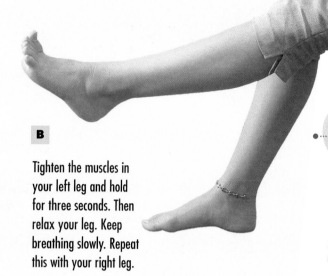

A

Sit so that you feel comfortable. Close your eyes and breathe slowly and rhythmically. Focus your attention on the sound of your breathing. Now, curl the toes of your left foot as tightly as you can. Hold for three seconds, then slowly let them relax. Slowly draw your foot upward, hold for three seconds, and then let it down to the floor again. Keep breathing slowly. Now repeat this with your right foot.

B

Tighten the muscles in your left leg and hold for three seconds. Then relax your leg. Keep breathing slowly. Repeat this with your right leg.

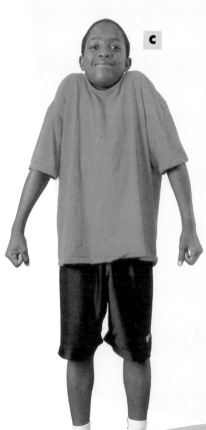

C

Push your belly out as far as you can, and hold for three seconds. Pull it in as far as you can, hold for three seconds, then relax. Take slow, rhythmical breaths. Pull your shoulders up toward your ears as if you were shrugging. Hold for three seconds, then relax. Keep breathing slowly.

D

Clench your left hand in a tight fist, hold for three seconds, then relax. Stretch your fingers apart as far as you can, hold for three seconds, then relax. Repeat with your right hand.

E

Push your lips out and squeeze your eyes shut as tightly as you can. Hold for three seconds, then relax. Open your eyes and mouth as wide as you can—as if you were screaming silently. Hold for three seconds, then relax.

Remain still and relaxed for a few more minutes. Focus on the sound of your breathing. See if you can feel more relaxed than you feel right now.

Develop

How Your Body Is Organized

Many parts of your body were involved in the exercise you just did. These include your skin, your bones, your heart, your lungs, your mouth, and your stomach. What other examples can you think of? None of these body parts functions on its own. Each part is an **organ**, which forms part of a body system. The organs that make up each **organ system** work together to perform a certain task or *function*. For example, the organs of your digestive system work together to break down food to supply your body with the energy and nutrients you need to survive. The following charts describe some of your body's organ systems.

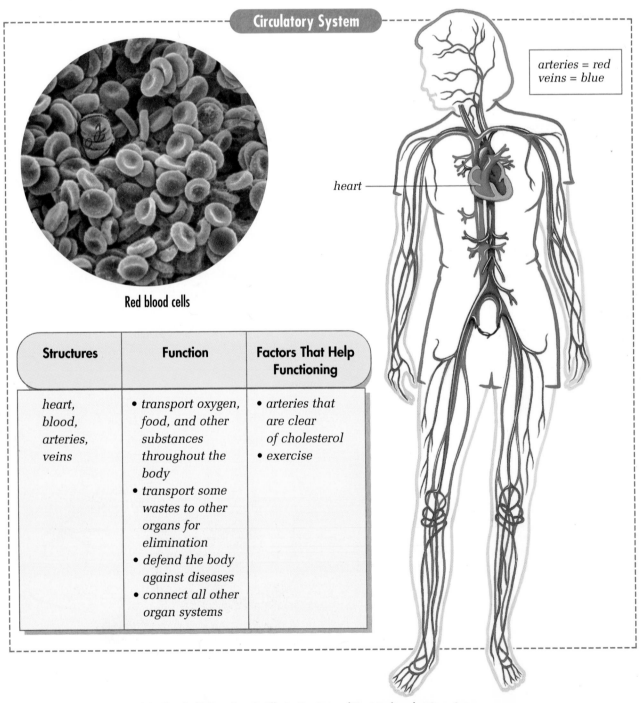

Circulatory System

arteries = red
veins = blue

heart

Red blood cells

Structures	Function	Factors That Help Functioning
heart, blood, arteries, veins	• transport oxygen, food, and other substances throughout the body • transport some wastes to other organs for elimination • defend the body against diseases • connect all other organ systems	• arteries that are clear of cholesterol • exercise

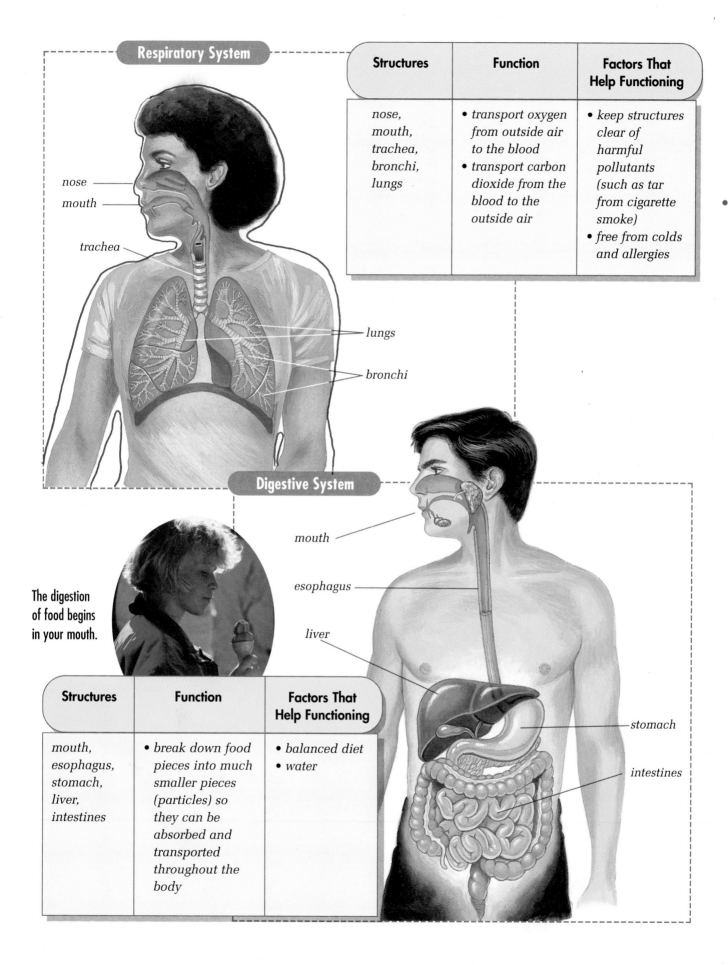

Respiratory System

nose

mouth

trachea

lungs

bronchi

Structures	Function	Factors That Help Functioning
nose, mouth, trachea, bronchi, lungs	• transport oxygen from outside air to the blood • transport carbon dioxide from the blood to the outside air	• keep structures clear of harmful pollutants (such as tar from cigarette smoke) • free from colds and allergies

Digestive System

mouth

esophagus

liver

stomach

intestines

The digestion of food begins in your mouth.

Structures	Function	Factors That Help Functioning
mouth, esophagus, stomach, liver, intestines	• break down food pieces into much smaller pieces (particles) so they can be absorbed and transported throughout the body	• balanced diet • water

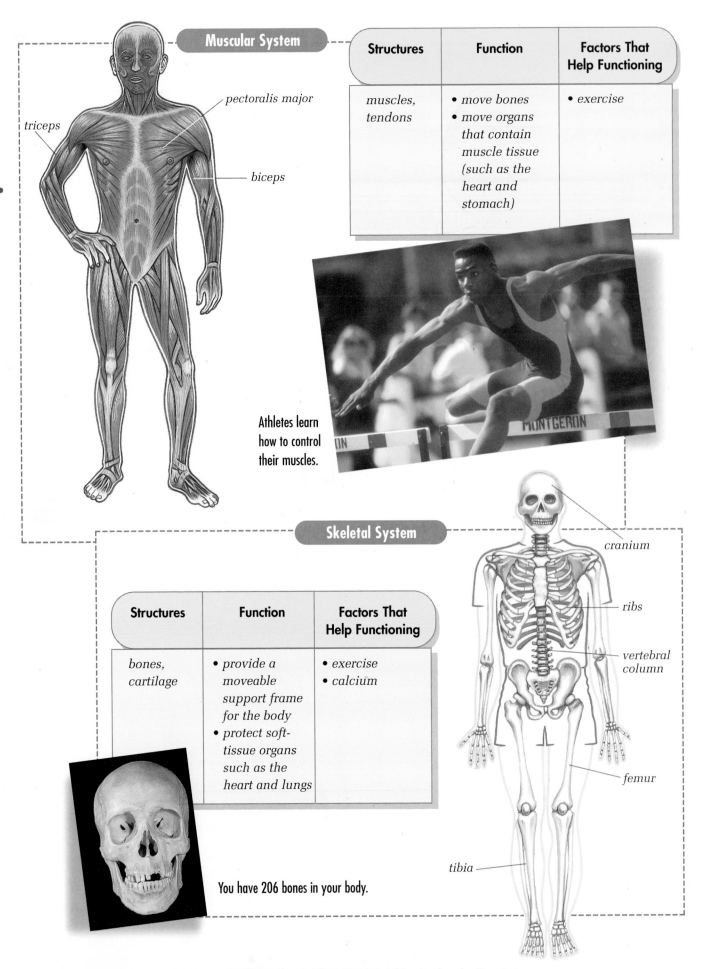

Muscular System

Structures	Function	Factors That Help Functioning
muscles, tendons	• move bones • move organs that contain muscle tissue (such as the heart and stomach)	• exercise

pectoralis major

triceps

biceps

Athletes learn how to control their muscles.

Skeletal System

Structures	Function	Factors That Help Functioning
bones, cartilage	• provide a moveable support frame for the body • protect soft-tissue organs such as the heart and lungs	• exercise • calcium

cranium

ribs

vertebral column

femur

tibia

You have 206 bones in your body.

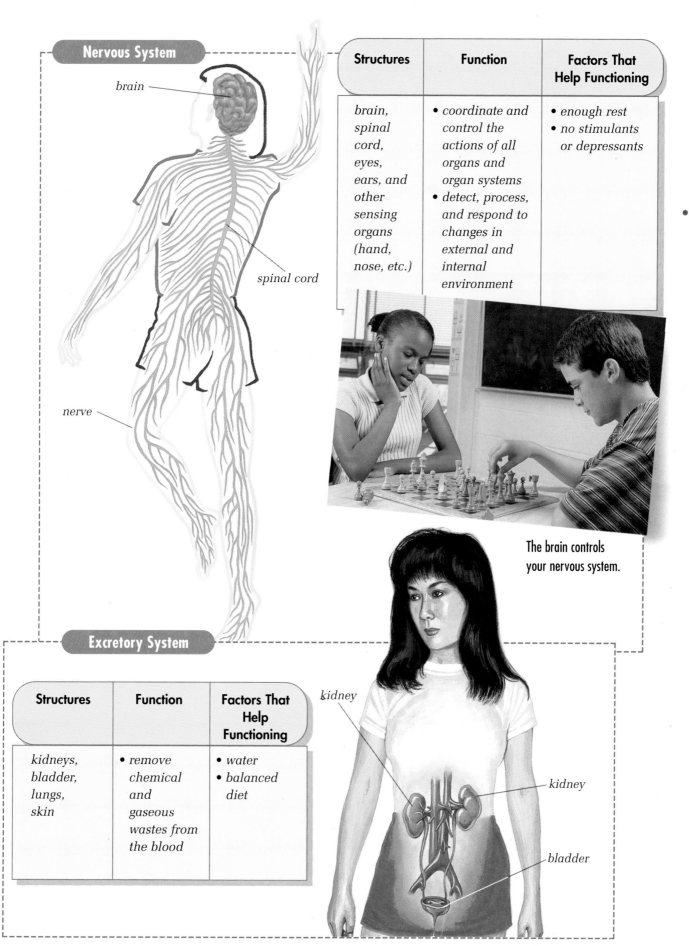

Nervous System

brain

spinal cord

nerve

Structures	Function	Factors That Help Functioning
brain, spinal cord, eyes, ears, and other sensing organs (hand, nose, etc.)	• coordinate and control the actions of all organs and organ systems • detect, process, and respond to changes in external and internal environment	• enough rest • no stimulants or depressants

The brain controls your nervous system.

Excretory System

Structures	Function	Factors That Help Functioning
kidneys, bladder, lungs, skin	• remove chemical and gaseous wastes from the blood	• water • balanced diet

kidney

kidney

bladder

Integumentary System

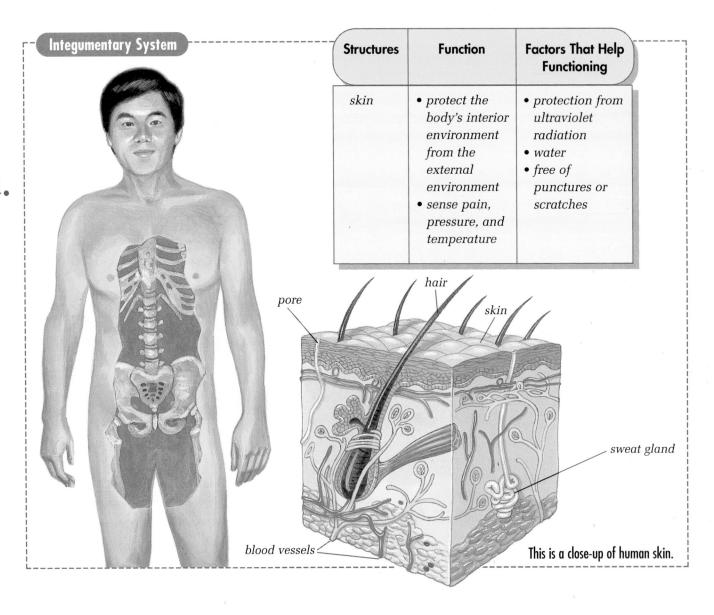

Structures	Function	Factors That Help Functioning
skin	• protect the body's interior environment from the external environment • sense pain, pressure, and temperature	• protection from ultraviolet radiation • water • free of punctures or scratches

pore

hair

skin

sweat gland

blood vessels

This is a close-up of human skin.

*info*BIT

Soaking Up the Rays

The sun's ultraviolet light can harm your skin. For many of the people on this beach, a brown substance in the skin, called **melanin**, helps block out some of these rays. Sunlight causes the skin to produce more melanin. That's why you tan if you stay out in the sun.

So why wear sun block if the melanin protects you? Many people's skin won't produce enough melanin when they are out in sunlight. Their skin burns instead of developing a tan. Also, even if melanin is easily produced, repeated exposure to the sun's ultraviolet rays over a long period of time greatly increases the chance of skin cancer. This is especially true for children. One bad sunburn could cause skin problems later in life.

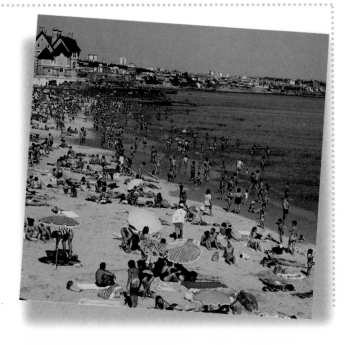

Working Together for Health

Your body's organ systems work together as a single unit for a common purpose: to support and maintain your life. This idea of working together as a unified, purposeful unit goes even deeper than systems. Each of your body's systems contains organs. The organs that make up each system work together as a single unit, too. Their common purpose is to support and maintain the healthy functioning of the system of which they are a part.

Each organ is made up of a group of **tissues** that work together. For example, your heart is made up of connecting tissue (to hold its shape together), muscle tissue (to help it to move), and nerve tissue (to coordinate its movement). Different organs are composed of different kinds of tissues. It all depends on the role (or function) that the organ serves.

Each of your tissues is made up of a group of smaller units that also work together, called cells. **Cells** are the smallest known functioning units of life. That's why scientists say that the cell is the most fundamental or basic unit of all living things.

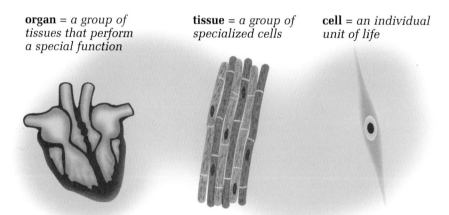

organ = *a group of tissues that perform a special function*

tissue = *a group of specialized cells*

cell = *an individual unit of life*

Body systems are made up of these three types of structures.

Communicate

1 a) Which of your organ systems were you aware of during the stress-relieving exercises you did at the beginning of this section?

   b) Which of your organ systems do you think were actually involved during the exercise? Provide details to support your answer.

2 Show your understanding of the relationship among these terms: *system, organ, tissue,* and *cell.* Use words, diagrams, flowcharts, or a combination of these to communicate your ideas.

3 Re-examine the organ system diagrams on previous pages.
   a) Does any one system seem to be more important than any of the others? Explain your answer.
   b) Do you think you could stay healthy if any of these systems were damaged, diseased, or missing? Why or why not?
   c) For one of the systems, suggest another factor that might affect how it functions.
   d) What does the title "Working Together for Health" mean to you?

1.2 CLOSE-UP ON THE CIRCULATORY SYSTEM

The circulatory system, like this highway interchange, is your body's transportation network.

Explore

Following are some early ideas about the circulatory system and its main organ, the heart. Today, after about 350 years of investigation, we know that only one of these early ideas is accurate. One is partially accurate. The rest have been shown to be incorrect. Do you know, or can you figure out, which is which?

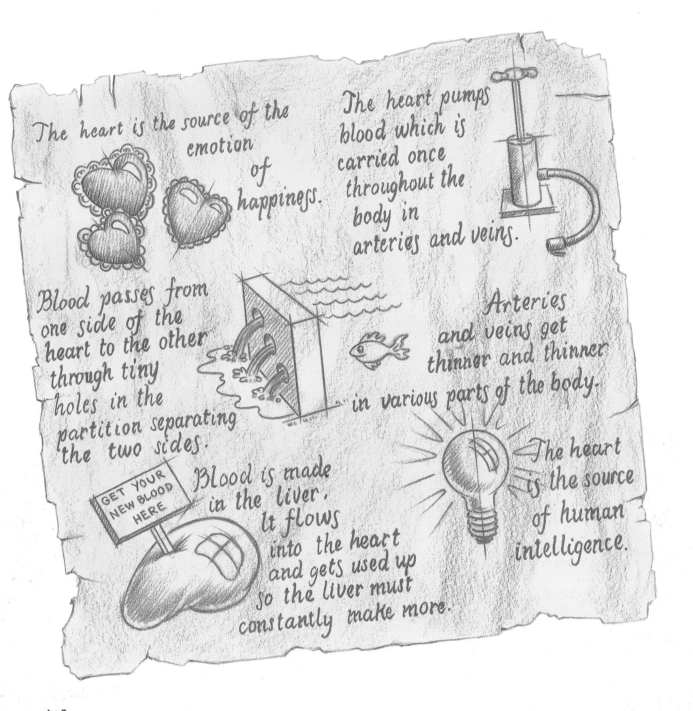

The heart is the source of the emotion of happiness.

The heart pumps blood which is carried once throughout the body in arteries and veins.

Blood passes from one side of the heart to the other through tiny holes in the partition separating the two sides.

Arteries and veins get thinner and thinner in various parts of the body.

GET YOUR NEW BLOOD HERE

Blood is made in the liver. It flows into the heart and gets used up so the liver must constantly make more.

The heart is the source of human intelligence.

Develop

Moving Things Around

You began life as a single cell. Nine months later, you had become about two trillion cells. By the time you stop growing, you will be made up of over 100 trillion cells!

Just like the living things in a pond ecosystem, each of your cells needs energy, oxygen, and nutrient particles to carry out its own life functions—and, therefore, your life functions. Unlike the living things in a pond, your cells are unable to obtain what they need by themselves. They rely on your body's transportation network, the circulatory system, to bring what they need and to remove wastes.

An engine powers this racing car. Does it serve the same function as your heart?

The "engine" of your circulatory system is the **heart**. This fist-sized organ has a mass of only about 300 g. However, what it lacks in size and mass it makes up for in function. Your heart must pump (expand and contract) an average of 70 times each minute for your entire life. It must exert enough pressure to push blood throughout your whole body continually. Fortunately, your heart is able to do this without rest and without your even thinking about it.

What is the effect of the pressure your heart exerts? The Problem Solver activity below can help you find out.

PROBLEM SOLVER

MODEL OF YOUR BEATING HEART

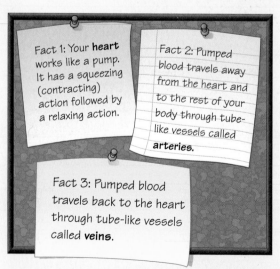

Fact 1: Your **heart** works like a pump. It has a squeezing (contracting) action followed by a relaxing action.

Fact 2: Pumped blood travels away from the heart and to the rest of your body through tube-like vessels called **arteries**.

Fact 3: Pumped blood travels back to the heart through tube-like vessels called **veins**.

Use these facts to design a model of your heart. Your model must help you appreciate the function of your heart, and the structure and function of the arteries and veins.

Here are some thoughts to help guide your design strategy.

• Your model doesn't have to be realistic, unless you want it to be. In other words, you don't have to use or make something that looks like a human heart.

• Brainstorm objects or devices you can use to represent the heart. Which might be

continued on next page ⸺▶

more important here: the object or device you use, or the action it simulates?

• Brainstorm objects or devices you can use to represent the arteries and veins. To help you choose, think about the role these blood vessels play.

Make your model and test it to find answers to the following questions. Write your answers in your Science Journal.

1 Compare the force with which blood moves when it first leaves the heart with the force it has when it's farther from the heart. Is it stronger, weaker, or the same?

2 Which do you think is thicker: an artery or a vein? Why might this be?

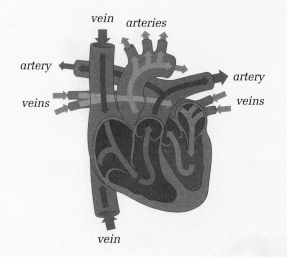

3 Some people develop fatty deposits of a substance called **cholesterol** in their arteries. These deposits make the diameter of the arteries smaller. How might this affect the circulatory system? How did you use your model to test this effect?

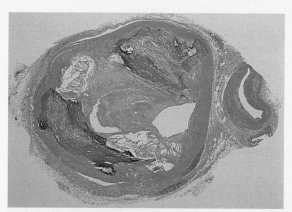

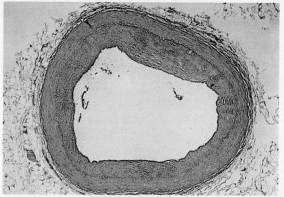

Which artery is clogged with cholesterol?

reSEARCH

If you lined up all the blood vessels in your body, end to end, they would form a tube more than 100 000 km long!

• Use library and Internet resources to find out more about how the circulatory system in your body works.

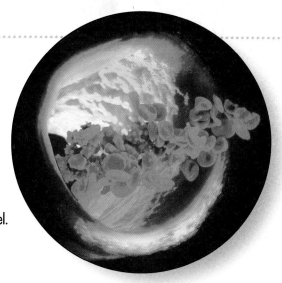

This is a cross-section of a blood vessel. Where are the blood cells?

1 a) Which blood vessels carry blood away from the heart?

   b) Which blood vessels carry blood to the heart?

   c) There are no visible structures joining these two kinds of blood vessels. How do you think blood gets from one to the other?

2 How might having narrower blood vessels affect the efficient functioning of the circulatory system? Explain your answer.

3 The heart is actually a double pump. One part pumps blood to the lungs, while the other part pumps blood to the rest of the body. One of these parts is larger and stronger than the other. Which would it be, and why?

4 Your heart must exert enough pressure to push blood throughout your entire body. How did your model exert pressure? How similar was this to the way your heart exerts pressure?

5 Assume that your heart beats at an average rate of 70 times per minute. How many times will your heart beat from the day you were born until the day you celebrate your next birthday?

1.3 THE INTERDEPENDENCE OF YOUR ORGAN SYSTEMS

Explore

A doctor can tell a great deal about your overall health by examining the functioning of your circulatory system. Why do you think this is so? What types of information about your digestive system could your blood provide? What types of information about your respiratory system?

Develop

Organ Systems Work Together

Your body's organ systems depend on one another. In other words, they are **interdependent**. This means they work together as a single unit to carry out all the functions that are vital to your survival.

The circulatory system provides an excellent example of the interdependence of organ systems. As you know, its function is to transport substances throughout the body, including water, nutrients (such as fats, sugars, proteins, vitamins, and minerals), and gases (such as oxygen and carbon dioxide). All of these are carried in blood.

Your circulatory system gets these substances from your other organ systems. For example, your digestive system provides the nutrients in a form your blood can transport easily. Your respiratory system brings in oxygen from the air outside your body, which is carried by your blood. At the same time, your respiratory system removes the carbon dioxide from your blood and releases it to the air.

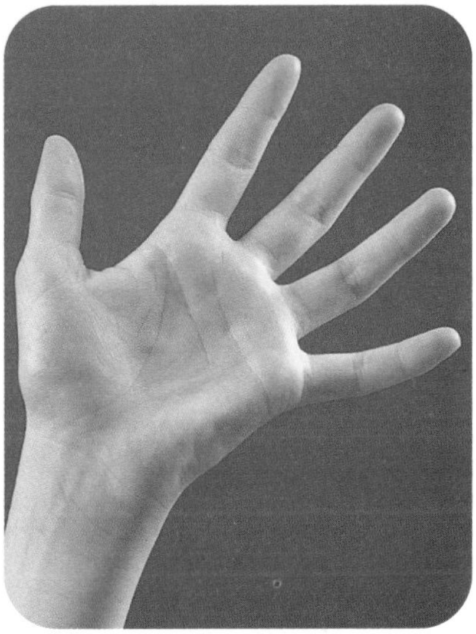

Take a moment to look at your hand. What a marvel it is! Think of what it can do, and what it helps you to experience. Consider also the organ systems of which your hand is a part. Which ones are obvious? Which other systems might be involved also? In your Science Journal, take some time to reflect on your remarkable hand.

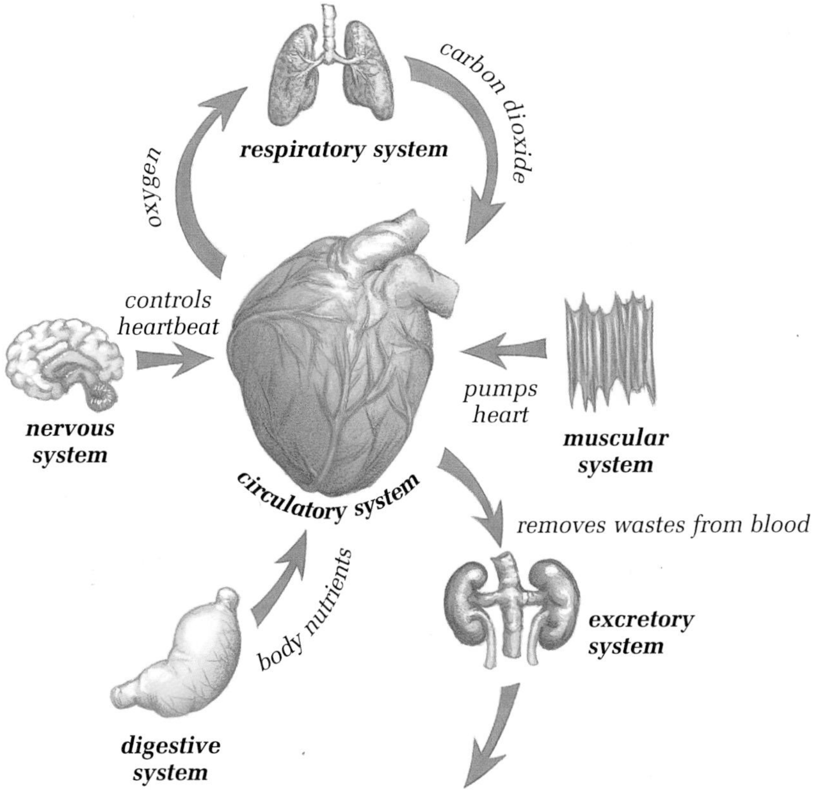

It follows that the digestive and respiratory systems depend on your circulatory system, too. Recall that all of your organs are made up of tissues, which are themselves made up of cells. Every cell needs nutrients and oxygen in order to function. Your body's cells cannot get these substances on their own. They depend on the circulatory system to provide them with what they need.

1 What does the word "interdependence" mean?

2 Everything you do depends on your organ systems. For example, eating involves the muscular system (throat muscles in swallowing), digestive system (food gets digested sending nutrients into the bloodstream), and excretory system (wastes leave the body).

   a) Draw a concept map to show how these systems are interdependent.

   b) Label the chains or connections. (For example, how are muscles involved? How are the excretory and respiratory systems involved?)

3 How many other examples of the interdependence of body systems can you think of? Make a list, and compare it with others in your class.

1.4 CHECK YOUR PROGRESS

1 Cheryl's heart beats an average of 74 times per minute when she is at rest. When she takes a jog around the neighbourhood, her heart beats faster. When she stops, her heart eventually returns to the resting rate of 74 times per minute.

   a) What reasons can you think of to explain these changes in heart rate (the number of times her heart beats in a certain amount of time)?

   b) In this example, what factors appear to affect heart rate?

   c) Do you think there are other factors that could affect heart rate? Use examples to support your answer.

   d) Which other organ systems are involved during the changes in Cheryl's heart rate? In what ways are they involved? Use the term *interdependence* in your answer.

2 The blood that leaves the heart is rich with oxygen. The blood that returns to the heart contains less oxygen. What do you think happens to the oxygen, and how does it happen? (Use your common sense, your imagination, or both, to answer this question. You will have a chance to revisit this idea at the end of this chapter.)

3 Do you think there are any organs that people can live without? Why or why not?

4 What factors affect how organ systems function? How do you think they affect the systems? (For example, what effect does smoking have on how the respiratory system functions? How does eating fatty foods affect the functioning of the circulatory system?) For each system, include at least one factor not mentioned in your text.

1 CELLS AND CELL SYSTEMS

info BIT

Florence Nightingale

Florence Nightingale was born in 1820 into a rich British family but became a nurse because she wanted to care for poor and suffering people. She is famous today because of the reforms she brought about in nursing and hospitals around the world.

5 What body systems are involved in playing soccer? How are these systems interdependent? Draw a concept map to illustrate this interconnectedness.

6 Our planet is home to perhaps as many as 50 000 000 different kinds of living things. These pictures show a few of them. How are these living things different from you? What similarities do you think you share with these and all other living things?

7 Interpret the data in the graph at right. Then re-read the reSEARCH about the total length of blood vessels. Based on this information, say how you think each of the following "what ifs" would affect the efficient functioning of the circulatory system.
a) What if the heart exerted less pressure than it normally does?
b) What if the heart exerted more pressure than it normally does?

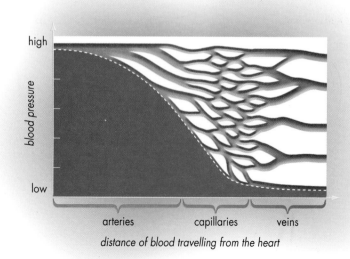

distance of blood travelling from the heart

2.0

The cell, in its structure and function, is the basic unit of all living things.

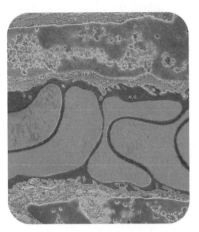

A capillary sliced lengthwise. Where are the red blood cells?

For a long time, the circulatory system presented an unsolvable puzzle. People could easily observe the arteries and the veins. They could see that these blood vessels branched out into smaller and thinner vessels. Some observers suspected that blood from the arteries returned to the heart through the veins. However, they could not observe any linking structures between them. They had reached the limits of human sight.

In 1660, an Italian scientist named Marcello Malpighi solved the puzzle. He looked at an intricate network of thin, hair-like vessels connecting arteries and veins in the lung tissue of frogs. These blood vessels were later called **capillaries**, from an ancient Roman word meaning "hair."

Malpighi's eyesight was no better than other scientists of his time. However, he lived during an exciting time in the history of modern science. By the early 1600s, a technological device had been invented that would change our understanding of life and living things. This device was the **microscope**.

2.1 THE MICROSCOPE EXTENDS THE SENSE OF SIGHT

Explore

How close can your eye come to an object? Try it with a ruler and a coin.

How small an object can you see with just your eyes? In your Science Journal, draw a line 1 mm long. (Or try making a circle that has a diameter of 1 mm.) Have you ever seen an organism this small? Can you think of any organisms that *are* this small?

Now look closely at the dot-pictures on this page. All of the dots in picture A are 1 mm in diameter. They are also 1 mm apart. (Use your ruler to verify this.) You can probably see each dot clearly. Can you clearly see the dots in picture B? What about in pictures C and D?

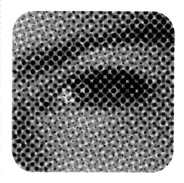

Dot Images

Look at this image close up. What do you see? Now look at it from a distance. What do you see?

Photographs in books, magazines, and newspapers are made up of tiny dots of colour and shade. This example has been exaggerated. The dots on a printed page are usually too small to see without magnification.

- Find out more about this process of using dots to reproduce photographs.
- What comparisons can you make between a dot in a picture and a cell in an organ?

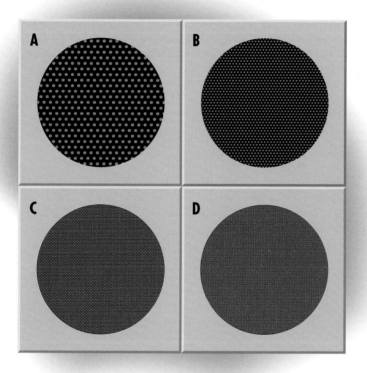

You probably can't see individual dots in picture D. This is normal. Most people with good eyesight can only see clear, defined images of things that are 0.1 mm or larger. This is a limitation of the human eye. To overcome this limitation and extend our sense of sight, we need the help of technology. We need a microscope.

Develop

Reviewing the Compound Light Microscope

A microscope magnifies (enlarges) the image of small objects. It also provides clear, defined images of those objects. The microscope you'll be using in class probably looks like the one shown on the next page. Take some time to review its parts and how they function. Then you'll be ready to take a closer look for yourself.

Microscope Parts and Their Functions

Any microscope that has two or more lenses is a *compound microscope.* (For more about lenses and how they affect the images of objects, see *Chapter 3: Optics.*)

When you view an object with a microscope, you are looking through the object. Because light must travel through the object for you to see it properly, you will see a lamp or other light source under the microscope's stage. That's why the full name for your microscope is **compound light microscope**.

Microscopes are valuable precision instruments. Like all scientific equipment, they must be handled with care. As a class, develop a chart to summarize the proper care and handling of your microscopes. Use these questions as a starting point for your ideas.

Compound Light Microscope*

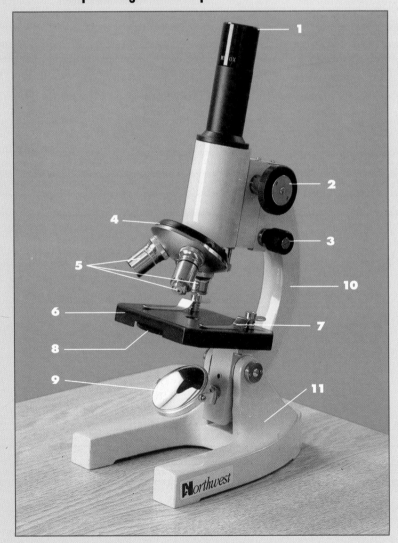

- How should you prepare your work area before bringing the microscope to it?

- How should you carry the microscope to your work area?

- In what position (upright? tilted?) should you keep the microscope? Why?

- What parts of the microscope should you keep clean? Why?

- How and where should you store the microscope when you've finished using it?

*See next page for legend

continued on next page ┄┄┄➤

Part	Function	Handling Hints
1 eyepiece	*acts like a magnifying glass*	*Try keeping both of your eyes open.*
2 coarse adjustment knob	*moves the body tube closer to or farther from the object to produce a clear, sharp image*	*Use this only when you're using the lowest-power objective lens.*
3 fine adjustment knob	*provides clearer, sharper images*	*Use this with any objective lens, but mainly with the medium-power and high-power objective lenses.*
4 revolving nosepiece	*holds the three objective lenses*	*When you change objective lenses, you'll feel or hear a "click" when the lens is in the right position.*
5 objective lenses	*provide different strengths (powers) of magnification*	*Avoid getting fingerprints or dirt on the lenses. They should be cleaned with proper lens-cleaning paper only.*
6 stage	*place where you put the slide that holds the object you want to view*	*Keep the stage dry.*
7 stage clips	*hold the slide firmly on the stage*	
8 diaphragm	*has different-sized holes that let different amounts of light pass through the object you're viewing*	
9 lamp	*directs light through the object you're viewing*	*If your microscope uses a mirror instead of a lamp, be very careful <u>not</u> to reflect direct sunlight into the microscope. You could damage your eyes.*
10 arm	*houses the adjustment knobs and helps you carry the microscope securely*	*When you carry your microscope from one place to another, hold the arm with one hand. Support the microscope with your other hand under the base.*
11 base	*serves as a foundation for the rest of the microscope*	*When you carry your microscope from one place to another, support it with one hand under the base. Use your other hand to hold the arm.*

*info*BIT

Peeking Inside

Fibre optics is a technology that allows light to travel down a flexible tube. Medical researchers have used fibre optics to create microscopes which can be used inside and outside the body. Some are tiny enough to be passed through a person's arteries. Other devices are used to help surgeons operate. The image you see in the background is actually the patient's eye!

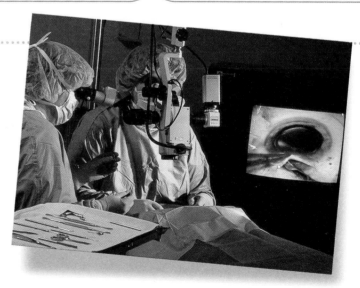

1 a) Which of the following could you see without a microscope? Why would you need one to see the others?
  - a liver cell (about 0.02 mm)
  - the head of a pin (about 1 mm)
  - an amoeba (about 0.1 mm)
  - a paramecium (about 0.23 mm)
  - a red blood cell (about 0.007 mm)

b) Did any of these sizes surprise you? Which one, and why?

2 In your Science Journal, make a labelled sketch of a microscope. Briefly explain how you would use a microscope to look at a slide of an amoeba.

2.2 CELLS AND THEIR STRUCTURES

Mycoplasma

Blue whale

Explore

The above left photo shows the smallest kind of organism scientists have discovered so far. It belongs to a group of organisms known as **mycoplasma**. These are so small that they had to be magnified over 18 000× to make this photo.

The organism on the right is the world's largest kind of animal, the blue whale. The whale is about 30 m in length. It's hard to believe that blue whales and mycoplasma have much in common. But they do. They have something in common with you, too, and with every other organism. They are made up of cells.

Cells are the individual, living units that make up all organisms. Some organisms are **multicellular**. This means that they are made up of two or more cells. Plants and animals are examples of multicellular (many-celled) organisms.

Other organisms are **unicellular**. They are made up of only a single cell. Most microscopic organisms are examples of unicellular (single-celled) organisms.

With a partner, open your Science Journals and jot down all the things you know or remember about cells. Here are some questions to help you focus your thinking. They'll also get you ready to examine cells in greater detail in the upcoming activity.

- How might the cells of a multicellular blue whale be different from the cell of the unicellular mycoplasma? How might they be similar?
- How might your cells be different from the cells of another animal or a plant? How might they be similar?

Develop

Looking at Cells

You're about to view cells under the microscope. Even at low power, you will probably see more than one cell. So it helps to be able to identify where one cell stops and another starts.

*info*BIT

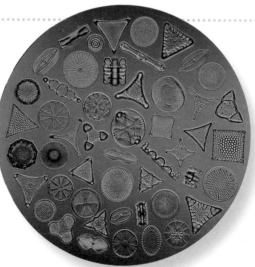

One-cell Wonders

Colossal Cell—One of the world's largest unicellular organisms is so big that you can see it with the unaided eye. It's called *acetabularia*, and it's a member of the plant-like algae family. Acetabularia measures from 5 cm to 7 cm! The largest cell in a multicellular organism is even bigger. It's the yolk of an ostrich egg.

Diatoms—These little glass pill-boxes are alive! Diatoms are tiny plant-like creatures made up of just one cell each. They live in lakes, oceans, and moist soil, and are an important part of the food chain.

COMPARING CELLS

The Question

In what ways are the cells of organisms similar and different?

Materials & Equipment

- *compound microscope*
- *one or more prepared slides of plant cells (for example, cells from a lily leaf or hibiscus stem)*
- *one or more prepared slides of animal cells (for example, skin cells)*
- *prepared slides of unicellular organisms such as amoebas or algae*

Procedure

1. Set up your microscope.
2. Get a prepared slide of plant cells, and put the slide on the stage. Position it so your specimen is above the hole in the stage. Then hold it securely in place with the stage clips.

Switching from Low- to Medium- to High-Power Viewing

- *When your glass slide is in place, look at the stage from the side. Make sure the low-power objective lens is above the slide.*

- *Use the coarse adjustment knob to bring the low-power objective lens as close as you can to the slide without touching it.*
- *Look through the eyepiece. Use the coarse adjustment knob to bring your specimen into focus.*

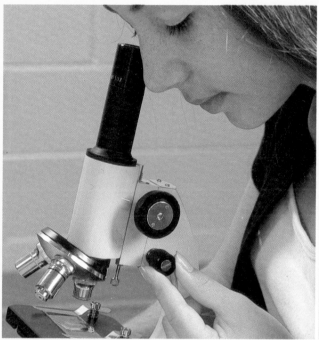

- *Use the fine adjustment knob to get a clear, sharp image.*
- *Keep looking through the eyepiece. Gently move the glass slide in different directions—a bit to the left, to the right, up, down. See what effect this has on the image.*

- *Move the specimen back to the centre of your view. Refocus using the coarse adjustment knob. Turn the revolving nosepiece to switch to the medium-power objective lens. (A "click" will tell you the lens is in place.) Focus the image with the fine adjustment knob.*

Caution!

Whenever you use the medium-power and the high-power objective lenses, focus your image using only the fine adjustment knob.

- *Move the specimen to the centre. Refocus with the fine adjustment knob. Switch to the high-power objective lens.*
- *Use the fine adjustment knob to focus the image.*

Hint!

When your specimen is focussed, try keeping both eyes open. If you concentrate on what you're looking at, all you'll see is your specimen. This method lets you relax your face muscles so you feel more comfortable. As a result, you can observe much longer.

continued on next page ······▶

2.2   Cells and Their Structures

3 Take your time to get familiar with what you can see at low, medium, and high power. In each case:

a) Count or estimate the number of cells you observe in the field of view. The **field of view** is the entire area you can see when you look through the microscope.

b) Notice the shapes of the cells and how they're arranged.

c) In your Science Journal, draw the view you see.

4 Remove the slide. Replace it with a prepared slide of animal cells. Again,

observe at low, medium, and high power. Repeat step 3.

5 Remove the slide. Get and observe the prepared slides of unicellular organisms. Again, observe at low, medium, and high power. Repeat step 3.

Keeping Records

6 Look over all your cell drawings. Choose one plant cell, one animal cell, and two unicellular organisms. Then use the following information about typical cell structures to help you label your drawings.

Cell Structures You Can Usually See with a Classroom Light Microscope

Many things can affect your ability to see details of the internal parts of cells. These factors include:

- the type of microscope
- the condition of the lenses (how clean, whether they're scratched, etc.)
- the quality of the prepared slides

Even so, you probably saw most, if not all, of the cell structures listed in the table below. Two of the structures are not present in some cells. If you are in doubt, re-check your observations. Set up your microscope again and double-check the accuracy and clarity of your drawings.

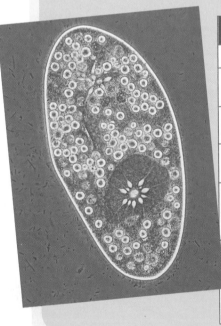

Cell Structure	Features That Can Help You Identify It
cell membrane	*looks like a thin line that surrounds the whole cell*
cell wall	*a rigid frame-like covering that surrounds the cell membrane*
chloroplast	*a green-coloured structure that may be oval or circular in shape*
cytoplasm	*a liquid inside the cell, which has grainy-looking bits in it*
mitochondria (singular is mitochondrion)	*very small sausage-shaped structures that may just be visible as tiny dots or grains in your microscope*
nucleus	*a fairly large, dark, spherical structure that's usually near the centre of the cell*
vacuoles	*clear, liquid-filled spaces in various places within the cytoplasm*

continued on next page ······▶

1
CELLS AND CELL SYSTEMS

Analyzing and Interpreting

7 What do you think are the differences between plant and animal cells? Give examples from what you observed.

8 Photosynthesis is the process that plants use to convert light energy, carbon dioxide, and water into their own food. Animals do not carry out photosynthesis. This fact suggests that plants have a photosynthesis-related cell structure that animals don't. What did you notice in plant cells that might suggest this structure? Explain how you arrived at your answer.

Forming Conclusions

9 Write a summary paragraph that answers the question: "In which ways are the cells of organisms similar and different?" Include diagrams in your explanation.

Communicate

1 In the Investigator activity, you observed several cell structures. Make a two-column chart with the names of the cell structures in the first column. In the second column, record your ideas about the role you think that each structure plays in the health and functioning of the cell.

2 You have personally observed several different kinds of cells. The photos on this page show some others.

a) Decide whether the cell in each photo is a unicellular organism or part of a multicellular organism. Explain how you made your decision in each case.

b) Use your experiences to identify as many cell structures as you can. In one sentence for each, explain what you think its functions are.

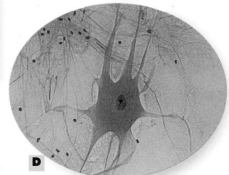

B

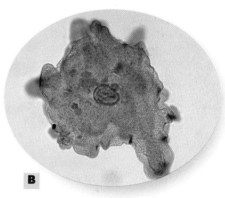

C

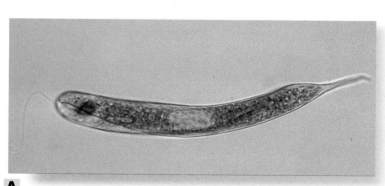

A

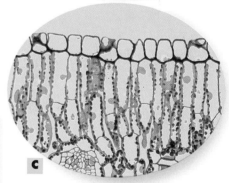

D

2.3 CELL STRUCTURES AND THEIR FUNCTIONS

Explore

Scientists use analogies to help them explain and focus their thinking. An *analogy* is a comparison to help you understand an idea, an object, a process, or all three. It compares the thing you're trying to understand to something that either looks or behaves like it. For example, to help understand living cells, one analogy is to compare the structures and functions of living cells to the structures and functions of a school. Use the pictures and statements below to explore this analogy.

- In what ways might the structures and functions of a school be like the structures and functions of a living cell?
- Exchange ideas with a partner. Keep in mind that analogies are only useful if they help you explain or focus your understanding. So add any details you wish to the school description to help make it a better or more useful comparison.
- If you prefer to develop a different cell analogy that makes more sense to you, go ahead.

The Vital Roles That Cell Structures Play

Develop

All cells carry out the processes that keep them alive and healthy. Various structures within a cell's cytoplasm carry out specific processes. These structures, in specific form and having specific function, are called **organelles**. In a way, cells are like living buildings or factories. For example, cells have:

- .a "command centre" that directs all cellular activities such as movement, growth, and other life functions
- a "power source" to provide energy for carrying out those activities
- a "controllable gateway" that lets needed materials in and waste materials out

Most cells display these characteristics. Because of this, scientists have constructed cell models like the ones shown below. You probably saw most of the organelles in these models in the Investigator activity in section 2.2.

Compare these cell models with the ones you drew in that activity.

- Which structures did you observe?
- Were there any you couldn't see? What might have prevented you?
- Pay close attention to the labels. Then outline some of the main functions for each cell structure.
- How does the function of each cell structure contribute to the overall health of the cell?

*re*SEARCH

You have observed cell structures using a compound light microscope. Using the higher power of an electron microscope, scientists have discovered many more cell structures. Use print or electronic resources to find out about the following cell structures and their life-supporting functions:

- endoplasmic reticulum
- Golgi bodies
- lysosomes
- nucleolus
- ribosomes

1 CELLS AND CELL SYSTEMS

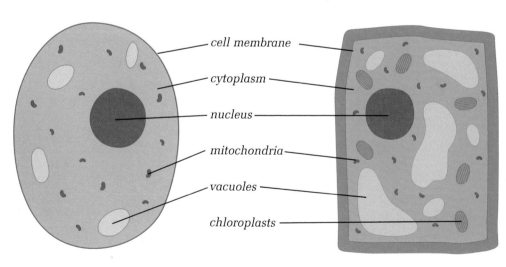

cell membrane
cytoplasm
nucleus
mitochondria
vacuoles
chloroplasts

Typical animal cell

Typical plant cell

CELLS IN 3-D!

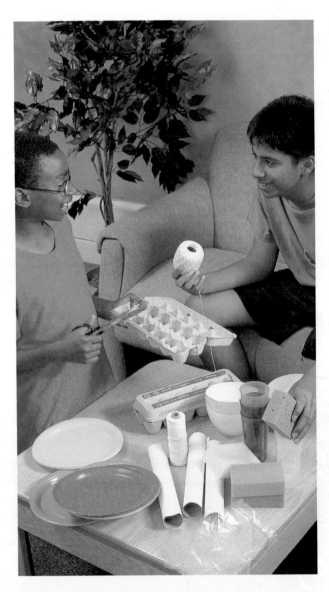

Procedure

1. Review what you know about cell structures and their functions. Brainstorm items that might be useful in representing each structure. Jot down each item as it occurs to you.

2. Take an informal inventory of items in your home. The kitchen, workshop, or craft cupboard can be great places to start looking. See what other items you might discover and add them to your list.

3. As your cell-model ideas begin to take shape, make some decisions. Do you want to make a model that you could eat when it's done? Would you like to build a model using only recycled materials? Are there any cell parts that you need to bake, freeze, mould, or put together?

4. When you've made your final decisions, construct your cell model. Be sure to share and compare it with your classmates.

5. Make a chart or mind map detailing all the items you used for your cell model. Which cell structures did you include? Why did you choose the item you did to represent each structure?

6. Pick any three items that you used. Pretend that they weren't available when you constructed your cell model. Which items could you use as replacements? Why would these replacements be better, worse, or equal to what you did use for your cell structure?

Cells look much more exciting and marvellous than the two-dimensional views you've seen through the microscope or in the photos. In this activity, you'll use common household items and your current understanding of cell structures and functions to design and make a 3-D model of a cell—either a generalized plant cell or a generalized animal cell.

1 Design a chart to record the following information:
   a) cell structures that you can see with a compound light microscope
   b) the functions of these cell structures
   c) whether these structures appear in animal cells, plant cells, or both

2 Scientists build generalized cell models based on multicellular organisms. Do you think there's such a thing as a generalized unicellular organism? Make a sketch to record your ideas of what one might look like. Include labels to describe the functions of all the structures you include.

3 How would the health of a cell be affected if one or more of its organelles were damaged? Give reasons to support your opinion.

2.4 CHECK YOUR PROGRESS

1. Identify the organisms on this page as unicellular or multicellular. Give reasons for your answers in each case.

A

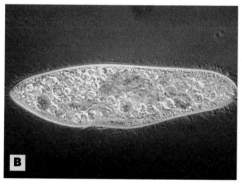

B

C

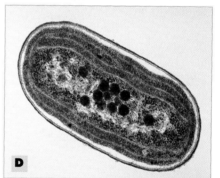

D

E

2 a) Sketch a plant cell as you remember it from your personal observations. Identify, using labels, the organelles and other cell structures that you observed.
   b) Do the same for an animal cell.
   c) Based on your observations and the sketches you just made, describe the key differences between plant cells and animal cells.

3 What is the function of a compound light microscope?

4 Your classmate is viewing a specimen using high power and is about to refocus using the coarse adjustment knob. What would you recommend your classmate do and why?

5 In your opinion, which structure or organelle is the most important to the health of a cell? Give reasons to support your answer.

MEDICAL LAB TECHNOLOGIST

How would you like a job that saves people's lives? a job that helps people get better from sickness? Most people think only doctors and nurses have jobs like this, but there's another important life-saving job—that of a lab technologist.

When doctors see a sick patient, they sometimes have an idea of what the problem is from the symptoms, but they're not totally sure. To find out exactly what's wrong, the doctor sends the patient's specimen (such as a blood or urine sample) to a medical laboratory. At the medical laboratory, a lab technologist takes the specimen and tests it. Infections, such as strep throat, and many serious diseases are often hard to identify without a lab technologist's help.

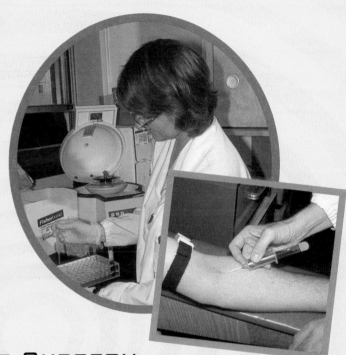

TRANSPLANT SURGEON

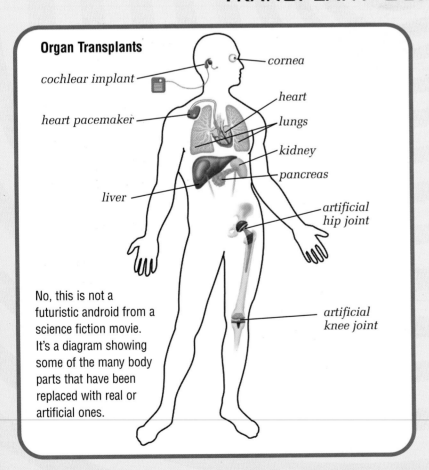

Organ Transplants

- cochlear implant
- cornea
- heart pacemaker
- heart
- lungs
- kidney
- pancreas
- liver
- artificial hip joint
- artificial knee joint

No, this is not a futuristic android from a science fiction movie. It's a diagram showing some of the many body parts that have been replaced with real or artificial ones.

If your car breaks down, you simply take it into the shop and an auto mechanic replaces the broken part that caused the problem. Is it possible to do the same thing for the human body? Since the first successfully transplanted kidney in 1954, surgeons have been doing just that! In Canada alone, there were 1533 transplant operations in 1996. Kidney transplants were the most common.

Transplant surgeons must be able to work quickly and calmly under pressure, because organs can only survive a short period of time without a blood supply. They also must be able to carefully remove all the blood vessels from the diseased organ and reattach them to the healthy one.

Cells must interact with their external environment to meet their basic needs.

To learn about living cells, you'll need to observe them. How can you observe living cells? You have practised some basic microscope techniques using prepared slides containing dead cells. Soon, you will develop more microscope skills by preparing living unicellular organisms for observation. First, though, you will explore the process of making your own prepared slides with non-living material.

*re*SEARCH

Optically Speaking

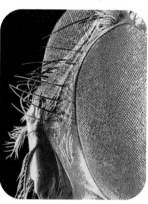

There are many types of microscopes, but not all microscopes use light.

- Choose another type of microscope and find out more about it.
- Compare this microscope with the compound light microscope you have been using. Why was its development important? How is it used? What type of information does this type of microscope provide?

Pond water organisms

3.1 PREPARING YOUR OWN SLIDES

Explore

You are about to prepare what scientists call a **wet mount**. This is a microscope slide that contains a specimen in a drop of water, covered with a small piece of glass or plastic called a **cover slip**. In the Problem Solver activity on the next page, you will learn how to make a wet mount using a non-living specimen: paper. Once you've mastered the skills, you'll apply them to making your own prepared slide of live plant cells.

HOW DO YOU PREPARE YOUR OWN SLIDES?

Preparing Your First Wet Mount

Follow these steps to make a wet mount of a lowercase letter "e."

1 Gather the following: a clean glass slide and cover slip, an eyedropper, tweezers (or a toothpick), a small cup of water, and your specimen—a letter "e" taken from a newspaper page.

2 Pick up the glass slide as shown in picture A. Place it in front of you.

3 Using an eyedropper, place one drop of water in the centre of the slide. Then use tweezers or a toothpick to lay your specimen—right-side up—on the drop of water.

4 Pick up the cover slip the same way you picked up the glass slide. Slowly lower it over your specimen as shown in picture B. Try not to trap air bubbles under the cover slip.

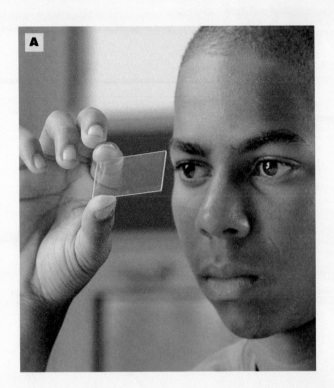

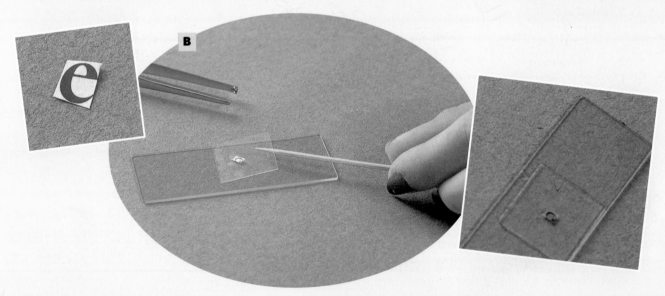

Testing Your Wet Mount

5 Set up your wet mount slide on a microscope. Before you view anything, make the following predictions based on your previous experiences. Make sketches to record your predictions.

CELLS AND CELL SYSTEMS

1

- How will your specimen appear when you observe it with low power?
- How will it change when you move the slide to the left? to the right? up? down?
- How will it change when you view it with medium power? with high power?

6 View your slide to test your predictions.

Preparing and Viewing a Cell Specimen

7 If you've ever looked closely at an onion, you may have noticed a thin, semi-transparent skin between the thicker layers. This skin is only one cell thick in most places, which makes it ideal for observing cells.

- How would you prepare a wet mount of onion cells? Decide what you would need, what you would do, and what cautions you need to exercise.
- Discuss the procedure with a partner. Then share your ideas with the whole class. When everyone has decided on what to do, and how to do it safely, prepare your wet mount.

8 View your specimen with a microscope, and make a sketch to record your observations. Be sure to label all the cell structures and organelles that you recognize. If there are any that you don't recognize, label them with a question mark.

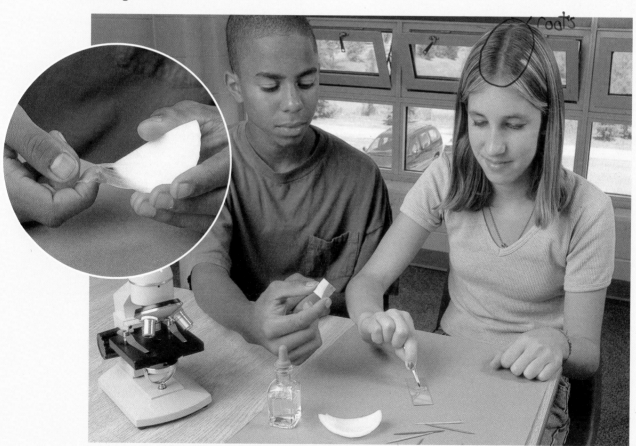

The cells in an onion bulb do not have chloroplasts. Can you figure out why? (Hint: What colour is an onion skin?)

Observing a Live Organism with the Microscope

Now that you know how to prepare cells for viewing, you are ready to observe a live unicellular organism: the **paramecium** (plural: paramecia). Because the paramecium is alive, it's worthy of the same respect and care you would show to any living thing. With a partner, discuss how you can show respect and care for unicellular organisms such as the paramecium.

INVESTIGATOR

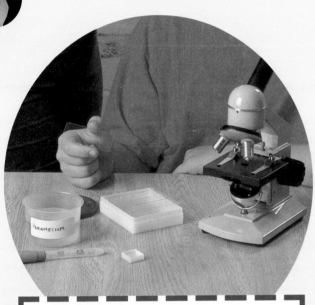

Caution!
Be careful when handling microscopic organisms. Wash your hands thoroughly when you have finished this activity.

Materials & Equipment
- *microscope*
- *glass slide*
- *cover slip*
- *eyedropper*
- *live paramecia (supplied by your teacher)*
- *small jar to carry the paramecia to your viewing area*
- *methyl cellulose*

OBSERVING PARAMECIA

The Question
What cell structures and organelles can you recognize in a living unicellular organism?

Procedure

1 Prepare a wet mount of live paramecia. Set up your slide on the microscope stage. Be sure the low-power objective lens is positioned over your specimen. Then observe your paramecia. Paramecia are fast! Take your time and concentrate on getting familiar with what you're observing, and how to keep your specimens in focus. After a little while, switch to medium power and observe. If you wish, try high power. Was this an improvement? Why or why not? Above all, enjoy watching these fascinating organisms.

2 Observe your specimens. Record any features and actions you find interesting. With a partner, brainstorm some questions you would like answered about your specimens.

3 You can slow down your paramecia by adding a tiny amount—less than a drop—of methyl cellulose. This is a syrupy liquid that thickens the water so it is harder for the paramecia to move

continued on next page ······➤

rapidly. The diagram below shows how to add methyl cellulose to your wet mount.

4 Observe your slowed-down specimens. Follow the instructions in step 5 for recording your observations.

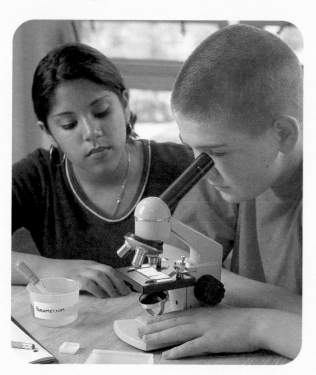

Keeping Records

5 Make an accurate drawing of one paramecium. Try to draw what you really see, not what you think or imagine might be there. Include labels to identify or describe the following details:
- shape
- colour
- size (how much of your field of view it occupies)
- all the cell structures and organelles that you recognize
- any cell structures and organelles that you don't recognize
- the power of the objective lens you're using

Analyzing and Interpreting

6 Describe how paramecia move. Use an analogy to help you describe their movement.

7 a) How did the methyl cellulose slow the paramecia's movements?
b) Suppose you didn't have any methyl cellulose available. Suggest another method you could use to slow the paramecia without harming them. Explain why you think it would work.

Forming Conclusions

8 Write a short story or draw a cartoon strip about a day in the life of a paramecium. Use your observations to help you include informative details such as how it moves, where it goes, what you think it eats, and what might eat it! Include as many cell structures and organelles as you can to support the details you include.

1 How did the plant cells that you prepared yourself compare with the prepared specimens you observed earlier?

2 Amoebas are common unicellular organisms that often share the same freshwater habitats as paramecia. Describe the steps you would follow to prepare amoeba specimens for observation.

3 Paramecia take in food and eliminate wastes, just like all other living things. Based on your observations, identify the structures you think are involved in these activities. Describe how you think they function.

4 Make up three questions about the life or behaviours of paramecia. Pick one of your questions and write a hypothesis that answers the question. (Remember: A **hypothesis** is a possible answer to a question. You usually phrase it so that it implies a way you could test it.)

The person who first observed unicellular organisms was a Dutch amateur scientist named Antony van Leeuwenhoek (pronounced LAY-ven-hook).

Find out about Leeuwenhoek and his microscopic investigations.

- What kinds of organisms did he discover?
- How did he communicate his findings?

3.2 INVESTIGATING THE NEEDS OF UNICELLULAR ORGANISMS

Explore

How would you respond to the situations pictured below and on the next page? Record your ideas in your Science Journal. What if you were a plant? In what ways might your responses to each situation be similar or different? Why? What if you were a paramecium? Record your ideas.

How Unicellular Organisms Meet Their Needs

Develop

Scientists often ask "what if" questions like those in the Explore activity above. "What if" questions often lead to ideas for experiments. Experiments always result in discovery—even if what you discover is something you already know.

Observation or **Experience** →
- **Questioning** (for example, asking "what if ...")
- **Hypothesizing** (making a reasonable guess that answers your question)
- **Experimenting** (designing a fair test — a controlled experiment)
- **Drawing Conclusions** (by comparing your results with your hypothesis)

→ **Discovery**

Before You Start...

Experiments offer many opportunities for making new discoveries for yourself. In this activity, you will plan and carry out an experiment based on your own "what if" questions.

The Question

In what ways do unicellular organisms meet their basic needs?

Your Task

1   This activity involves asking your own questions about unicellular organisms, planning your own experiments to investigate one of those questions, and drawing your own conclusions from them.

2   Use the question stated at the beginning to help you brainstorm all the questions you have about the lives and behaviours of unicellular organisms. Then review your questions to see which ones intrigue you enough to investigate further. Do you see opportunities for experiment that could help you answer your questions?

3   Select a question and write a hypothesis to answer it. Then plan an experiment to test your hypothesis.

4   Make sure your experiment is a fair test of your hypothesis. How will you know?

5   Decide what equipment and materials you will need. Ask your teacher what live unicellular organisms are available.

6   Write up the procedure you'll follow to perform your experiment. Obtain your teacher's approval and carry it out.

7   Decide how you will record your results in a clear, meaningful manner. Examples include

Caution!
Be careful when handling microscopic organisms. Wash your hands thoroughly when you've finished this activity.

diagrams, data tables, graphs, and flowcharts. The method or methods you use will depend on the kind of experiment you design.

8   Explain how you decided on the experiment you planned. Which variable did you consider changing? Why did you select the one you did?

9   What do the data you collect mean? Are there other ways to interpret them?

10   Based on the experiment you planned and carried out, write a summary statement that answers a question that you have asked.

11   Share your results with your classmates.

1 CELLS AND CELL SYSTEMS

1   All organisms, both unicellular and multicellular, share the
    same basic needs. This means that they need:
    •   suitable temperatures and living conditions
    •   food for energy
    •   a way to eliminate wastes
    •   to grow and develop
    •   to respond to changes in their environment
    •   to reproduce to make more of their kind
    a) Give an example describing how unicellular organisms meet
        each of their basic needs.
    b) Which basic need or needs did you investigate in the
        Experiment on Your Own activity? Which unicellular
        organism did you use? What did your results tell you about
        how this organism meets its needs?

2   Imagine that you have been asked to make a presentation to a
    class of Grade 5 students. The topic is "The Needs of
    Unicellular Organisms."
    a) Organize and develop a presentation that communicates the
        procedure and results of your experiment.
    b) Describe how you might change your presentation if you
        were doing it for a group of visiting parents. Why would you
        make these changes?

3   The flowchart on page 43 shows one way to represent the
    scientific process of discovery. Do you see any flaws or
    weaknesses in this model? Modify it to show the scientific
    process of discovery as you understand it.

4   You usually measure size (length) in units such as metres,
    centimetres, and millimetres. Because most unicellular
    organisms are much smaller than 1 mm, scientists use another
    measuring unit to describe them: the micrometre. Its symbol is
    µm. (µ is the Greek letter m.) One micrometre is one-millionth
    of a metre (1 µm = 0.000 001 m) or one-thousandth of one
    millimetre (1 µm = 0.001 mm). Based on this information,
    answer the following questions.
    a) A typical amoeba is about 100 µm long. How many
        millimetres is that?
    b) A typical paramecium is about 0.23 mm long. How many
        micrometres is that?
    c) Bacteria, among the smallest unicellular organisms, are
        0.5 µm. How many millimetres is that?
    d) Viruses are even smaller than bacteria. Some of the smallest
        viruses are 0.05 µm. How many millimetres is that?

reSEARCH

Water Bears

Not all microscopic organisms are unicellular. For example, the members of one group of microscopic animals fondly referred to as "water bears" are multicellular. They range in size from 0.05 mm to 1.2 mm. (So the largest water bears are just in the range of your unaided sight.) These animals are amazing survivors. Some can form a protective covering that lets them sleep safely in temperatures as hot as 150°C and as cold as −270°C. They can also withstand more than 1000 times the amount of radiation that would kill a human!

•   Find out more about water bears. Why do they have to withstand such extreme conditions?

3.3 HOW SUBSTANCES MOVE INTO AND OUT OF CELLS

Explore

Right now, each cell in your body is bringing water, gases, and food inside itself. Each of your cells is using these substances to supply itself, and you, with the matter and energy you both need to survive. At the same time, each of your cells is generating waste products that also must be removed.

This process of bringing substances into your cells and removing substances from them is important to your survival. But it isn't unique to humans. The same process is also happening, right now, in every organism on earth. The cell has a structure that permits this vital exchange of substances between the inside and outside of the cell. It is the **cell membrane**. Many substances move through the cell membrane by a process called **diffusion**. Observe the "mini-experiments" shown here to develop an idea of this process.

Experiment #1

Dropping In

In a moment, Roberta is going to place a drop of ink into a beaker of room-temperature water. Predict what will happen to the ink drop over time. Make individual sketches to show how you believe the ink drop will look:

a) as soon as it's dropped into the water
b) 5 s after being dropped into the water
c) about 20 s later
d) about 60 s later
e) several minutes later

When you've finished sketching, test your predictions.

Experiment #2

Smell Detective

Martin volunteered to carry drinks to the class hosting a surprise party for a retiring teacher. He isn't sure which classroom is the right one, but he does know the students plan to serve pizza and popcorn.

Explain how Martin could use the smell of popcorn and pizza as a clue.

Design an experiment to test how quickly a smell could travel from one end of your classroom to another.

Experiment #3

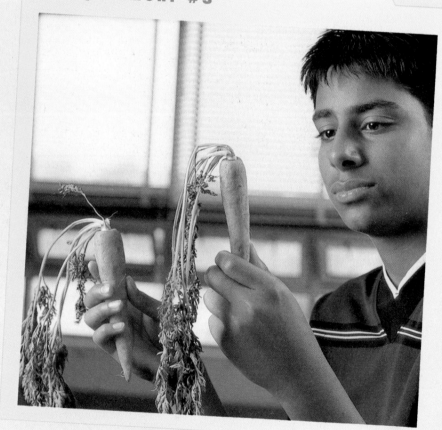

Back from the Brink

Alex didn't mean to leave these plants in the warm car so long. He decides to place them in a container of water and check on them every half-hour or so for several hours to see if they will become firm and healthy again.

Repeat Alex's experiment for yourself, using a limp piece of celery or carrot. Place it in a container of water and check on it every half-hour or so for several hours. What do you notice?

You have just seen diffusion in action. Write a sentence explaining what you think it is.

The Cell Membrane and Diffusion

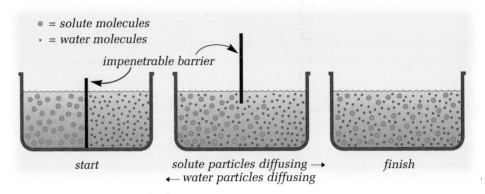

- = *solute molecules*
- = *water molecules*

impenetrable barrier

start   *solute particles diffusing →*   *finish*

← water particles diffusing

Diffusion is the movement of particles from an area where there are more of them to an area where there are fewer of them. In other words, diffusion moves particles from a more concentrated area to a less concentrated area. It's a "balancing out" or "evening out" process that continues until the concentration of particles is the same everywhere.

An Example of Diffusion — Making Tea

The tiny openings in this tea bag are large enough to allow water to pass through, along with the substances that make the flavour of the tea, but they are small enough to keep in the tea leaves themselves. How is a tea bag similar to a cell? How is it different?

Many substances move in and out of cells by diffusion. The cell membrane acts like a wall with extremely tiny openings that allow some particles to pass through.

These openings are small enough to keep the cell's cytoplasm and its contents inside. They are also small enough to keep most substances in the cell's external environment out. However, some substances are able to pass from the outside in and from the inside out. So the cell membrane allows the particles of some substances to pass through it, but not others. Because of this fact, scientists say that the cell membrane is **selectively permeable**.

One of the substances that can pass through the cell membrane is oxygen. Most cells need oxygen to perform cellular respiration. Oxygen particles are small enough to pass through the cell's selectively permeable membrane into the cell. This movement of oxygen happens by diffusion, and it happens naturally. That's because the concentration of oxygen is usually higher outside the cell membrane than it is inside. As a result, oxygen simply diffuses into the cell. The cell doesn't have to do anything to make it happen.

The Cell Membrane and Osmosis

Water is another substance that has particles small enough to diffuse through the cell membrane. The amount of water inside a cell must stay fairly constant. If the water concentration inside the cell gets too low, water from outside the cell naturally diffuses in. If the concentration gets too high, water naturally diffuses out of the cell.

The diffusion of water is vital to the survival and health of cells. For this reason, scientists give it a special name: osmosis. **Osmosis**, then, is the diffusion of water particles through a selectively permeable membrane. The water particles move from an area of higher concentration (where there are more water particles) to an area of lower concentration (where there are fewer).

Communicate

1 a) Use the term "selectively permeable" in a sentence that clearly demonstrates its meaning.
   b) What is the function of a cell's selectively permeable membrane?
   c) How does this function contribute to the health of the cell?

2 The terms diffusion and osmosis seem to have similar meanings. Explain how they are similar. Then give a reason why scientists use two separate terms.

3 a) In the Diffusion Mini-Experiment #3, you observed the result of diffusion on a plant. Describe what you observed and identify the process involved.
   b) Although you didn't observe the celery or carrot cells directly, you can still infer what happened to them. Describe what must have happened.

4 Fish species that live in fresh water have to remove excess water as waste from their bodies. Fish species that live in salt water have bodies that keep in as much water as possible. Using what you know about osmosis, explain these observations.

*info*BIT

Reverse Osmosis
A process called reverse osmosis can be used to purify water. Impure water is pumped through a membrane which allows water particles through, separating dissolved salts, some bacteria, and organic material from the water. To make the purified water even safer to drink, other filters, such as charcoal, are also used. Reverse osmosis units allow ocean sailors to have a constant supply of drinking water.

Have you wondered why unicellular organisms are so small? Does it surprise you that there aren't any single-celled creatures the size of a dog or elephant?

Explore

Unicellular organisms are tiny because there are limits to how large they can grow. One of the reasons involves diffusion and osmosis. These vital processes work well only over very short distances. For example, it takes an oxygen particle a fraction of a second to diffuse over a distance of 10 µm. To diffuse over a distance of 1 mm takes several minutes! Do you see how unicellular organisms benefit by being microscopic?

Multicellular Organisms Have Specialized Cells

Like all living things, unicellular organisms grow and develop. When they reach the limits of their size, like the amoeba shown here, they reproduce. Amoebas do this by dividing in two, which results in two smaller, identical copies of each organism.

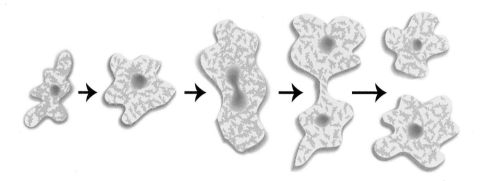

Your cells reproduce this way, too. That's how, for example, your body replaces the 50 000 000 or so skin cells that it naturally loses each day! Your body cells also reproduce to repair tissues that get damaged. For example, if you scrape your elbow, your skin cells reproduce to form new skin tissue.

Your skin cell can do this because it's specialized for this function. You and most other multicellular organisms are made up of **specialized cells**. This means that there are various kinds of cells, and each kind carries out a specific function or functions needed to support life. Each kind of cell has specific structures that enable it to carry out its functions. For example, the function of your **red blood cells** is to carry oxygen to all the cells of your body. To do this, the red blood cells often must travel through extremely small blood vessels. Their thin, pliable disc shape enables them to do this.

Red blood cells do not reproduce in the same way as skin cells. When red blood cells mature into the shape shown here, they lose their nucleus. Since the nucleus controls cell division (among other functions), red blood cells can't reproduce by simply dividing to make more of themselves. The only way your body can make more red blood cells is by relying on specialized tissues in another body system. Most bones of the skeletal system contain a tissue called **marrow**, with specialized cells that make red blood cells.

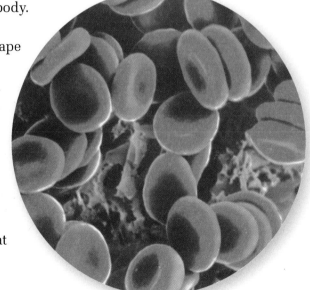

Red blood cells

The Body's Nerve Centre

This strange-looking tree is actually a nerve cell. It's called a *purkinje* cell, and it comes from a part of your brain called the cerebellum. Your brain and nervous system are made of billions of nerve cells. These cells are what let you think, touch, taste, move, and see.

Specialization means that the cells of a multicellular organism must work together to support their own lives, as well as the life of the whole individual. For example, the cells that make up the tissues of your liver rely on other organ systems to provide them with oxygen and nutrients by diffusion.

Communicate

1. For what reasons do the cells that make up multicellular organisms need to reproduce?
2. Is a red blood cell more specialized than an amoeba, or is it the other way around?
3. What are the advantages of having specialized cells? Are there any disadvantages? Explain your answer.

3.5 WHAT YOUR CELLS AND ORGANS NEED, SO DOES YOUR BODY

Explore

Why do you think you need to drink water regularly and breathe oxygen? You need water and oxygen because your cells, tissues, and organs all have these basic needs in order to function properly. For example, water keeps cells from drying out, and it transports nutrients in and wastes out. If you were to examine a drop of blood under a microscope, you would discover that a large part is water. In fact, your body is about 70% water! You need to drink water not only because you feel thirsty, but because your cells and organs are thirsty.

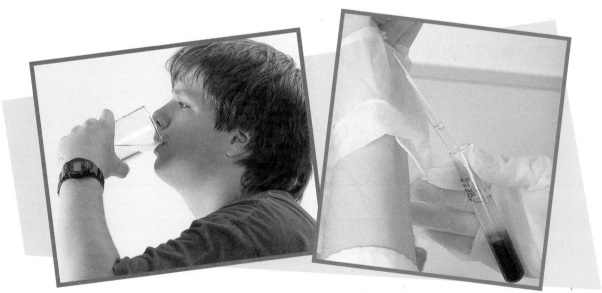

Why do you get thirsty?

Blood is made up of about 50% water.

ic Body Needs

Think about the other needs that your body has. In the next activity, you'll research some of these needs and find out how they help your body to function.

BASIC BODY NEEDS

Work with a partner or a group to brainstorm a list of what you think your body needs to help it survive.

- Research two body elements (cells, tissues, organs, or systems) in your list that depend on each need.
- Organize your results into a chart where you also explain the body element's function with each need. This chart shows an example that's been started for water.
- Compare and exchange your research results with other groups.

Some Basic Needs of the Body		
Need	*Body Element*	*Function*
water	• cell	• transports nutrients and wastes
	• excretory system	• helps regulate waste disposal

Communicate

1 Briefly explain how your body might get each of the basic needs listed in the above Problem Solver activity.

3.6 CHECK YOUR PROGRESS

1 Choose one of the items below. Using words, pictures, or both, explain how you would prepare it to view with a microscope. Also make a sketch showing what you think it would look like under low, medium, and high power. (Ask your teacher if you can set up a microscope to verify, and if necessary, modify your sketches.)

a) a hair from your head

b) a fleck of dandruff

c) a grain of pepper

d) a grain of salt

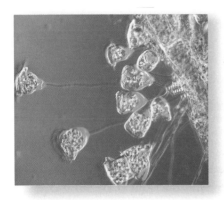

Vorticella

2 Examine the unicellular organism at left closely. Based on your observations, experiences, and intuition, make as many inferences as you can about its features, abilities, and behaviours.

3 Imagine that an amoeba is placed in a solution of salty water. The concentration of salt in the solution is greater than the salt concentration of the amoeba's watery cytoplasm. What will happen, and why? Be sure to use the proper science terms to communicate your understanding.

4 Explain the term cell specialization as you understand it.

5 Choose a basic need of your body and explain how it helps your body's cells, tissues, or organs function.

6 The following pictures show examples of specialized cells from tissues of multicellular organisms. Some are tissues you would find in plants. Others are tissues you would find in you! Look at the cells in the pictures. What can you infer about these cells? How does their shape help them do their job in the body? What function do you think each cell performs?

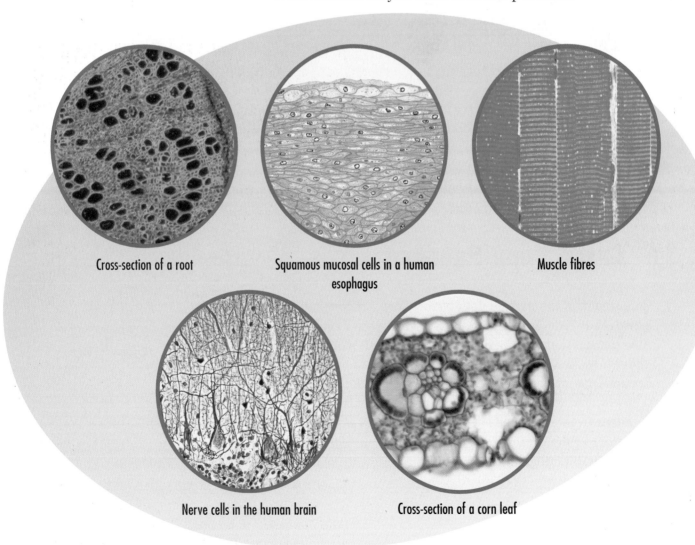

Cross-section of a root

Squamous mucosal cells in a human esophagus

Muscle fibres

Nerve cells in the human brain

Cross-section of a corn leaf

INVESTIGATING CELLS

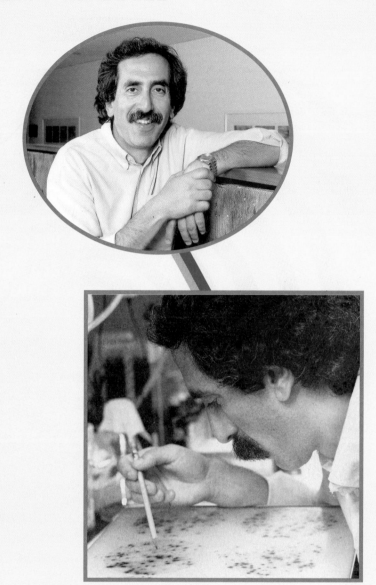

Alan Bernstein is a scientist at Mount Sinai Hospital in Toronto. In his research, he studies the way cells communicate with each other. "Almost all diseases are caused by a breakdown in communication between cells in our bodies," says Dr. Bernstein. "Once we discover how cells communicate, we can use this information to treat diseases like cancer."

Dr. Bernstein looks at how *stem cells* in your bone marrow communicate. (Note: These stem cells in your body are not the same as the stem cells in a plant you looked at earlier. Stem cells in your body produce cells that are different from themselves. Stem cells in a plant are just cells that are located in the stem.) Stem cells in your bones make the blood cells for your body. Blood cells die off very quickly—about 1 million every second! Stem cells make sure these blood cells are replaced with new ones. But how can they tell when more blood cells are needed?

Special particles called *signal proteins* stick halfway out of each stem cell. These particles act like radio antennae for the stem cell! They pick up signals sent by other cells that tell the stem cell whether to produce more blood cells or not.

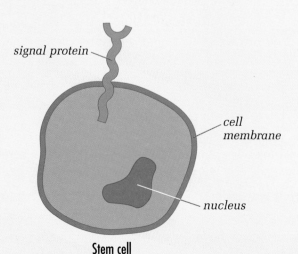

signal molecule from another cell

signal protein

cell membrane

nucleus

Stem cell

Dr. Bernstein and his research group have discovered the unit of hereditary information, or gene, in our bodies that makes this signal protein. When someone's signal proteins are not working properly, the person can get cancer. Dr. Bernstein hopes that one day it will be possible to treat cancer patients with the normal gene.

Despite hard work, Dr. Bernstein loves his job. "Science is a common language for people of all ethnic, cultural, and racial backgrounds," he says. "When I study a disease, it's not just a Canadian problem—it's a human problem."

BIG IDEA

4.0

The health of a plant depends on the health of its cells and tissues.

Water lily

Giant saguaro cactus

Daffodil

Deciduous tree

Wheat

Sundew, a carnivorous plant

Each kind of plant has its own features and abilities to survive and flourish in its usual environment. As you can see, there are different plants for almost every kind of environment you can imagine. However, plants have several characteristics in common. For example, plants need a way to:

- collect the sun's light energy to perform photosynthesis
- take in carbon dioxide gas
- take in water and dissolved minerals
- transport water and minerals to all parts of the plant
- transport energy-rich food to all parts of the plant

Most plants also have three structures that help them meet their needs. These are the **roots**, **stems**, and **leaves**.

With a partner, do the following.

- Identify the three plant structures in each photo on the previous page. If any structure isn't visible, either say where you would expect to find it, or make a sketch to show where it is.
- Make a simple two-column chart in your Science Journal. In the left column, jot down the five plant needs listed on the previous page. In the right column, say which structure or structures you think help a plant meet each need.
- What might a cell in each plant organ look like? In what ways might they be different from one another? In what ways might they be similar? Make some quick sketches to record your ideas. Include labels to identify the cell structures you think are present, and what function they serve.

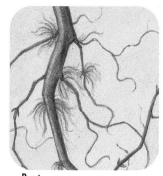

Root

Stem

Leaf

4.1 THE EFFECT OF WATER ON PLANT CELLS

Explore

Have you ever watered a dry, wilted plant? Maybe the plant wilted because it was left too long in a hot, dry place. Maybe it just didn't get watered often enough. Were you able to water the plant and see it come back to life?

Water is vital to the survival of plants. One reason involves the process of **photosynthesis**. Recall what you know about this process.

- Why is water important for photosynthesis?
- Can you think of any other reasons why plants need water?

Why is a sprinkler system necessary?

Develop
Watering the Plant

In section 3.3, you learned about how substances can move across a cell's selectively permeable membrane. Healthy cells are able to control or regulate the amount of a substance that enters or leaves them. What do you think happens if there's too much or not enough of a substance—water, for instance? You'll have a chance to examine this question for yourself in the next activity.

INVESTIGATOR

WATER AND PLANT CELLS

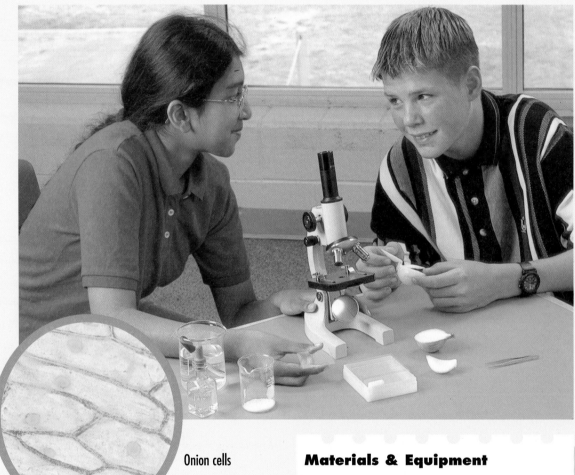

Onion cells

The Question

What will happen to plant cells when they are placed in pure water and in salty water?

Materials & Equipment

- *thin slice of onion*
- *compound microscope*
- *glass slide*
- *cover slip*
- *distilled (pure) water*
- *salt solution*
- *medicine dropper*
- *paper towelling*

continued on next page ·······➤

Procedure

1. The cells of onion skins are easy to see with a classroom microscope. Start by preparing a wet mount of a thin slice of onion skin. Make sure that light can be easily seen through the skin. Use distilled water, rather than regular tap water.

2. Observe your onion specimen under low, medium, and high power. Pick a few cells that you can see clearly. In your Science Journal, sketch what they look like. On one of these sketches, label all the organelles and other cell structures you know.

3. Take the slide off the microscope stage. Place two or three drops of the salt solution at one edge of the cover slip. Then touch a small piece of paper towelling to the other edge of the cover slip. This will draw the salt water under the cover slip so it is in contact with the specimen.

4. Repeat step 2. Pick a few cells you can see clearly. (Do not waste time trying to locate the same cell you sketched before.)

5. Again, take the slide off the microscope stage. Rinse the medicine dropper to remove the salt solution. Place two or three drops of fresh distilled water at one edge of the cover slip. Use the technique you learned in step 3 to "rinse out" the salt solution from your wet mount. Then add a few new drops of distilled water to the specimen.

6. Repeat step 2.

Keeping Records

7. Make a drawing of a typical onion cell in each of the following situations. Use labels to identify clearly the colour, size, and shape of the cell, and any changes you observed.
   - onion cell in distilled water
   - onion cell in salt solution
   - onion cell returned to distilled water

Analyzing and Interpreting

8. How did the salt solution affect the onion cells?

9. What happened when you replaced the solution with distilled water?

Forming Conclusions

10. Explain what happened in this activity. Use any special scientific terminology you've learned to assist you.

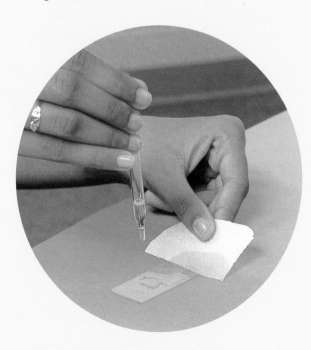

1 Why do plants wilt if they aren't given the water they need?

2 Examine the set-ups shown in the following diagrams. Two similar-sized, peeled potatoes have "wells" drilled in them as shown. The well in potato A is completely filled with distilled water, and the well in potato B is filled with a concentrated sugar solution. Each well is plugged with a rubber stopper carrying a very thin glass tube that reaches into the well. Each potato is placed in a container of distilled water so that the bottom half is covered in the water. Answer the following questions and give reasons to support your predictions.

a) Explain why liquid rises up the thin glass tube in both cases.

b) Predict what will happen to the liquid level in the glass tube in each case after the set-ups have been left overnight.

c) Predict what the cells of potato A and potato B will look like after the set-ups have been left overnight.

d) Suppose potato B is placed in sugar solution instead of distilled water at the start, using the same concentrated sugar solution as in the well. Predict what will happen to the liquid level in the glass tube and the potato cells after the set-ups have been left overnight.

e) Predict what will happen if you use a less concentrated sugar solution outside than in the well of potato B.

f) Predict what will happen if you use a more concentrated sugar solution outside than in the well.

g) How can you change the set-up of potato A to show the same result as in part f)?

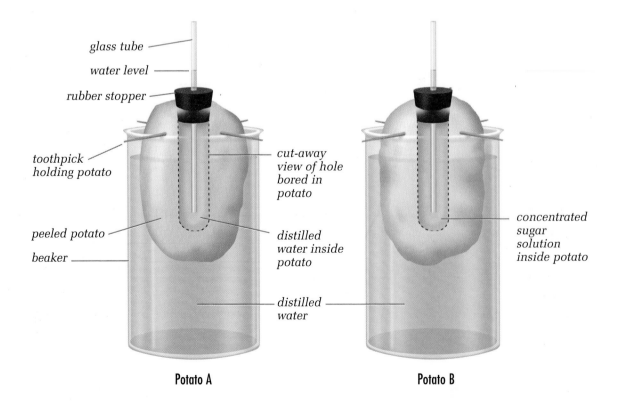

Potato A   Potato B

4.0   The Health of a Plant Depends on the Health of Its Cells and Tissues

4.2 THE STRUCTURE AND FUNCTION OF LEAF CELLS

Explore

In the Investigator activity in section 4.1, you observed part of an onion skin from a "top-down" view. If you were looking at a more typical plant cell—for example, a cell from an elodea leaf—here's a way to get a different angle on what you see.

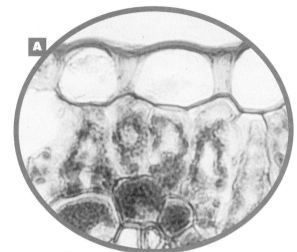

Cross-section of a corn leaf

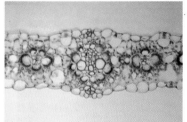

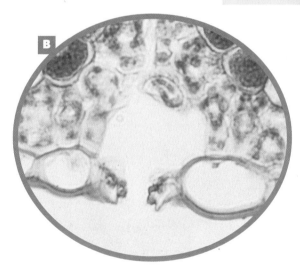

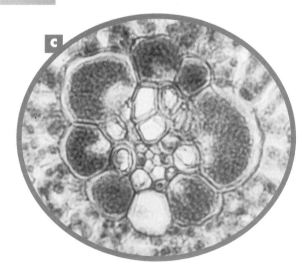

- Examine the centre photograph of the cross-section view of a leaf. Locate a group of cells that look like those in A. Where are they, near the top or the bottom of the leaf?
- Locate a group of cells that look like those in B. Where are they? Are there more in some areas than in others?
- Locate a group of cells that look like those in C. What could be the purpose of this cell group?

- There are pockets of air inside a leaf. Identify where these air pockets are.
- Can you find chloroplasts? If so, in which cells? Why do you think they are in these cells and not in others?

Based on your observations, reasoning, and imagination, explain why you think the cells are arranged the way they are in your plant leaf.

Leaf Cells and Tissues

This diagram shows a simplified view of a leaf cross-section. The labels identify some of the main tissues and cells. Try to match the tissues and cells in the diagram to the cross-section photos on the previous page.

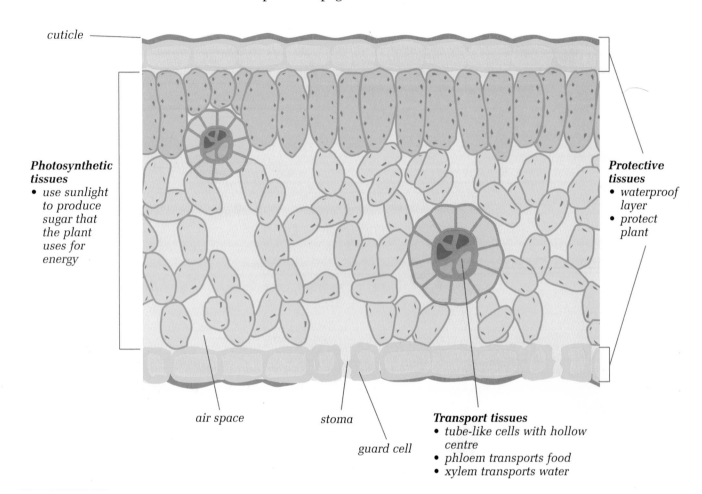

cuticle

Photosynthetic tissues
• use sunlight to produce sugar that the plant uses for energy

Protective tissues
• waterproof layer
• protect plant

air space

stoma

guard cell

Transport tissues
• tube-like cells with hollow centre
• phloem transports food
• xylem transports water

Communicate

1 a) Name the plant organ that you observed in this section.
   b) Identify the tissues that make up this organ.
   c) Describe the cells that make up each of the tissues in this organ.

2 a) Identify one specialized leaf tissue and one specialized leaf cell.
   b) Describe the structure of the tissue and cell you identified.
   c) Explain the function of the tissue and cell you identified.

3 How does the structure of a plant leaf help it move water, food, and gases?

4 Use an example to describe how water and gases move into and out of leaf cells during diffusion.

4.3 THE TRANSPORT SYSTEM IN PLANTS

Explore

You have seen that the leaves of green plants have specialized cells and tissues for collecting sunlight and carbon dioxide, two of the three main requirements for photosynthesis. However, leaf cells cannot carry out this essential, life-supporting function without the third main requirement: water.

As you might expect, plants have specialized cells and tissues for absorbing and moving water. In other words, plants have a transport system. You will look for evidence of this system in the next activity.

INVESTIGATOR

OBSERVING EVIDENCE OF PLANT TRANSPORT

The Question

What inferences can you make about the way substances are transported throughout a plant?

Materials & Equipment

- *a white, long-stemmed carnation or Queen Anne's Lace*
- *2 different colours of food colouring (such as red and green)*
- *two 500 mL beakers or water bottles*
- *straws*
- *a sharp knife*
- *a cutting board such as a sheet of cardboard, plywood, or plastic*
- *watch or clock*
- *ruler*
- *tap water*

Caution!

Be very careful when handling the knife. This is especially important during step 3 of the Procedure.

continued on next page ·······▶

1

CELLS AND CELL SYSTEMS

Procedure

1. Add cool or room-temperature tap water to the beakers or bottles so they are about three-quarters full. Try to make sure they have the same volume of water. Put some red food colouring in one and green food colouring in the other. Wait until the colour diffuses throughout the water in the beakers.

2. While you're waiting, prepare the carnation. You will want the flower to have a stem about 25 cm long. Use your knife to trim the bottom of the stem as necessary.

3. Hold the flower-head steady and pierce the stem with the knife blade. Then run the blade carefully down the stem to split it along its entire length. You may need to pause now and again so you can move your hand to steady the stem.

4. Insert one side of the split stem into the red water and the other into the green water. Use the straws to support the carnation so it stands upright.

Keeping Records

5. Design a chart to record your observations over time intervals of one, two, and three days.

Analyzing and Interpreting

6. Describe what happened to the plant.
7. Which plant parts were involved?
8. Which plant parts were not involved? (In other words, were you working with a complete plant?)
9. Did you observe diffusion or osmosis in this activity? If so, say where.

Forming Conclusions

10. Give one possible explanation for what you observed. Use your reasoning and your understanding of cells to guide you.
    a) How much confidence do you have in your explanation? If you're very confident, say why. If you aren't, say what additional information would give you greater confidence.
    b) Suggest an idea for an experiment that would help you test your explanation. (If possible, design the experiment, show it to your teacher, and then carry it out.)

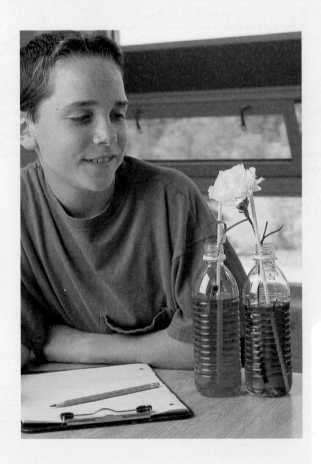

The Function and Structure of Root Cells and Stem Cells

The root and stem of a plant both play an important role in the transport of materials through the plant. In addition to this role, they each have other functions that support the plant's life. Root cells and stem cells therefore have different structures that reflect these other functions.

Root Cells and Tissues

Taproot—carrots

Fibrous root—sunflower sprout

There are two main kinds of roots: *taproots* and *fibrous roots*. Both kinds anchor a plant firmly in the ground. They also help provide support for the stem. Most importantly, roots absorb water and dissolved minerals from the soil, and transport these substances up to other plant parts.

Root hairs on a radish seedling

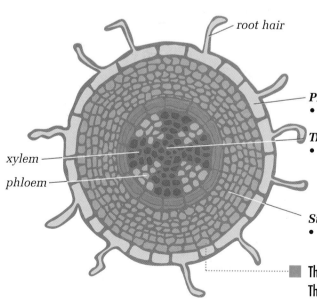

root hair

xylem

phloem

Protective tissues
• *absorb water from soil*

Transport tissues
• *phloem and xylem are surrounded by a circle of cells*

Storage tissues
• *store food*

This diagram shows a simplified view of a root cross-section. The labels identify some of the main tissues and cells.

Expensive Gates

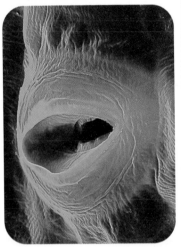

Two crescent-shaped cells close together form the opening of a stoma.

Plants need to take in carbon dioxide from the air and have tiny pores, called **stomata**, that allow air to move inside their tissues. However, plants pay a price for this need. Most of the water that plants absorb from the soil—more than 90%—is lost into the air through those same openings. The water evaporates inside the photosynthetic tissue layer of the leaf and then diffuses out of the openings.

- What would you predict about the number of stomata in a desert plant? In a marsh plant? Why?

Stem Cells and Tissues

Stems provide support for a plant's leaves so they can collect sunlight. In some kinds of plants, stems perform photosynthesis. Most importantly, stems transport water and dissolved substances between the roots and the leaves and throughout the rest of the plant.

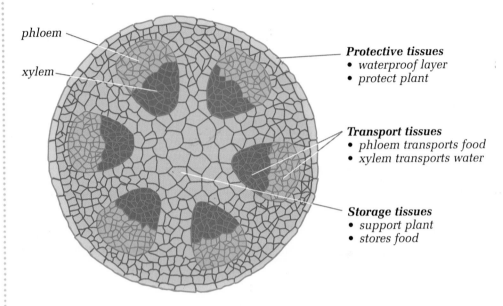

phloem

xylem

Protective tissues
- *waterproof layer*
- *protect plant*

Transport tissues
- *phloem transports food*
- *xylem transports water*

Storage tissues
- *support plant*
- *stores food*

This diagram shows a simplified view of a stem cross-section. The labels identify some of the main tissues and cells.

Communicate

1 a) Name the plant system or systems that you observed in this section.
   b) Name the plant tissues that you observed in this section.
   c) Describe the cells that make up each of these tissues.

2 How do the structure of plant roots and stems enable them to move water, food, and gases? Use a diagram to help explain your answer.

3 Use an example to describe how water and gases move into and out of root cells during diffusion.

4 Would you expect a plant that lives in water to have strong roots? Why or why not?

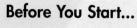
Experiment
ON YOUR OWN

Before You Start...

Have you ever given or received flowers from someone? How did they look at first? How did they change over time? Why did this happen?

Selling fresh, vibrant cut flowers is big business. Flower shops use a variety of methods to keep plants fresh-looking for as long as possible. What's the science behind these methods? Use your understanding of plant cells and tissues to help you solve the following problem.

The Question

Which substance, technique, or both, will keep flowers from wilting for as long as possible?

Your Task

1 Make a hypothesis.
2 Decide what materials and equipment you'll need to test your hypothesis. For example:
   a) What kind of plant will you use, and how many will you need?
   b) What substances do you need to test your hypothesis?
   c) Where can you find what you need, and what substitutions could you make, if necessary?
   d) How will you troubleshoot for safety?
3 Plan your procedure. For example:
   a) What evidence are you looking for to support your hypothesis?
   b) How long will you run your experiment?
   c) How will you collect your data?
   d) What variables are you working with, and how can you make sure that your test is fair?
   e) How will you record your results?
4 Write up your procedure and show it to your teacher.
5 Carry out your experiment.
6 Compare your results with your hypothesis. Were you able to support it? If not, what possible reasons might there be?
7 How did you keep water moving through the plant's roots, stems, and leaves? Can you explain your results in terms of water moving through the plant?
8 Share and compare your experimental design and findings with your classmates. How do your results compare with theirs?

4.4 CHECK YOUR PROGRESS

1 a) Write a sentence that explains why plants need a transport system.

   b) Give examples to support your explanation.

2 Use words, sketches, or both, to describe how a water particle gets into a plant, and what happens to it. Your answer can be creative, but it must also be scientifically accurate.

3 Imagine you are a producer of a television gardening show. Outline a script for a segment of the show that explains why water is important for plants. Prepare your script in two columns: one for visuals and one for speech (on-camera dialogue and narration).

4 In which plant tissues would you expect to find more air spaces? Explain your reasoning.

5 Create an information booklet that explains and illustrates root and stem tissues and specialized cells. Be sure to describe the structures of the tissue and cells you identified and explain their functions.

6 Compare the external structures of the plants shown here. Infer how they are adapted for living in their environments. If necessary, do some quick fact-checking to verify your inferences.

7 Big Idea 4.0 states, "The health of a plant depends on the health of its cells and tissues." What does "health of its cells and tissues" mean to you? Give three examples to support this Big Idea.

BIG IDEA
5.0 Your health depends on the health of your cells.

You can tell the difference between a healthy pond ecosystem and an unhealthy one by examining its living components. A healthy ecosystem is full of life, with each living thing able to get what it needs from its environment. There is plenty of oxygen, a source of energy, and enough nutrients. The wastes that these organisms produce do not build up into dangerous amounts.

In the same way, the body of a healthy multicellular organism, whether a person or a rose bush, depends, in turn, on the health of each and every cell. The first requirement for healthy cells is that they are able to get the oxygen, energy, and nutrients they need to survive. That's where this Big Idea will start.

5.1 HOW VITAL SUBSTANCES ARE TRANSPORTED TO AND FROM YOUR CELLS

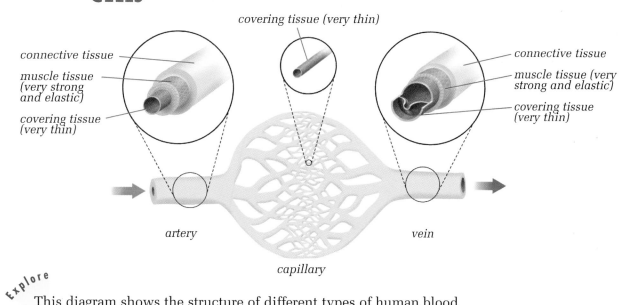

connective tissue

muscle tissue (very strong and elastic)

covering tissue (very thin)

covering tissue (very thin)

connective tissue

muscle tissue (very strong and elastic)

covering tissue (very thin)

artery

vein

capillary

Explore

This diagram shows the structure of different types of human blood vessels. Examine it carefully. With a partner, discuss your answers to these questions.

- In what ways are the tissues that make up these blood vessels the same? In what ways are they different?

- Look at the arteries and the veins. Do the differences in their structure make sense with regard to their function?
- In section 1.2, you designed a model of the pumping action of the heart through arteries and veins. Review your model and recall your reasons for choosing the materials you used. How do these materials compare with real arteries and veins?
- Why is the structure of capillaries so much simpler than the structure of arteries and veins?

Develop

The Gas Exchange Process

Your cells need oxygen to release energy through cellular respiration. They also need to rid themselves of the carbon dioxide waste gas that they produce during this process. Two body systems work together so that cells can exchange these two gases.

The respiratory system draws oxygen-rich air into the lungs through a series of tube-like passageways. These passageways narrow until they end in about 600 000 000 tiny, air-filled sacs called **alveoli**.

The tissue that makes up the air sacs is only one cell thick. Notice also that the air sacs are enveloped in a mesh of **capillaries**.

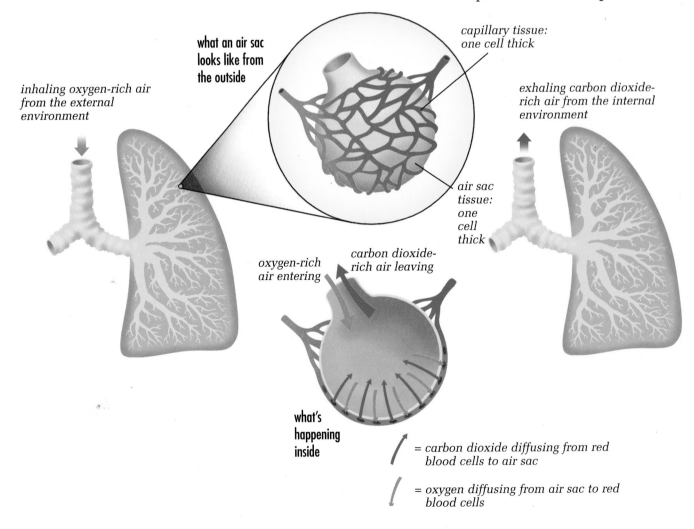

what an air sac looks like from the outside

capillary tissue: one cell thick

inhaling oxygen-rich air from the external environment

exhaling carbon dioxide-rich air from the internal environment

air sac tissue: one cell thick

carbon dioxide-rich air leaving

oxygen-rich air entering

what's happening inside

= *carbon dioxide diffusing from red blood cells to air sac*

= *oxygen diffusing from air sac to red blood cells*

5.0 Your Health Depends on the Health of Your Cells

Capillary tissue is also only one cell thick. This means that the distance between the air inside the air sacs and the blood inside the capillaries is very short. If you think back to what you have learned about diffusion, you probably have a good idea of what this means.

The air in the air sacs has a high concentration of oxygen and a low concentration of carbon dioxide. The blood in the capillaries surrounding the air sacs has a low concentration of oxygen and a high concentration of carbon dioxide. So oxygen naturally diffuses from the air sacs into the capillaries. Carbon dioxide naturally diffuses in the other direction. In one second, blood travels through all the capillaries in your lungs. That's all the time it takes for your blood to take in as much oxygen as it can hold and release its carbon dioxide waste.

• Why do you think it's important to breathe deeply when exercising?

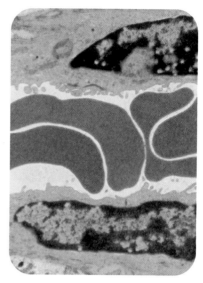

Red blood cells in a capillary

How Do Other Vital Substances Reach Your Body Cells?
The diagram below is a simplified view of the path that blood travels through your body. You've already developed an understanding of what happens in the area labelled A. Now, do the following:

• In your Science Journal, summarize your understanding of gas exchange using words, pictures, or both.
• Then extend and apply your understanding. Recall that cells need energy, as well as oxygen, for cellular respiration. This energy comes from nutrients such as carbohydrates, fats, and proteins. Explain what you think happens in the area labelled B for cells to get the oxygen and nutrients they need. (That's a big area, of course. So decide on one or two examples to focus your answer.)

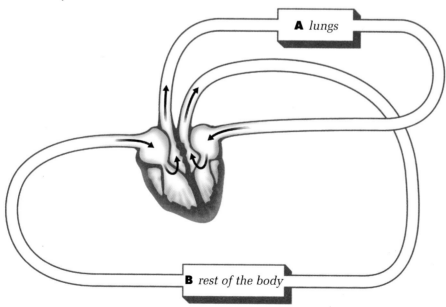

A *lungs*

B *rest of the body*

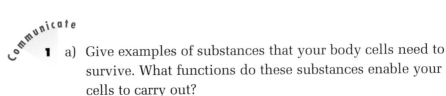

1 a) Give examples of substances that your body cells need to survive. What functions do these substances enable your cells to carry out?

   b) Describe the similarities between the needs of your cells and the general needs of your body.

2 What might be the effect or impact of the following imaginary situations?

   a) The covering tissue of your capillaries is much thicker.

   b) Air-sac tissue is much thicker.

3 a) Examine the digestive systems of the animals shown in the following diagrams. In what ways are the structures of these systems similar and different?

   b) Based on your answer to a), describe how the functions of these structures may be similar and different.

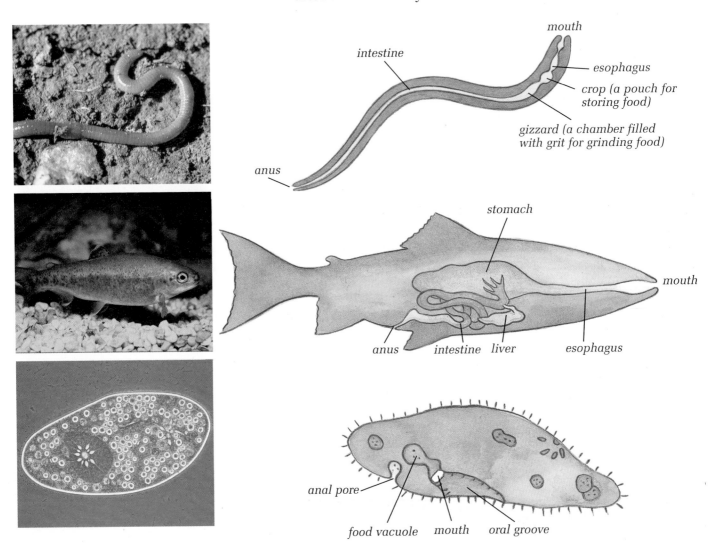

mouth

intestine

esophagus

crop (a pouch for storing food)

gizzard (a chamber filled with grit for grinding food)

anus

stomach

mouth

anus   *intestine*   *liver*   *esophagus*

anal pore

food vacuole   *mouth*   *oral groove*

4 Why is the food you eat directly related to your health? Use your understanding of cells to answer this question.

5.2 FACTORS THAT AFFECT THE HEALTH OF YOUR CELLS

Gases such as oxygen and carbon dioxide dissolve easily in water. So do solids such as sugar and salt. In fact, more substances dissolve in water than in any other solvent.

This amazing property of water is vital to every cell, tissue, organ, and system in your body. Your health—your very survival—depends on it!

- Discuss this idea with a partner. Use as many detailed examples as you can.

Develop

Healthy Cells Make a Healthy Body

Many factors affect the health of your cells, and therefore, your own health and well-being. These factors include:

- diseases or conditions that you have inherited from your family
- sensitivity to environmental conditions (such as smog) or specific substances (such as pollen, dust, or dairy products)
- how you respond to physical, emotional, and psychological stresses
- how you treat your body in general (for example, by making choices about diet, exercise, sleep, and smoking)

You have learned a great deal about cells and their life-supporting functions. The next activity gives you a chance to extend and enhance your understanding. You will take a more in-depth look at a specific organ system.

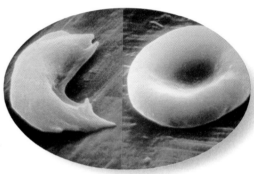

The sickle-shaped blood cell on the left causes anemia.

Cells That Affect Your Body

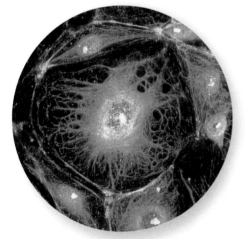

These cancer cells are from a tumor.

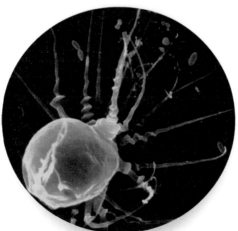

A white blood cell attacking a bacteria cell.

These are the virus that cause polio.

1 CELLS AND CELL SYSTEMS

HEALTHY CELLS FOR LIFE

Maintaining a Healthy Body

CANADA'S

Food Guide

TO HEALTHY EATING
FOR PEOPLE FOUR YEARS
AND OVER

Health Santé
Canada Canada

Enjoy a variety
of foods from each
group every day.

Choose lower-
fat foods
more often.

Grain Products
Choose whole grain
and enriched
products more often.

Vegetables and Fruit
Choose dark green and
orange vegetables and
orange fruit more often.

Milk Products
Choose lower-fat milk
products more often.

Meat and Alternatives
Choose leaner meats,
poultry and fish, as well
as dried peas, beans

The Question

What is the best action plan that outlines your recommendations for maintaining the health of our body systems?

Background Information

1 To make your recommendations, you need more information. Working in groups of five, have each group member choose one of the following body systems to investigate further.

continued on next page ⋯⋯➤

a) circulatory system
b) digestive system
c) nervous system
d) excretory system
e) respiratory system

2 Use the guidelines below to focus your investigation. Record the process and results of your research with notes, diagrams, flowcharts, tables, and graphs. (Some of these may not apply in all cases. Use your judgement to choose the best methods for recording your data and information.)

a) List the system's main organs, tissues, and cells. Give examples of key features or specializations of the cells that contribute to the healthy functioning of the system.

b) List other body systems that depend on this system and those that this system depends on. Briefly describe the nature of this interdependency.

c) List at least three examples of scientific developments that have improved our understanding of this system and its cells. Briefly describe each example.

d) Describe at least three ways that we have used our new understanding to improve or safeguard human health.

e) Identify at least two helpful and two harmful substances that alter the way the cells of this system function. Describe the impact of these changes on its tissues and organs. Include possible effects on other body systems and on the body as a whole.

3 Share your discoveries with other members of your group. Consult with other groups as well. You may have gathered information that they can benefit from, and they may have done the same for you.

In Your Opinion

4 What do you think is the best way to maintain your body's health? Develop a plan and outline your recommendations. For example:
- Decide on the kind of exercise you would like to maintain for your body and body systems.
- Write up a balanced diet plan that provides you with the nutrition you need.
- List the things you can do to reduce stress and enjoy each day.

5 Once you have made your plan, post it where you can refer to it daily. That way you can remind yourself to live each day in a healthy, happy way that will help you build toward a long and successful future.

Communicate

1 Based on the research you have done, give two examples of ways that research about cells has improved human health.

2 Based on the research you have done, give two examples of substances that change the way cells function. Describe their effect, and the consequences of their effect.

3 Choose three types of cells in your body. For each, describe how it contributes to your health.

5.3 DEVELOPING A THEORY FOR DISEASE

Explore

Have you ever fallen off a bike and received a wound that needed attention in the hospital? Have you ever cut yourself with a knife so that you needed stitches? Have you or has anyone you know ever seriously broken a bone?

If you answered "yes" to any of these questions, consider yourself lucky. Why? Because you're alive. If you had lived before the beginning of modern medicine, you would probably have died from your injury. In those days, 50% of people who had some kind of punctured wound and went to the hospital died of infection. That means that if you and your friend lived then and you both cut yourselves and went to the hospital for treatment, the chances were that *one of you would be dead within a week!*

Develop

The First Vaccine

That's quite a startling fact. Doctors long ago were really quite helpless when it came to treating their patients for some illnesses and injuries.

During the 1600s and 1700s, people in Europe and the rest of the world suffered and died from a disease called **smallpox**. Victims broke out in a rash filled with pus (called pox). They developed chills, high fever, nausea, and muscle aches. Up to 40% of those infected died and many of the survivors were left blind.

Then in the late 1700s, Edward Jenner, an English country doctor, noticed an interesting coincidence. Milkmaids who had had cowpox, a mild and related form of smallpox, rarely got smallpox. He concluded that contracting the milder cowpox made them immune to the more serious smallpox. Jenner began infecting people with cowpox on purpose. These people became immune to smallpox and Jenner had created the world's first **vaccine**.

Smallpox was a cruel disease. At one time, it was the leading cause of death in Europe, with over 400 000 people dying each year. Edward Jenner (1749–1823) discovered how to prevent the disease. He called his procedure *vaccination*, from the Latin word *vacca*, which means "cow."

Watch Out for Germs!

But what caused disease and infection? That's what doctors and scientists couldn't figure out. Jenner and others tried for nearly 90 years to come up with at least one other vaccine that would prevent disease. They failed, because they just didn't understand what they were dealing with.

The French chemist, Louis Pasteur, did. He was the first person to identify living micro-organisms as "germs." He suggested and later proved that germs were the cause of most infectious diseases. Using this knowledge, he found a way to prevent and cure many common but deadly diseases.

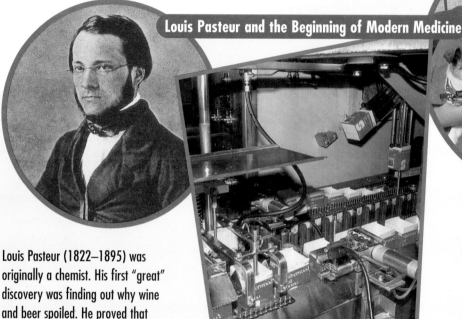

Louis Pasteur and the Beginning of Modern Medicine

Louis Pasteur (1822–1895) was originally a chemist. His first "great" discovery was finding out why wine and beer spoiled. He proved that yeast was actually a micro-organism and not a chemical, which is what people thought. More importantly, he showed that it was a micro-organism floating in the air that made the wine and beer go bad.

Pasteur worked tirelessly to produce vaccines and cures for cholera, anthrax, swine erysipelas, and rabies. Now each year, pet owners take their dogs and cats to veterinarians for annual rabies vaccination shots.

Pasteur realized he needed to kill the harmful micro-organisms in wine and beer to keep them from spoiling. His solution was simple but effective. He heated the wine and beer to 60°C, which killed the micro-organisms but didn't change the taste. This process of heating food became known as **pasteurization**. It is still used today for fruit juices, milk, wine, and beer.

Cleaning Up the Germs

Pasteur's discovery of germs led to other discoveries in medicine. For example, Joseph Lister (1827–1912) was an English surgeon. Many of his patients died of infection even though their operations were successful. He thought that these infections were caused by Pasteur's "germs" entering the surgical wounds. So he introduced the practice of cleanliness and sterilization to medical procedures. Before Lister, doctors and nurses never thought about keeping themselves or their patients' wounds and incisions clean.

TRACKING DOWN DISEASE

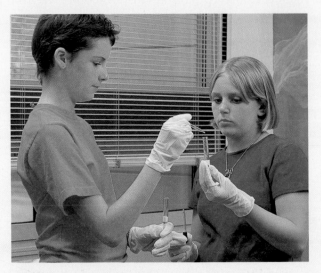

Before You Start...

Long before modern medicine, people realized that certain diseases were spread from person to person. It was important then to find the source and isolate the person or persons until the disease had run its course.

Here's your chance to play medical detective. This simulation models how an infectious disease might spread in a group.

The Question

How difficult is it to find the source of a disease?

Materials & Equipment

- *clean test tubes*
- *labels for test tubes*
- *eyedroppers*
- *protective gloves*
- *standard solution*
- *phenol red solution*

Procedure

1 Write your name on a label and place it on your test tube.

2 Put on your gloves. Don't allow the solutions to touch your skin. Remember, you are simulating an infectious disease!

3 Obtain from your teacher 5 mL of a standard solution in your test tube.

4 Choose a partner. Put one drop of your solution into your partner's test tube. Have your partner add a drop of solution to your test tube. Gently shake the test tube to mix the solution.

5 Record the name of your partner in your Science Journal.

6 Repeat steps 4 and 5 with two other partners.

7 Add 1 drop of phenol red solution to your test tube. Record the colour of your solution.

Analyzing and Interpreting

8 What colour was your test tube? Were you infected or are you disease-free?

9 If you were infected, from whom did you get the disease? How many in the class became infected?

10 As a class, try to track the transmission of the disease. Who was its source?

Forming Conclusions

11 What inferences can you make about the way diseases are spread?

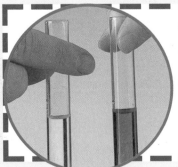

- If your test tube turned red, you are disease-free!
- If your test tube turned yellow, you are infected!

1 In your opinion, how important is scientific research in solving problems of human health and nutrition? Give reasons to justify your answer.

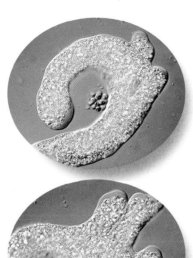

5.4 CHECK YOUR PROGRESS

1 a) Which two body systems work together during the process of gas exchange?
   b) Describe how they work together in this process.
   c) Is this an example of interdependency? Why or why not?

2 Are there any body systems that a person could live without? Give reasons to explain your answer.

3 a) Identify three factors that affect human health, and explain how.
   b) In section 5.2, you read that these factors "affect the health of your cells, and therefore, your own health and well-being." Explain how this is true.

4 These pictures show how the amoeba gets the food it needs to survive. Describe the structures you think are involved. Then infer how the amoeba eliminates its wastes.

5 The study of medicine goes back thousands of years to ancient times. Why do you think it took so long to discover the cause of disease?

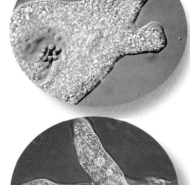

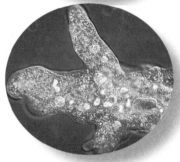

---

*info***BIT**

Medical Breakthroughs

In 1928, Scottish biologist Alexander Flemming (1881–1955) accidentally made a discovery. While examining a harmful disease-causing germ (or bacteria), he noticed that a light blue mould had killed some of the germs. The mould was *Penicillium notatum,* and so he named his germ-killing substance **penicillin**. He realized that this mould could be used to kill all sorts of germs that make people sick. It was the world's first **antibiotic**.

Today penicillin and other antibiotics are used to treat many diseases, including meningitis, pneumonia, diphtheria, and blood poisoning.

Penicillium mould on an orange

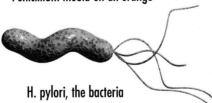

H. pylori, the bacteria that causes stomach ulcers

For over a century, doctors were convinced that stomach or peptic ulcers were mainly caused by stress. Then in the early 1980s, two Australian doctors, Barry Marshall and Robin Warren, discovered a bacteria in the stomach lining of patients with peptic ulcers. They believed the bacteria was the cause, not stress. For years the medical community refused to accept their findings. Then in 1985, Dr. Marshall swallowed a sample of the bacteria to prove his point. He quickly developed a stomach inflammation that was known to cause ulcers. Later studies showed that this bacteria could be killed by antibiotics.

Boost Your Performance!

BOOST YOUR PERFORMANCE!
Run Faster!   Jump Higher!   Throw Further!

Champion Mountain Climber Ray Peak
"Super Duper Energy Bars are fantastic! They give me that boost of energy I need to reach the summit!"

It seems that every day, product ads and media articles pronounce amazing claims. Like the ad for SuperDuper Energy Bars, the claims offer a "quick-fix" solution to real health concerns. *Take this bar and your energy worries are over! Down this pill and your cold is gone forever!*

But how do you know if these claims are true? For example, will SuperDuper Energy Bars really help you reach that summit? Follow the path our researcher took to prove or disprove SuperDuper's claims.

NUTRITION INFORMATION
PER 60 g SERVING (1 BAR)

ENERGY.................................236 Cal
                                        980 kJ

PROTEIN...................................10 g

FAT...2.5 g
CARBOHYDRATE....................45 g

Read the Label

Research starts with the product. Most energy bars contain high levels of carbohydrates.

Carbohydrates are found in many of the foods we eat, including rice, pasta, and bread. Your body uses carbohydrates as fuel to do energetic activities, like running a marathon or climbing a mountain. If you run out of fuel from carbohydrates part way through an athletic event, your performance will drop quickly. Consuming carbohydrates *before* this happens will boost your performance.

Look on the Web

To check out carbohydrates, our researcher first went to the Internet. But beware. There's so much information on the Web that it can be time consuming and frustrating trying to find what you need. Also, some information found on the Web may not be accurate. It's always a good idea to get information from a variety of different print and media sources.

Energy Bars Get Zapped!

Out exercising and need a quick energy boost? Are you reaching for the latest athletic food fad, an energy bar?

The ads claim that energy bars provide athletes with a superhuman burst of energy. But according to researchers at Jock University, a bowl of oatmeal provides the same amount of carbohydrate energy as an energy bar. Eight endurance-trained female cyclists consumed either an energy bar or oatmeal two hours before a 60-minute cycling workout. The researchers found no performance difference between the two groups. Perhaps if oatmeal had a more exciting name, like "Oatmeal Burst," athletes would flock to it as well as energy bars.

Ask the Experts

Next, the researcher found an expert on nutrition. Experts can be found in all sorts of places: universities, businesses, government agencies.

- Brainstorm all of the places you might find someone who knows something about your topic. (See In Your Opinion.)
  - Draw up a list of questions that you might ask the expert.

According to nutritionist Thomas Wolever, your body can store enough fuel from carbohydrates to give you about two hours of non-stop energetic activity. So if you work out for only twenty minutes, you'll still have plenty of fuel left over. Gobbling up more carbohydrates will not improve your performance. "If you're just going out and playing a game of football or baseball," says Wolever, "an energy bar probably won't make a whole lot of difference."

Look It Up in Newspapers and Magazines

Our researcher spent hours going over newspaper and magazine articles. It's always useful to read what others have already written. Most libraries carry back issues of certain newspapers and magazines. But don't believe everything you read. Just because it's in print doesn't mean it's true. Check to see if the article mentions where it got its facts. Then check out this new source of information.

Check Out Scientific Studies

Finally, our researcher read the scientific studies on energy bars. A proper scientific study is one that has been peer-reviewed. This means that the scientists who did the study presented the results of their work to other scientists, their peers, for review. Quite often, advertising claims are based on research done by the company—research that has not been peer-reviewed by the scientific community.

In Your Opinion

1. How did the above information change your opinion of energy bars?
2. Research one of the following products to discover if the claims made about them are true. Think about what sources of information you can use: library, Internet, magazines, experts, your own knowledge of science.
   a) a herbal remedy such as echinacea
   b) a meal-replacement drink
   c) a body care product such as moisturizer, shampoo, or acne cream
3. When you're finished, ask yourself: How did the information I found change my opinion of the product?

PROJECT

Getting Started

You are an executive of the Learn-Through-Play Gaming Company. The Company's mission is to develop toys and games that are fun, safe, reliable, and educational. The president has discovered that you have been learning about cells and cell systems. She thinks this makes you the best candidate to oversee the development of a new game. This game is intended for children aged 9 to 11. Its aim is to teach how cells contribute to the healthy functioning of organisms. Just what the game will be like is up to you and the other members of your design team. However, the company president has outlined the following four conditions.

1 The game can be focussed on one or more of these themes:
   • the needs of unicellular and multicellular organisms
   • the structure and function of plants and their cells
   • cells, tissues, organs, and systems in the human body
2 The game's characters must be cells.
3 The game's setting can be a small puddle or pond, the inside of a plant, or the inside of a person or other animal.
4 The game must "teach well" and "sell well." To "teach well," it must be scientifically accurate and have easy-to-follow directions. To "sell well," it must be appealing to look at and fun to play.

Before You Start...

Begin by reviewing your progress. Look through your Science Journal and this chapter. With a partner, discuss the needs that cells have and how cells meet those needs. Compose a list of important ideas that you think people should know about cells, tissues, organs, and body systems. Afterward, share your list with other groups. In what ways are your lists similar and different? Are there any additions you would like to make to your list?

The Question

How can you design a game that will teach players about cells and their role in maintaining an organism's health?

Procedure

1 Brainstorm features of different games that you enjoy playing. Are they board games? card games? role-playing games? What makes the games fun? Are the rules clear and easy to follow? Share these features with your teammates. Make sure one member of your team takes notes.

2 Look at the results of your brainstorming. Begin to focus your ideas. Here are some questions you could ask yourselves.
  a) Which theme would you like to use for your game?
  b) What kind of game would you like to design?
  c) Which elements will be fairly easy to incorporate? Which ones may need some researching or additional thought?
  d) What materials and equipment will you need for your game? What alternatives are there if you can't get or find what you need?

3 The president of the company will judge your game based on the criteria outlined in the Assessment Checklist. How will you ensure that your game meets these criteria?

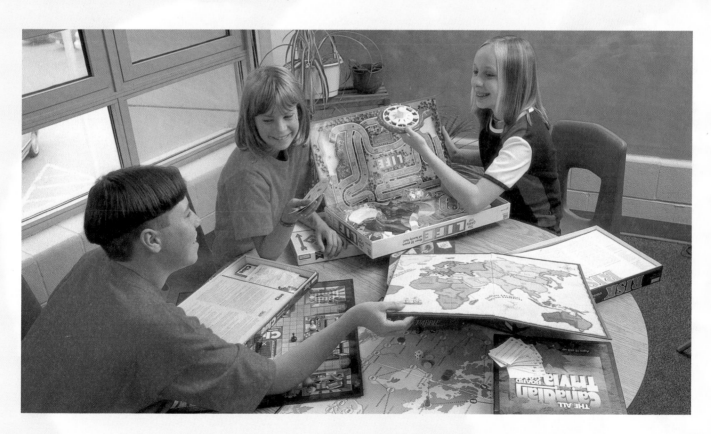

continued on next page ·······>

Assessment Checklist

If your game focusses on unicellular organisms, players should be able to:

❑ identify a variety of single-celled organisms
❑ describe ways that single-celled organisms survive and meet their basic needs
❑ identify organelles and structures of single-celled organisms
❑ explain the function of selectively permeable membranes in single-celled organisms

If your game focusses on plants, players should be able to:

❑ describe the structures and organelles of a typical plant cell
❑ identify specialized cells in roots, stems, and leaves and explain their role in moving water, gases, and food throughout the plant
❑ explain the function of selectively permeable membranes in plant cells
❑ identify specialized structures that enable different kinds of plants to live in certain environmental conditions

If your game focusses on the human body, players should be able to:

❑ describe the structures and organelles that make up a typical animal cell
❑ explain the function of selectively permeable membranes in animal cells
❑ describe diffusion and osmosis in human body cells and tell why they are important
❑ describe the organization of cells into tissues, organs, and body systems
❑ describe how the needs and health of the human body are linked to the needs and health of its cells
❑ identify at least four body systems and explain how they are interdependent

Is your game:

❑ fun to play?
❑ appealing to look at?
❑ something that people would or could play more than once?

4 If you have access to graphics software, you might like to create some or all of your game components on the computer. For example, illustrations and printed instructions can be printed out and mounted on cardboard.

Share and Compare

5 An important step in developing any successful game is to let people play it and give you their feedback. This is the best way to find out if any rules or instructions are unclear or confusing. Player feedback also lets you know whether people find the game interesting and fun.

a) Make sure at least several different people or groups try out your first working design. The more feedback you get, the more information you have to work with.

b) When you have completed your game, present and share it with the rest of your class.

c) Be prepared to modify the rules if necessary. Receive and offer constructive feedback so everyone can improve the quality of the games.

Observations and Reflections

6 How well does your game meet the specified criteria?

7 In your opinion, how well did your game communicate your understanding of the Big Ideas you explored in this chapter? Be as specific as possible in your answer.

8 If you redesigned your game, what did you change? Why? How did these changes improve your game?

CHAPTER REVIEW

Using Key Terms

1 Design a mind map that demonstrates your understanding of the terms below.

> cell
> diffusion
> multicellular
> organ
> organelle
> osmosis
> tissue
> selectively permeable
> system
> unicellular

Reviewing the Big Ideas

2 List some of the factors that can affect your health.

3 a) What do these terms have in common, and how are they different: *artery, capillary, vein*?

   b) The layer of muscle tissue that surrounds your arteries is much thicker than the layer that surrounds your veins. How does this difference in structure suit the function of arteries and veins?

4 Agree or disagree with this statement, and give two examples to support your decision: *The organs of humans are interdependent.*

5 Infer the significance of the following information.

   a) Marta is breathing (inhaling and exhaling) 12 times per minute. She is filling her air sacs with 4200 mL of oxygen-rich air each minute.

   b) Douglas is breathing 20 times per minute. He is filling his air sacs with 3000 mL of oxygen-rich air each minute.

   c) Cathy is breathing 30 times per minute. She is filling her air sacs with 1500 mL of oxygen-rich air each minute.

6 a) Which of these terms do scientists use to describe the most basic unit of all living things: *tissues, organs, cells, body systems*?

   b) Explain how the other three terms are related to the one you chose in a).

7 a) Draw a labelled diagram comparing a typical plant cell and a typical animal cell.

   b) Explain any differences between the cells you drew.

8 Different kinds of specialized cells have different shapes. They often have different organelles, or different numbers of them. For example, the cells that make up muscles have many mitochondria, while the cells that make up skin have very few. Infer a reason why.

9 (a) In this diagram, which particles can move through the selectively permeable membrane? Explain why.

   (b) Is this an example of diffusion or osmosis? How do you know?

   (c) Look closely at the diagram. What do you notice? Why do you think this happened?

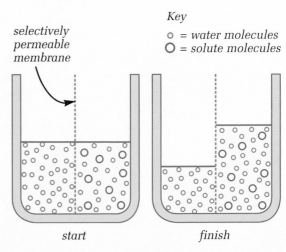

selectively permeable membrane

Key
o = *water molecules*
O = *solute molecules*

start   *finish*

10 In what ways are the needs of your individual cells related to the needs of your whole body?

11 The carrot in photo A was put in a dry, warm place for several days. Then photo B was taken. Compare the mass of the carrot in both photos. Explain your findings.

A

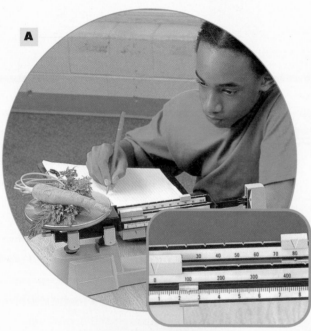

B

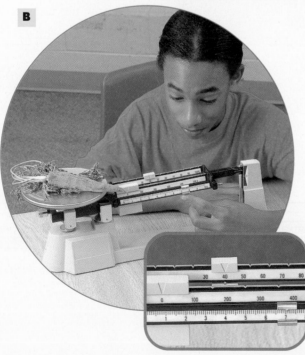

Connecting the Big Ideas

12 Explain how the five Big Ideas that you have explored are related to one another. Your explanation can be in the form of a mind map, an illustration, or a written summary.

13 When scientists think about the possibility of life on another planet, they want to know if that planet has water. In fact, scientists find it hard to imagine life without water. Why might that be?

14 Give at least one example to describe how root cells are specialized to help plants get what they need to survive. Then do the same for plant stem cells and leaf cells.

15 a) You have probably observed at least two different unicellular organisms in this chapter. Compare the similarities and differences of all the unicellular organisms you have personally observed in this chapter. Use a chart or a mind map to record your answers.

   b) In what ways are these organisms similar to a human cell? In what ways are they different?

16 a) Which of the unicellular organisms in the following photos are probably producers in microscopic ecosystems? Which ones are consumers? Give reasons for your answers. (If you're unsure, say so—and say why.)

b) Explain the differences between producers and consumers.

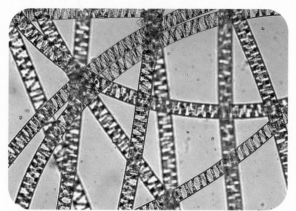
Spirogyra

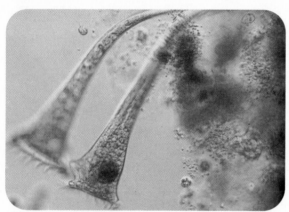
Stentor coeruleus

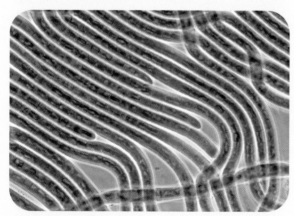
Oscillatoria tenuis

Using the Big Ideas

17 Your friend has a bad cold, and has been coughing and sneezing around you. Several days later, you develop a cold. Explain how this could have happened. (Hint: Use your understanding of cells and what they need to survive to help you.)

18 Reread the infoBIT about water loss in plants in section 4.3 (Expensive Gates).
  a) Why would water vapour naturally move out of the leaf and into the air?
  b) The leaves of some plants have adaptations to deal with this water-loss problem. For example, the epidermis cells in this leaf are specialized to grow a mat of fine, fuzzy hairs. How do you think these hairs help the leaf conserve water?

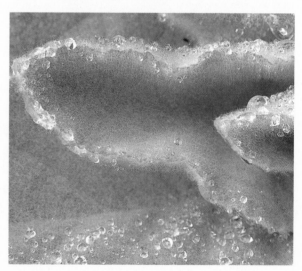

19 Meat and fish are sometimes preserved from spoiling by salting them or by placing them in a salty solution. What effect do you think the salt has on these foods? (Hint: Think about the basic needs that all living things have.)

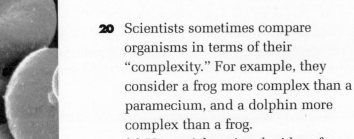
20 Scientists sometimes compare organisms in terms of their "complexity." For example, they consider a frog more complex than a paramecium, and a dolphin more complex than a frog.

(a) How might using the idea of complexity help a scientist?

(b) What do you think about the use of this idea? Do you find it helpful or informative? Why or why not?

21 a) Design a brand new plant. Start by choosing an environment for it. For example, will your plant live in a tropical rain forest or a city park? Will it float on the surface of a pond or cling to a mountainside? Will its climate be very dry? cold? hot? humid?

b) Based on your choices, decide on the adaptations that will help it survive. Think about the specialized cells and tissues it will need and what organs these might form.

c) Sketch your design, including details of its external and internal (cellular) structure. Share your sketch with other students to see if they can infer what environment your plant is adapted for. Be prepared to provide reasons for all the details you included.

d) If you like, construct a model of your plant using an appropriate computer program, or using wire and papier mâché. Then display your finished model for others to share.

22 Identify at least two things that you can do to improve or maintain your state of health. Describe the impact and effect of each of your choices.

Self Assessment

23 Reflect on your experiences in this chapter—the questions you've asked and answered, the new questions you may have, and the work you've done.

a) Select one piece of work that you put a lot of effort into. (The piece of work could be—for example—an experiment you designed, an idea you "wrestled with" to understand, or a model you constructed.)

b) Select one piece of work that you're especially proud of.

c) Select one piece of work that you're unsatisfied with, or think you could have done better on.

d) Give reasons for each of the selections you just made.

FLUIDS

The earth is a planet covered and immersed in what scientists call *fluids*. Fluids are substances that are able to flow and to take the shape of their containers. Both water, which covers the surface of the planet, and air, which completely surrounds it, are fluids. Your body depends on fluids as well. Besides the air you breathe, your heart, which is an organ that moves fluids, pumps blood (a fluid) throughout your body. Many of the devices and means of transportation we use today depend upon the nature of fluids: mechanical pumps of all kinds, jacks and lifts, braking systems, boats, and even airplanes.

In this chapter, you will discover that fluids have many different properties. You will investigate the relationships among some of these properties and have a chance to apply what you learn to building devices that use fluids in a variety of ways.

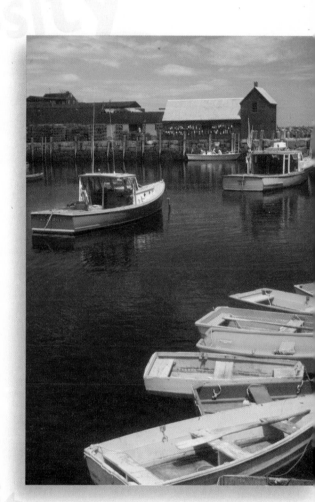

BIG Ideas

1.0 All fluids demonstrate the property of viscosity, or the internal friction that causes a fluid to resist flowing.

2.0 Density is another important property of fluids.

3.0 Fluids exert a buoyant force on objects that allows some objects to float.

4.0 Understanding the properties of fluids helps in designing and building useful devices.

THE JAR-CAR RACE CHALLENGE

Jar-cars are jars of equal size that are half-filled with solids and liquids. They also have a tight lid. Here are the Challenge Rules:

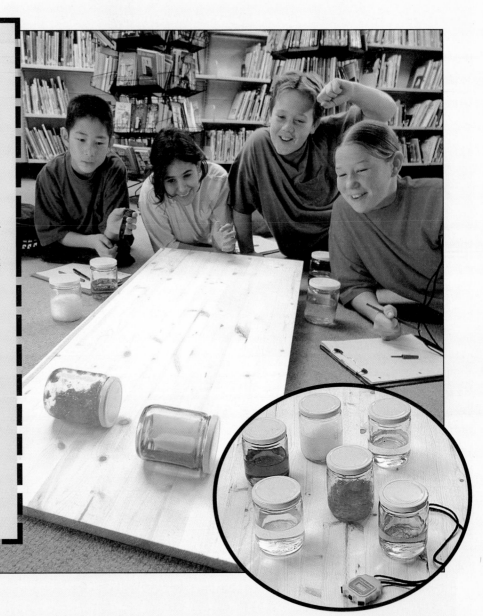

Jar-Car Race Rules

- All the jars must have the same amount of material in them (by volume, not mass).
- You can use any substance approved by your teacher.
- The racing track is a board at least 60 cm long that is raised at one end by placing it on three or four books.
- To race, roll your jar-car down the racing track and time how long it takes to reach the end of the track.
- Before rolling the jar-cars, predict which jar-cars will roll the fastest.

Here are some hints to help you race:

- When you release the jars, just let them go. *Make sure you don't push them.* Also, make sure they will not fall very far if they slip off the track.

- Roll each jar three times. For each substance, take the average time for the three trials. Make a graph that shows your predictions and the final results of the jar races.

Invitation to Explore

Creative Canadians

In 1978, the Canadian government asked two University of Waterloo scientists, Alan Plumtree and Alfred Rudin, to design a reliable hand-operated water pump suitable for use in developing countries. The government required that the new pump meet the following criteria:

- It had to be durable enough to work continuously for 18 hours a day.
- It had to be cheap enough for poorer countries to afford.
- It had to be simple enough for villagers to maintain and repair themselves.
- It had to be designed so that it could be manufactured within developing countries, creating jobs and making spare parts readily available.

When the University of Waterloo scientists were researching pump designs, they noticed a pump at a Mennonite community in southern Ontario. It was practical and reliable and had been used for generations. With this pump as a model, the inventors designed a hand pump made out of a plastic tubing called polyvinyl chloride (PVC). In the past, pumps were made of iron and steel, materials that are scarce and costly in many developing countries. PVC is inexpensive and available everywhere around the world. Plus, PVC doesn't rust! The new PVC pump was light, sturdy, cheap to build, and easy to install and maintain.

Canadian Invention Brings Water to African Villages

RESEARCHERS AT THE University of Waterloo in southern Ontario have developed a low-cost, shallow-well pump that can easily be used in developing countries.

Since the early 1980s, many African and Southeast Asian communities have utilized the pump to bring clean drinking water to their villages.

Now, with the help of the International Research Centre in Ottawa, these inexpensive pumps are being made all over the developing world.

Mennonites in southern Ontario have used hand pumps like this one for generations.

A city canal in Bangkok, Thailand

Clean Drinking Water

Three-quarters of all the people on earth don't have clean drinking water. The rivers and lakes from which they collect water are often polluted, causing dysentery and cholera. Groundwater, on the other hand, is clean because it has been "filtered" by the soil. Unfortunately, a pump to draw water out of the ground is too expensive for many rural villages. Even if they can afford a pump, villagers often don't have the expertise or the spare parts for repairs when it breaks.

Thanks to these Canadian inventors, villagers in developing countries are building and maintaining their own water pumps. As of 1996, over 11 000 hand pumps were being used in 13 developing nations. Local manufacturing provides readily available spare parts, and modifications to the basic design can be made based on local conditions. For example, in Sri Lanka, they decided to use a leather washer instead of a plastic one in their version of the pump. The advantage of the leather one is that it can be made locally. In Malawi, the spigot on the pump has to be made out of black metal because the original white plastic one was eaten by hyenas. The hyenas thought the white spigots looked like bones and kept chewing them off the pumps!

These villagers in Thailand are being trained to maintain and repair a University of Waterloo hand pump recently installed in their village.

Invitation to Explore

The PVC water pump is a good example of the importance of understanding a concept so that you can apply that understanding to different situations. In this case, the inventors knew about the properties of fluids and how a water pump operates. They applied this knowledge to developing a better pump that would work reliably for long hours and be easy to fix. In this chapter, you will work with fluids to develop an understanding of their properties.

What Is a Fluid?

A fluid is any substance in a gas or liquid state.

reSEARCH

Canadian International Organizations

The International Development Research Centre (IDRC) is a crown corporation that worked with the University of Waterloo to develop the hand pump pictured on the previous pages.

• Find out more about IDRC and other Canadian international organizations, such as CIDA (Canadian International Development Agency).

Focus Your Thoughts

1 Think about science activities that you have done or read. Make a list of words that you consider are related to fluids. These may be words you know from previous science classes or words you learned in this section. You don't need definitions, just a list of words.

2 Group the words into categories that make sense to you. For each category, choose a title that describes those words.

3 For each category, think of an example that represents the grouping.

4 Could the jar-car races be considered a fair test? Explain your answer.

5 Which container rolled the fastest? What was different about its contents?

6 Why was the University of Waterloo pump so useful in developing countries?

All fluids demonstrate the property of viscosity, or the internal friction that causes a fluid to resist flowing.

Fluids can be found everywhere. We drink them, we breathe them, and we use them. But how much do you know about fluids? In this Big Idea, you will have an opportunity to investigate an important property of fluids called viscosity.

1.1 INVESTIGATING VISCOSITY

Explore

The **Particle Theory of Matter** attempts to explain matter in a number of ways. It describes:

- a model of matter
- the different states of matter
- what happens when matter changes states.

This model helps you understand and explain observations you will make when investigating matter. Can the Particle Theory be used to describe fluids and how they behave? And what exactly are fluids? Look at the four main points of the Particle Theory shown below. Make notes on what you think would be a good definition of fluids.

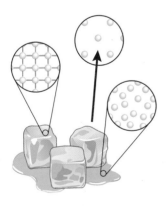

1 *All matter is made of tiny particles. Different substances are made of different particles.*

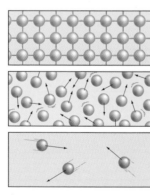

2 *The tiny particles of matter are always moving and vibrating.*

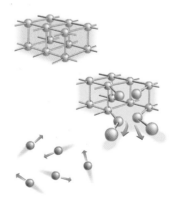

3 *In a liquid, they are close and slide around each other. In a gas, they are far apart.*

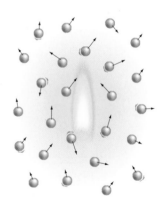

4 *Adding heat to matter makes the particles move around faster and vibrate faster.*

Develop
Viscosity

Most people think of liquids when they hear the word "fluids." But gases are also fluids. In fact, we can think of a **fluid** as any matter that has no fixed shape but that takes the shape of its container. For example, the air in a bicycle tire takes the shape of the tire. The air in a beach ball takes the shape of the ball. In the same way, water in a bottle takes the shape of the bottle, but in a bowl, it takes the shape of the bowl. In this chapter, you will investigate the properties of fluids. In many of these activities, you will use the Particle Theory to help explain your observations.

One property of fluids is how they move or flow. Think about the fluids you have used in the last couple of days. How would using them be different if they didn't flow the way they usually do? For example, what if soda pop was like a thick syrup or ketchup was like water? In both these situations, the properties of the fluids are dramatically different. With your partner, identify three fluids that you have used, and describe what they would be like if they were thicker as well as thinner. Here is an example:

Fluid	Thicker	Thinner
Shampoo	– hard to get out of bottle	– would take a lot to wash hair

How fluids flow is determined by a property called viscosity. **Viscosity** is a liquid's internal resistance or friction that keeps it from flowing. Recall from the Particle Theory that the particles in a liquid slide around and roll over each other. In a gas, the particles move around more easily because they are far apart. In a fluid, the greater the friction or rubbing between the particles, the higher the viscosity. Fluids with a high viscosity do not flow as easily as fluids with a low viscosity.

Flow Rate

Juice has a low viscosity.
Ketchup has a high viscosity.

86

There are several ways to determine the viscosity of fluids. Two common ways you will investigate are the bubble method and the ramp method. Both methods measure how fast a liquid flows through a tube or its **flow rate**.

- In the **bubble method**, you time how long it takes an air bubble to rise through a tube of fluid. The length of time the bubble takes indicates how hard it is for the air bubble to move up through the fluid.
- In the **ramp method**, you time how long it takes a fluid to flow down a ramp.

THE BUBBLE TEST

The Question

How can you compare the viscosity of different liquids?

Materials & Equipment

- *5 clear plastic tubes (cut into lengths of 5 to 30 cm)*
- *10 stoppers or plugs (eyedropper bulbs, binder clips, etc.)*
- *stopwatch*
- *funnel*
- *5 liquids: water, liquid furniture or floor polish, shampoo, pancake or table syrup, vegetable oil*

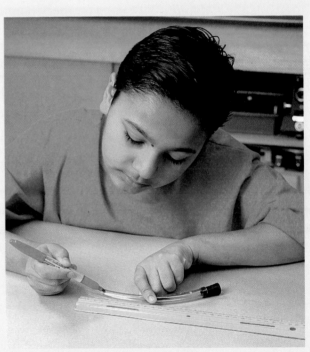

Step 2: mark each tube at 2 cm from end.

Procedure

1. Before your group begins the investigation, make sure you have enough equipment to test all five liquids.
2. Make a mark on each tube at 2 cm from the end.
3. Place a stopper in the unmarked end of a tube. Use the funnel to fill the tube up to the mark with one of the liquids.
4. Seal the marked end of the tube with a stopper.
5. Hold the tube vertically. At the moment that you turn the tube upside down, start your stopwatch. Make sure to hold the tube straight vertically and by only one end.
6. Record the time it takes for the bubble to reach the top of the tube.

continued on next page ······➤

Step 5: turn tube upside down.

7 Repeat steps 5 and 6 two more times with the same tube and record the times.

8 Repeat steps 3, 4, 5, 6, and 7 and for each liquid.

Keeping Records

9 Record your results in a table similar to the following.

Time for Bubble Test				
Fluid	Trial 1	Trial 2	Trial 3	Average Time

Analyzing and Interpreting

10 Look at the three measurements you took for the first liquid. Is one of these measurements very different from the other two? If so, circle this one and do not include it when you calculate the average time. Do the same for the readings for all the other liquids. There could be an error in these circled measurements. You will look at them later in question 14, part d).

11 Calculate the average time that each bubble took to move up its tube of fluid.

12 Based on your results, list the fluids in order from most viscous to least viscous.

13 Share your results with your class.

Forming Conclusions

14 Write a summary for your investigation using the following questions as a guide:
a) What did you do?
b) What question were you trying to answer?
c) What were your results?
d) What sources of error or problems did you encounter? (If you had an error in measurement, describe how you think it happened.)
e) What is one thing you learned in this activity?

*info*BIT

Valves in Your Veins
Most of the larger veins in your body contain one-way valves. They ensure that blood flows in the correct direction.

Blood flowing the correct way through a vein pushes the flaps of the valve open.

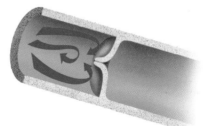

If blood tries to flow backward through a vein, the valve closes.

Viscosity Is Important

Look at the list of fluids you identified at the beginning of this lesson. Each of the fluids you identified would be quite different if its viscosity was different. This is true for many fluids. For example, when you are cooking, you may need to change the viscosity of gravy. If the gravy's viscosity is too low, you might need to add more flour. If its viscosity is too high, you need to add water. Milkshakes and ice cream have thickeners already added to them to make sure that they have the right viscosity.

Communicate

1 Write a short paragraph to describe viscosity. Include at least two examples of fluids and use the words *flow*, *fluid*, *particles*, and *viscosity* in your description.

2 Which of the following materials is the most viscous? Which is the least viscous? How could you determine this?
   a) syrup
   b) house paint
   c) water

3 Describe two substances that are useful because of their viscosity.

1.2 THE EFFECT OF TEMPERATURE ON VISCOSITY

What will happen to the viscosity of these liquids?

Table syrup on hot pancakes   Flowing lava reaches the ocean   Olive oil put into a refrigerator   Room temperature engine oil into a hot engine

1.0 All Fluids Demonstrate the Property of Viscosity, or the Internal Friction That Causes a Fluid to Resist Flowing

Explore

Earlier in this Big Idea, you thought about different fluids and what would happen if their viscosity changed. What might cause a fluid's viscosity to change? Think back to the last activity, The Bubble Test. As you held the straws in your hand, the liquid may have heated up a little. Did you notice a change in the time it took for the bubble to rise between the first, second, and third trials?

Temperature is one factor that can have a big effect on viscosity. In the next activity, you will use the ramp method to design a way to test the effect of temperature on different fluids.

Develop

The Ramp Method

The ramp method of testing viscosity involves pouring a fluid down a ramp and timing how long it takes to get to the bottom. By pouring the same amount of another fluid and timing it, you can compare the viscosities of different fluids. You can also investigate the effect of temperature on viscosity by testing the same fluid several times. First you test the fluid at room temperature. Then you warm it in hot water or cool it in an ice bath, and test it again. In the next activity, you design your own tests.

PROBLEM SOLVER

HOW FAST CAN IT GO?

In the previous Investigator activity, you used the bubble method to test five fluids. Now you will use the ramp test to determine the effect of temperature on the viscosity of one of these five fluids.

- You will use one of the five fluids used in the Investigator activity, a glass or metal ramp, a stopwatch, hot water, and cold water.

- Design a fair test that will allow you to collect evidence to demonstrate the effect of temperature on viscosity. Write out your procedure and show it to your teacher for approval.
- If there is time, repeat this test with one or more of the other four fluids.
- Carry out your test. When you are done, create a one-page summary poster explaining your results.

Understanding Viscosity and Temperature

Your Problem Solver activity may have showed how a change in temperature can affect the viscosity of a fluid. As the temperature increases, the viscosity of a liquid decreases. The opposite is also true. As the temperature decreases, the viscosity of a liquid increases. These changes can greatly affect manufactured devices.

*re*SEARCH

Multi-grade Motor Oil

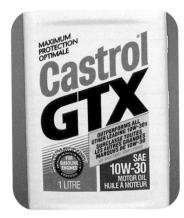

10W30 is a common multi-grade oil used in Canada.

The Society of Automotive Engineers (SAE) assigns all motor oils a viscosity number between 5 and 50. The higher the number, the higher the viscosity. An SAE 30 oil is suitable for summer use, while SAE 10 oil can be used for winter driving. Multi-grade motor oil, such as SAE 10W30, has compounds added to it that allow the oil to flow easily at cold temperatures, but prevent it from thinning out too much when hot.

- If your family has a car, which oil does it use? Why does it use this grade?
- Find out what the difference is between 5W30 and 10W30 oil.

A car owner will use oil with a different viscosity, depending on the season. In colder weather, if an oil becomes too thick, it cannot function as well in the engine. Therefore, when the weather is cold, an oil with a low viscosity is used. The oil takes longer to thicken up as the temperature drops, so it remains effective longer. During warm weather, a higher viscosity oil is used. This oil takes longer to thin out. Thin oil is less effective as a lubricant. Manufacturers add chemicals called viscosity modifiers to motor oil to change the oil's characteristics. Some of these modifiers help to improve fuel economy or oil performance in extreme temperatures.

Communicate

1 Look at the other posters in your class that summarize the results of the ramp test.
a) Do your results agree with others?
b) Are there differences? Why do you think differences might occur?
2 In a fair test, you have to keep most variables the same so that you can see what the effect of one variable is.
a) What things did you keep the same for each test?
b) What did you change during the tests?
3 How does temperature affect the viscosity of a liquid?
4 You are given three samples of the same shampoo at three different temperatures: 35°C, 50°C, and 75°C.
a) Which sample would have the highest viscosity? Which sample would have the lowest viscosity?
b) Support your answer with data collected from your Problem Solver activity.
5 Review the results of the jar-car race in the Invitation to Explore. How does viscosity relate to these results?

1.3 CHECK YOUR PROGRESS

1 What is a fluid? Give an example of a fluid you have used in the past day.
2 Use the Particle Theory of Matter to explain what viscosity is and why temperature affects viscosity.
3 Describe two methods used to test viscosity.
4 When you pour cereal into a bowl for breakfast, the cereal takes the shape of the bowl. Is cereal a fluid? Explain your answer.
5 Give some examples of how an understanding of viscosity benefits people.

2.0 Density is another important property of fluids.

You have already studied one important property of fluids—viscosity. Think about how the Particle Theory helps you explain your observations about viscosity and the effect of temperature on it. This Big Idea is about the property of substances called density. You will have an opportunity to apply your understanding of the Particle Theory once again as you study density in fluids.

2.1 WORKING WITH FLUIDS

Explore

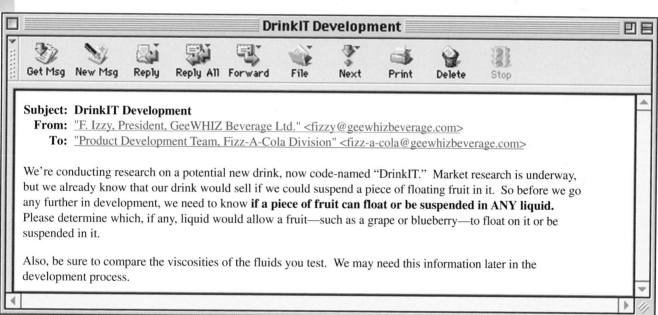

DrinkIT Development

Get Msg   New Msg   Reply   Reply All   Forward   File   Next   Print   Delete   Stop

Subject: **DrinkIT Development**
   From: "F. Izzy, President, GeeWHIZ Beverage Ltd." <fizzy@geewhizbeverage.com>
   To: "Product Development Team, Fizz-A-Cola Division" <fizz-a-cola@geewhizbeverage.com>

We're conducting research on a potential new drink, now code-named "DrinkIT." Market research is underway, but we already know that our drink would sell if we could suspend a piece of floating fruit in it. So before we go any further in development, we need to know **if a piece of fruit can float or be suspended in ANY liquid.** Please determine which, if any, liquid would allow a fruit—such as a grape or blueberry—to float on it or be suspended in it.

Also, be sure to compare the viscosities of the fluids you test. We may need this information later in the development process.

Develop

Using the Properties of Fluids

Imagine you have just received that e-mail from your boss. As part of the Research and Development Department at Fizz-A-Cola, you now have to get to work!

SINK OR FLOAT?

- Using the instructions in the e-mail on the previous page, design a procedure that will allow you to collect the data F. Izzy is asking for.
- Show your procedure to your teacher for approval, and then do your testing.
- You can use any three liquids you wish or any combination of them.

- Remember that you need to have some way of collecting information so you can report on your results.

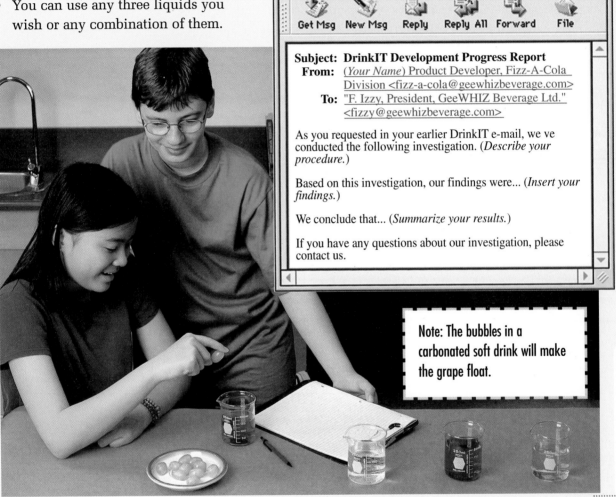

DrinkIT Development Progress Report

Get Msg   New Msg   Reply   Reply All   Forward   File

Subject: DrinkIT Development Progress Report
From: *(Your Name)* Product Developer, Fizz-A-Cola Division <fizz-a-cola@geewhizbeverage.com>
To: "F. Izzy, President, GeeWHIZ Beverage Ltd." <fizzy@geewhizbeverage.com>

As you requested in your earlier DrinkIT e-mail, we ve conducted the following investigation. (*Describe your procedure.*)

Based on this investigation, our findings were... (*Insert your findings.*)

We conclude that... (*Summarize your results.*)

If you have any questions about our investigation, please contact us.

Note: The bubbles in a carbonated soft drink will make the grape float.

Communicate

1. Were you able to float a piece of fruit? If you were, describe how you did it. If you were unable to, describe your results.
2. What was the most interesting part of your research?
3. You may have noticed that sometimes your fruit sank and sometimes it floated. Why do you think this happened?

2.2 DENSITY AND VISCOSITY

Explore

Here is an example of some data that was collected in the last activity. One student, Derek, used cranberry juice, tomato paste, peach juice concentrate, and a grape in his research.

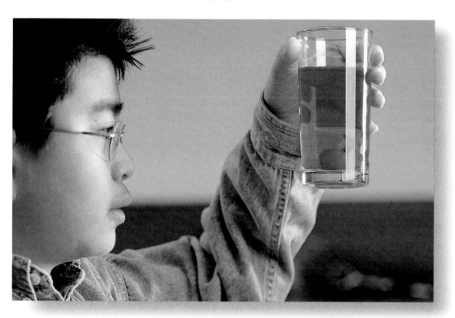

Fluid	Grape Sank	Grape Floated on Top	Grape Floated in Middle	Viscosity [1 is most viscous, 3 is least]
cranberry juice	✓			3
tomato paste	✓			2
peach juice concentrate		✓		1

Why did the grape sink in some liquids and not in others? The reason for the difference is a property of fluids called density. **Density** is the amount of matter or number of particles in a given volume. Think about the differences in density between the different fluids as you examine the results from Derek's investigation.

Develop

Density

In the DrinkIT Problem Solver, you had to keep a number of variables constant throughout the investigation. So which variables changed? *Each fluid was different.* The amount of matter in each fluid sample changed. Recall that the Particle Theory of Matter states that all matter is made of tiny particles. It also states that different substances are made of different particles. So the particles in each fluid are different from the particles in every other fluid tested. The result is each substance has a different density.

Solids	A flowing liquid	Burning gases

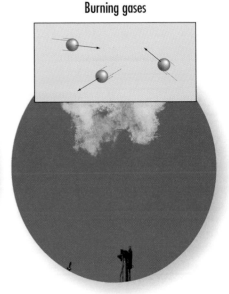

You may also recall that the Particle Theory describes how these particles behave in each of the three states of matter. When matter is a solid, the particles are close together and fixed in place. In a liquid, they are close together, but can slide around and over each other. In a gas, the particles are far apart and move around rapidly. In our investigation, the fluids used were all liquids. The particles in the liquids could roll over each other.

Earlier in this chapter, you learned that viscosity is a measure of the amount of friction between the particles in a fluid. From Derek's investigation, you can see that the greater the viscosity, the greater the density of the fluid. Notice that the grape floated on the fluids with high viscosities. These fluids had densities greater than that of the grape. The grape sank in fluids with low viscosities. These fluids had densities less than the density of the grape.

So, if the density of the grape was *less* than the density of the fluid, *the grape floated*. If the density of the grape was *greater* than the density of the fluid, *the grape sank*. Is this always the case? In the next section, you have a chance to do more investigating to help you answer this question.

Density affects how a substance will float in a liquid.

2.0 Density Is Another Important Property of Fluids

Communicate

1 What is the relationship between viscosity and density in the fluids used in Derek's investigation?

2 Why did the grape sink in the cranberry juice?

3 Which of the three fluids had the most particles in the volume used and which had the least? How do you know?

4 There are three states of matter shown in this picture. Based on the Particle Theory, draw what you think the particles look like for each state.

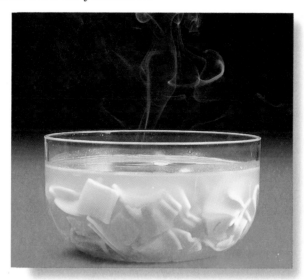

2.3 FINDING THE DENSITY OF SUBSTANCES

Explore

As you probably have realized, not all substances have the same density. That's because certain characteristics of substances differ. In this section, you will investigate some of these characteristics and learn how to calculate density.

PROBLEM SOLVER

DENSE AND DENSER

You have six identical jars full of two sets of different materials in front of you.

• For each set of substances, make a list, ranking them in order of highest density to lowest density.

• What variable will you have to consider for the substances in Set 2?

• You may use any method you like to determine your ranking, but you cannot open the jars. It may help to remember the jar-car activity you did at the start of the chapter when you rolled jars of different substances down a ramp.

• Be prepared to explain your reasons for your ranking.

continued on next page ······▶

- The list to the right tells you what is in each jar. If a substance has been changed, your teacher will tell you.
- Keep your ranking handy because you will be testing some of these substances later. You will be able to compare your ranking with your test results.

Contents of Jars

Set 1	Set 2
• *water*	• *sand*
• *corn syrup*	• *small stones*
• *shampoo*	• *wood chips*

Weight and Mass

You may have done your ranking by lifting each jar and determining how heavy it was. When you did this, you were experiencing the combined weight of the jar and the substance in it.

Weight

Weight is a measure of the force of gravity on an object. The force of gravity is measured in newtons (N), named after Sir Isaac Newton (1642–1727), the English mathematician and scientist. A force of 1 N is about the amount of force exerted by an apple in your hand. So the weight of the apple is 1 N.

Mass

The **mass** of an object measures the amount of matter or number of particles that are in the object. Consider what you learned about density. Is there a relationship between the density of an object and its mass?

If you were to go to the moon, you would find that the force of gravity is one-sixth of that on earth, but the mass of an object on the moon is the same as on the earth. So what would happen to the astronaut's weight when she travels to the moon?

If you had the same volume of gold and concrete, which would have the greater mass? Which would be heavier (have the greater weight)? How could you find out without using a scale?

- Which would weigh more: the same volume of gold on earth or on the moon?
- Which would have the greater mass: the same volume of gold on earth or on the moon?

Develop
Determining Density

Now that you've ranked your materials and have an understanding of mass, you'll determine the density of substances in the next activity.

CALCULATING MASS/VOLUME RATIO

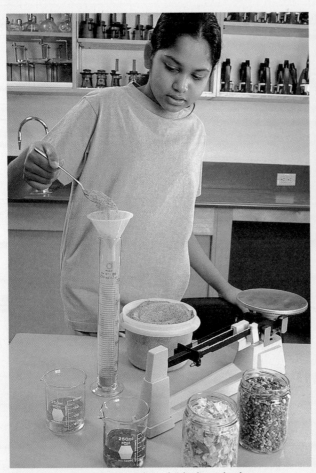

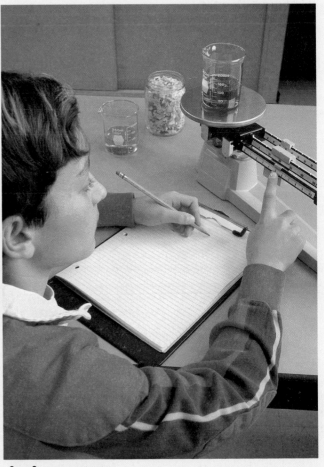

Step 2: pour 100 mL into graduated cylinder or beaker.

Step 3: measure mass.

The Question

How can you calculate the density of a variety of solids (mechanical mixtures) and liquids?

Materials & Equipment

• *500-mL beaker*
• *200–300 mL graduated cylinder*
• *triple beam or electronic balance*
• *water, sand, corn syrup, small stones, shampoo, wood chips*
• *graph paper*

Procedure

1. Measure the mass of the beaker and record it in your table.
2. Pour 100 mL of the first substance into the graduated cylinder or beaker and record the volume in the table.
3. Place the beaker containing the substance on the balance and measure the mass. Record the mass in your table.
4. Repeat steps 2 and 3 with volumes of 200 mL, 300 mL, 400 mL, and 500 mL of the same substance.
5. Repeat this procedure for each substance.
6. Clean and return your equipment to the proper location.

Keeping Records

7 In your notebook, make a table like the one shown below to record your data. Use a table like this for each substance.

Substance	Volume of Substance (mL)	Mass of Beaker (g)	Mass of Beaker and Substance (g)	Mass of Substance Only (g)	Mass/Volume Ratio

Analyzing and Interpreting

8 Find the mass of each substance by subtracting the mass of the beaker from the total mass of the beaker and substance together.

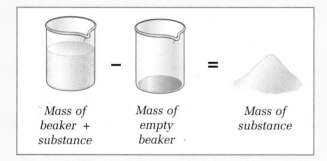

Mass of beaker + substance	−	*Mass of empty beaker*	=	*Mass of substance*

9 Find the ratio of the mass to the volume by dividing the mass of the substance by the volume for each volume you measured. What is the average ratio for each substance? This ratio is the density of each substance.

For example:

- 242 mL of a substance has a mass of 424 g

- the mass to volume ratio is

$$\frac{424 \text{ g (mass)}}{242 \text{ mL (volume)}}$$

- Density $= \dfrac{424 \text{ g}}{242 \text{ mL}} = \dfrac{1.75 \text{ g}}{1 \text{ mL}}$ or **1.75 g/mL**

10 Set up a line graph with mass on the vertical axis and volume on the horizontal axis. Plot your results for the first substance. Draw a straight line through or close to the points.

11 Plot your results for the other substances on the same graph. Label each line.

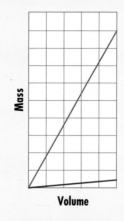

How will you determine what increments you will use for each axis?

12 Compare the slopes of the lines. Which slope is the steepest? Which slope is the most gradual?

13 Can you see any relationship between the average ratio for each substance and the slope of each line on your graph?

14 Compare your calculated densities for the substances with the predictions you made when you did the Problem Solver at the beginning of this section. Was the ranking of the densities you predicted the same or was there a difference?

Forming Conclusions

15 Write a summary paragraph that explains how you calculated the density of the substances used in this investigation. Your summary should include the words *substance*, *volume*, *mass*, *graph*, *slope*, *ratio*, and *density*.

1 The table below shows mass and volume data for baby oil. What happens to the mass of the baby oil as the volume changes?

Mass (g)	Volume (mL)
0.8	1.0
1.6	2.0
2.4	3.0
3.2	4.0

2 a) What is the density of the baby oil?
  b) What happens to the density as the mass and volume change?

3 Suppose you were to graph the baby oil data. Would the slope of the line for the baby oil be steeper or more gradual than one for water? (The density of water is 1.0 g/mL.)

4 a) What is the relationship between mass and weight?
  b) If you were to travel to Mars where the force of gravity is about one-third that of earth's, would your body mass change or would your weight change? Why or why not?

2.4 EXPERIMENTING WITH DENSITY

In the DrinkIT activity, you observed how a piece of fruit would float in some fluids, but not in others. The volumes of all the fluids were held constant. But the amount of matter or mass of the fluid changed depending on the fluid used. Did you notice that the higher the viscosity, the greater the density? If the grape's density was higher than the fluid, it sank. If the grape's density was lower, it floated. What will happen if we keep the mass of the fluid the same but change the volume?

Changing the Volume

Volume and Displacement

When a substance is placed in a fluid, a curious thing happens. The volume of the fluid rises. Try it. Put an object that will sink into a graduated cylinder filled with 100 mL of water. Note how much the water level rises. This rise in volume takes place because the substance moves aside, or *displaces*, an amount of water equal to its volume.

The following investigation will help you develop your understanding of volume and density. You have observed what happens to fluids when the volume is kept constant and the mass varies for different substances. In this activity, you will keep the mass constant and observe what happens to the volume.

WHAT HAPPENS TO THE VOLUME?

The Question

Will objects of similar mass displace the same volume when placed in water?

Materials & Equipment

- *triple beam or electronic balance*
- *water, copper pennies, corn syrup, cylindrical wood block, rectangular eraser, iron filings, shampoo*
- *100-mL graduated cylinder*
- *stirring rod*

Procedure

1. Make a prediction about the densities of the substances you will be testing by listing them in order from highest to lowest density.

2. Use the balance to measure out 25 g of each substance. You might have to cut the eraser.

3. Use the graduated cylinder to measure the volume of each sample and record it in your table. Make sure to clean the graduated cylinder each time before measuring the next substance.

Step 2: measure 25 g.

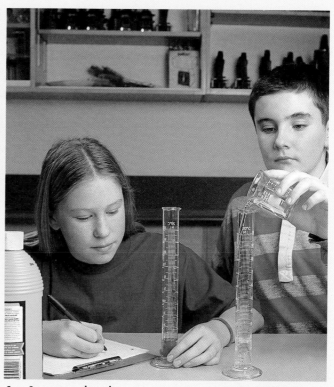

Step 3: measure the volume.

Step 4: put 40 mL of water into a graduated cylinder.

continued on next page ······▶

4 Put 40 mL of water into the graduated cylinder.

5 Place the 25 g of the first substance to be tested into the water in the graduated cylinder. If the substance floats, use the stirring rod to push it down so that it's just completely submerged. Stir well to get rid of any air bubbles. Record the new volume.

> **Caution!**
> Don't push the stirring rod too far down into the water. Otherwise, it will create a false reading for the new volume of water.

6 Clean the graduated cylinder and repeat steps 3 and 4 for each remaining substance.

7 Clean and return your equipment to the proper location.

Keeping Records

8 Record your results in a table like the one shown below.

Analyzing and Interpreting

9 Calculate the volume displaced by each substance (column 6). You do this by subtracting the initial volume of water in the cylinder (column 4) from the total volume after the substance was added (column 5).

10 For the liquids, compare the displaced volume (column 6) with the original measured volume (column 3). Are these numbers the same or different? Why do you think this is so?

11 Calculate the density of each substance. You do this by dividing the mass (column 2) by the displaced volume (column 6).

Forming Conclusions

12 Explain how to find the density of a substance. Describe how your predicted order of densities compared with your calculated results.

1 Substance	2 Mass of Substance (g)	3 Vol. of Substance Used (mL)	4 Initial Vol. of Water in Cylinder (mL)	5 Vol. in Cylinder after Substance Added (mL)	6 Displaced Vol. (mL) (column 5 minus column 4)	7 Density of Substance (g/mL)
water						
copper pennies						
corn syrup						
wood block						
eraser						
iron filings						
shampoo						

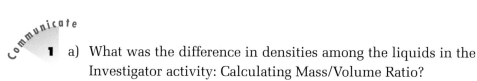

Communicate

1 a) What was the difference in densities among the liquids in the Investigator activity: Calculating Mass/Volume Ratio?

b) What was the difference in densities among the solids in this activity?

c) Make a table of the solid and liquid densities. Use this table to predict which solids will float in which liquids.

2 Using your understanding of the Particle Theory of Matter, how do you think the densities of gases would compare with those of liquids and solids?

3 a) What is the density of 27.1 g of mercury that displaces 2 mL of water?

b) What is the density of 5.25 g of silver that displaces 0.5 mL of water?

c) What is the density of 28.5 g of lead that displaces 2.5 mL of water?

d) If you had 100 mL of each substance, which one would have the greatest mass?

4 The density of fresh water is 1.0 g/mL. Look at the densities you have calculated for your various substances. Can you infer anything about how objects float and sink based on their densities?

---

*info*BIT

Eureka!—The Mind of Archimedes

Archimedes (287 B.C.–212 B.C.) was a Greek mathematician. He is famous for many inventions and mathematical discoveries, but he's probably most remembered for his bath!

About 2300 years ago, the king of

Syracuse summoned the famous scientist and mathematician. The king suspected that his new crown was not made of pure gold as promised but had some silver in it. He wanted Archimedes to find out—but without damaging the crown. While thinking hard about this problem, Archimedes decided to have a relaxing, hot bath. As he lowered himself into the tub, he noticed water overflowing its sides. At that instant, he realized he had solved the king's problem! In his absent-mindedness, he jumped out of the tub and ran naked down the street shouting "*Eureka! Eureka!*" (Greek for "I've got it! I've got it!")

What did Archimedes discover? When he saw the water overflowing from the bathtub, he realized that his body was

displacing the water. The volume of water he displaced was equal to the volume of his body. He could now test the king's crown in the same way to determine its volume.

Archimedes knew that gold has a higher density than silver—it's nearly twice as dense. If the crown were made with pure silver that equalled the mass of the king's gold, for example, its volume would be greater. It would, therefore, displace *more* water than if it were made of pure gold. Even if a small amount of silver were used, the volume of the crown (and the water it displaced) would still be greater than the same mass of pure gold. And what did Archimedes discover when he performed his test? The crown was indeed not pure gold.

Experiment ········►
ON YOUR OWN

This commercial hydrometer can be used to measure the sugar content of syrup. Why do you think someone might need this information?

Before You Start...

One way to measure the density of a liquid is with a **hydrometer**. You may have seen hydrometers like the one in the photo for sale. In this activity, you will work in groups to design and build your own hydrometer. You will use a variety of solutions to make a series of pre-determined densities. Your group will then use the hydrometers in an investigation to determine the density of unknown liquids.

The Question

How can you build a hydrometer to determine the density of unknown liquids?

Materials & Equipment

- *graduated cylinder*
- *clear plastic straws (10 to 15 cm long)*
- *modelling clay*
- *fresh water*
- *salt water*
- *ruler*
- *permanent marker*
- *funnel*
- *sand or lead BBs*
- *a variety of liquids*

Construct It

1 Read through the whole activity and use the list of materials and equipment to help you determine how you will construct and test your hydrometer. Collect everything you need before you start the experiment.

2 Fill a 250-mL or greater graduated cylinder full of water so the water bulges around the rim of the cylinder.

3 Take a straw and seal one end with modelling clay.

4 Use a funnel to pour the sand or drop lead BBs into the straw. Carefully place the straw in the graduated cylinder. *(Caution! Some water will spill when you add the straw.)* Be sure to add enough material to make the straw float upright with about 1 cm above water.

Step 4: pour sand into the straw.

5 Use a permanent marker to draw a line on the straw at the water level. You now have a hydrometer calibrated for the density of fresh water, which is 1.0 g/mL.

6 Next, each group will calibrate their hydrometers to the density of one of the solutions shown in the table below.

a) Before you begin, calculate the density of each solution.

Solution	Mass of Solution (g)	Volume of Solution (mL)	Density (g/mL)
1	253.0	250	?
2	265.7	250	?
3	272.4	250	?
4	287.1	250	?

7 Empty the water from the graduated cylinder, and fill the cylinder almost to the top with the salt solution. Place your hydrometer in the cylinder.

8 Mark the new level on your hydrometer.

Use It

9 Your teacher will give you two unknown samples. To determine the densities of the unknown samples, work with three other groups who calibrated their hydrometers differently. The four hydrometers will give you a range of densities from which to choose.

10 When you have determined the densities of the unknown samples, write a short report that describes what you did, your results, and one new thing you learned in this activity.

11 You have measured the density of water at room temperature. Do you think there will be a difference in density if the water is warmer or colder than room temperature? Make a prediction and test it out.

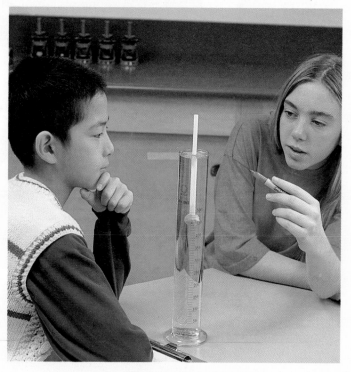

This hydrometer has been calibrated for water at a density of 1.0 g/mL.

2.5 DENSITY AND THE PARTICLE THEORY OF MATTER

Which fluid has a higher density, the one on the right or the one on the left?

The picture above shows a different kind of thermometer. It is Galileo Galilei's thermometer (or thermoscope), first invented in the 1590s. Each temperature bulb acts like a hydrometer and floats to the top when the water's density is the same as the bulb.

- What relationship do you think there is between density and temperature?

Explore

So far, in the activities in this Big Idea, you have been collecting evidence to describe density. Earlier, when you tried to suspend a piece of fruit in a liquid, you observed that sometimes the fruit sank and sometimes it floated. The fruit sank when its density was greater than that of the liquid, and it floated when its density was less than that of the liquid. You observed that different fluids had different densities when the volume was constant and the mass changed.

You also investigated the relationship between mass and volume for different amounts of the same substance. You were able to graph your results to determine the density of each fluid used.

Density is the mass per unit of volume, which can be measured in mL or cm³. Density is calculated by dividing the mass of a substance by its volume.

$$\text{Density (D)} = \frac{\text{Mass (m)}}{\text{Volume (V)}}$$

The units for the density of liquids and gases are usually given in g/mL or kg/L.

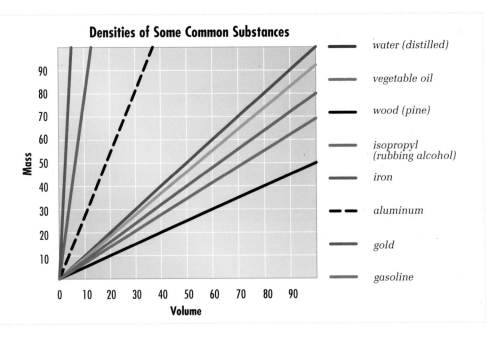

Densities of Some Common Substances

- water (distilled)
- vegetable oil
- wood (pine)
- isopropyl (rubbing alcohol)
- iron
- aluminum
- gold
- gasoline

In another Investigator activity, you kept the mass the same and noticed that different substances displaced different volumes of water. Using the known mass and the displaced volume, you were able to determine the density of each substance tested.

Next you constructed a hydrometer to measure known and unknown densities of concentrated salt solutions and unknown liquids. Finally, you investigated the effect of changing temperature on the density of water. Now it's time to tie these observations back to the Particle Theory of Matter.

You can determine a substance's density if you know the mass and volume of a sample of the substance.

Develop Density Changes with Temperature

The **Particle Theory of Matter** states that for each substance, the number of particles in a given volume remains constant if the temperature is kept constant. You have observed this in all the activities you've done in this Big Idea. Density does not change as long as the temperature stays the same.

According to the Particle Theory, the particles begin to vibrate when energy is added to a substance. As a solid changes to a liquid and eventually to a gas, the particles vibrate and move more rapidly. This affects the density of the substance in several ways.

As particles move more rapidly, the space between them increases. This can cause two things to happen. First, the volume can increase. This means that the density decreases. Why? Because the particles need more room to move. So, the volume increases, but the number of particles does not. You noticed this when you tested the densities of cold water and warm water. The warm water had a lower density than the cold water. That's why warm water floats on cold water. If you swim in a lake, you may have noticed patches of warm water on the surface.

What would happen if the fluid being heated were a gas? For example, what would happen if you left a partially inflated children's wading pool out in the sun?

As the fluid (air) inside the pool's walls heats up, the particles move more rapidly and farther apart. This causes a pressure increase, and the pool is inflated more than when it was cooler. No air has been added to the pool, though. The air in it has expanded because of the heat. So the same number of air particles still fill the pool walls, but what has happened to the density?

*info*BIT

Volume and Mass of Water

Thanks to the metric system, there is a very simple relationship between the volume and mass of water at 4°C.

- 1 mL of volume occupies the space of 1 cm^3.
- 1 mL of water has a mass of exactly 1 g.
- Therefore, if you were to fill a container measuring 4 cm by 3 cm by 2 cm with water, you could find the mass of the water without having to use a scale.

Volume of Container (V) = Length (L) $\times$ Width (W) $\times$ Height (H)

V = LWH

V = 4 cm $\times$ 3 cm $\times$ 2 cm

V = 24 cm^3

1 cm^3 of water = 1 mL, which has a mass of 1 g

Therefore: 24 cm^3 of water has a mass of 24 g

1 What units are usually used for measuring the density of solids? of liquids?

2 Use the Particle Theory of Matter to describe what happens to the density of a substance when it cools.

3 Is there a mistake in any of the following directions for this water-play air mattress? Explain your answer.

WARNING

This air mattress should not be used by children without adult supervision.

Do not inflate.

Keep away from sharp objects to prevent punctures.

2.6 CHECK YOUR PROGRESS

1 Make a list of all the words related to density in this Big Idea. Use these words to make a concept map to illustrate your understanding of density. Save your concept map for future use.

2 How are viscosity and density related?

3 What is density and how do you measure it?

4 What happens to the density of a fluid as it warms up?

5 In the graph below, which fluid has the highest density and which has the lowest? How do you know?

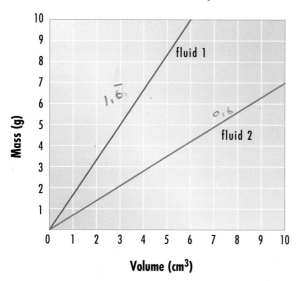

6 Which is denser—10 g of shampoo or 10 kg of shampoo?

7 Which is denser—water at 15°C or water at 60°C?

*info*BIT

Frozen Water

Most fluids become denser as they cool down to their freezing temperature and turn into a solid. Water is an exception. It reaches its greatest density at 4°C (1.0 g/mL). Below that temperature, water becomes less dense as its temperature drops from 4°C to 0°C.

In the fall, as the weather becomes colder, the water in a lake starts to cool. When the water on the surface cools down to 4°C, it sinks because it is denser than the warmer water below. As the winter air continues to cool, the temperature of the surface water drops below 4°C. That water floats on top of the denser water, and eventually this upper water freezes. That's one reason why a lake freezes from the top down!

The density of ice is 0.92 g/mL. Can you explain why ice floats?

CARDIOLOGIST

Imagine a pump no bigger than a clenched fist that pumps 7200 L of a fairly thick fluid through more than 95 000 km of tubing every day for 80 years. This extraordinary device is the human heart!

Its job is to pump blood throughout the body, supplying all living cells with nutrients while carrying away waste products. A cardiologist is a doctor who treats diseases and disorders of the heart.

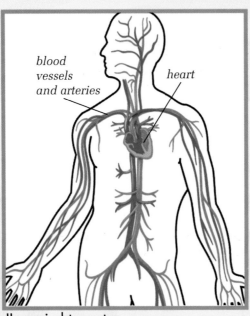

blood vessels and arteries

heart

Human circulatory system

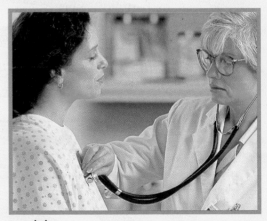

A cardiologist examines a patient.

Some common heart ailments include:
- *myocardial infarction:* a type of heart attack
- *hypertension:* an increase in pressure inside the blood vessels that causes the heart to work harder
- *arrhythmia:* an irregular heartbeat

SWIMMING POOL CONTRACTOR

A swimming pool contractor installs and repairs swimming pools. But there's more to this job than just digging a hole in the ground and filling it with water. If this were the case, pool water would quickly become contaminated with leaves, dirt, bacteria, bits of skin, old Band-Aids, and hair. To make sure this doesn't happen, a pool contractor installs a system of drains, inlets, pipes, pumps, and filters to keep the water clean and fresh.

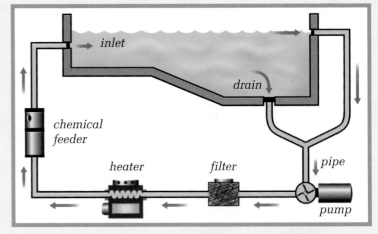

inlet

drain

chemical feeder

heater

filter

pipe

pump

Swimming pool circulation system. How does it resemble the human circulatory system?

A pool contractor is a little like a doctor. When something goes wrong with a pool's circulatory system, the contractor must be able to quickly diagnose and correct the problem.

Swimming pool under construction

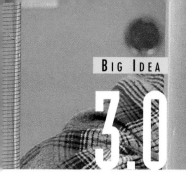
Fluids exert a buoyant force on objects that allows some objects to float.

If you dropped a metal bar into the water, what would happen to it? Yet a ship made of metal can float. Buoyancy is what allows a ship to float in water. Buoyancy is another important property of fluids.

3.1 FLOATING AND DENSITY

Explore

You have had an opportunity to build a hydrometer and determine the density of a variety of fluids. You marked your hydrometer for a given density. If you test a liquid with a higher density, the hydrometer floats higher. If you test a liquid with a lower density, the hydrometer floats lower.

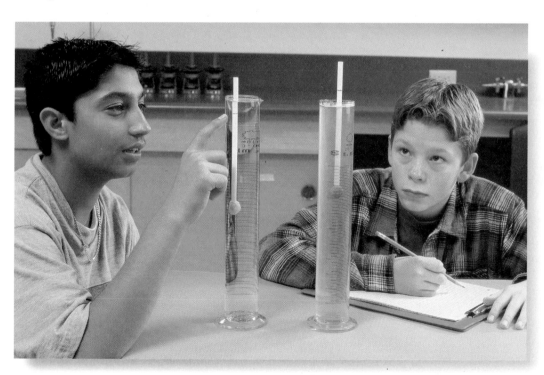

Student-made hydrometers testing the density of two different liquids

What caused the hydrometer to go up or down? Some force must have been working against gravity to allow the hydrometer to float. What was that force? Do you think density played a role?

When an object is at rest, forces acting on it are said to be **balanced**. When an object is moving, the forces are said to be **unbalanced**.

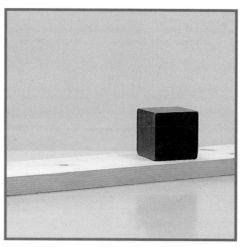

What will happen to this block if no force is applied to it? Are the forces balanced or unbalanced?

What do you think will happen to this block? Are the forces balanced or unbalanced?

Develop
Average Density

To determine the force that opposes gravity, let's examine how objects float on some fluids, but not on others.

PROBLEM SOLVER

WHAT FLOATS ON WHAT?

Materials

- *25 mL of corn oil*
- *25 mL of water*
- *25 mL of glycerin*
- *25 mL of corn syrup*
- *steel ball*
- *rubber ball*
- *small block of plastic*
- *small piece of wood*

Your teacher will demonstrate this activity.
- Predict the order in which these substances will arrange themselves top to bottom, if you put them all together in one container.
- Record what happens after all the substances are combined. Draw a labelled diagram of the result.

Look at your prediction. What were the reasons for your prediction? Did you base it on the weight of the objects, the density, or the state of the material? If you chose density, you were on the right track. A difference in density was the reason for the liquids separating out and the solids floating within the different liquids. Less dense liquids and solids floated on denser liquids. But there is more to the story.

Is this always true? Think about the ship in the water. Isn't the density of the metal in the ship greater than the density of water?

Boats and other objects that appear to have a greater density than water float because their *average density* is less than the density of water. **Average density** takes into consideration all the different substances that exist within a given volume. So, for a ship, steel or other metals form the ship's structure, but the ship also contains a large volume of air. A solid ship of steel would sink, but a ship with air inside will float.

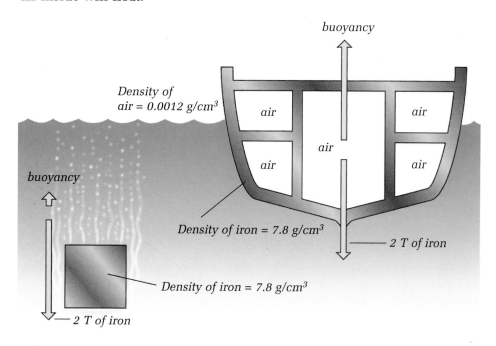

buoyancy

Density of air = 0.0012 g/cm³

air air air air air air

buoyancy

Density of iron = 7.8 g/cm³

2 T of iron

Density of iron = 7.8 g/cm³

2 T of iron

A solid block of iron weighing 2 tonnes will sink in water. Its density of 7.8 g/cm³ is almost eight times as great as water. The buoyancy force wouldn't be great enough to keep it afloat. Now suppose you were to build a boat with the 2 tonnes of iron. Its weight still would be the same, but as you can see in the illustration, the buoyancy force would equal the weight of iron, and the boat would float. Why do you think the average density of a boat is so much less than the metal of its hull?

PROBLEM SOLVER

plastic bottle

eyedropper

water

SINK OR SWIM

Here is an example of buoyancy magic that's not magic at all.

- Fill a plastic pop bottle about $\frac{3}{4}$ full of water. Float an eyedropper or any other small sealed tube of air on the surface of the water. (See illustration at left.)
- Tightly seal the lid of the bottle.
- Now, squeeze the bottle with your hand so the sides go in.
- Can you explain what happens?

- Use your library or the Internet to find other examples of average density.
- Check out blimps, fish, or any other object or living thing which has an average density that may allow it to float.
- Why do you float feet down in the water instead of head down?

Communicate

1 The following liquids were poured into a tube.
   a) Draw what the tube would look like after the liquids settled. How do you know this?
   b) What calculations do you need to do to help predict the answer?

Fluid	Mass (g)	Volume (mL)
antifreeze	252	200
distilled water	100	100
rubbing alcohol	40	50

2 If a block of ice with a density of 0.917 g/mL were dropped into the tube, where would it end up?

3 What is the difference between density and average density?

3.2 BUOYANCY

Explore

From your investigations, you have seen that an object sinks when its density is greater than the density of the fluid it is in. But what happens when an object floats in a liquid? When an object is in a liquid, the force of gravity on the object pulls the object down. The liquid, however, exerts an opposite force, called the **buoyant force**, and tries to push the object up. If the density of the liquid is greater than the density of the object, the buoyant force that the liquid exerts on the object will be greater than the force of gravity acting down on the object. The object will float. If the density of the object is greater than the liquid, the force of gravity will be greater than the buoyant force acting on the object. The object will sink.

Develop

Discovering the Buoyant Force

In previous investigations, you determined the volume of different substances in the same way that Archimedes did. That experience will help you with the next activity, where you will investigate buoyant force.

A MYSTERY

As part of their study of buoyant force, three students did the following investigation. They took a 200-g object and used a spring scale to measure the force of gravity on it. This measurement was 2.0 N. They then dropped the mass, suspended by the spring scale, into three different liquids, as shown in the photos.

In each case, they found that the object appeared to weigh less. How could this be if the mass of the object was always the same? Did they make a mistake in their measurements?

Work with your group to brainstorm possible explanations for these observations. As you brainstorm, consider the following questions:

- Does density play a role in these observations?
- In the air, gravity pulls the mass down. Now there seems to be something pushing the mass back up. What is that?

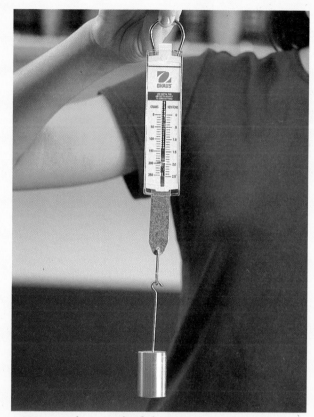

A 200-g mass has a weight of about 2 N.

Water

Molasses

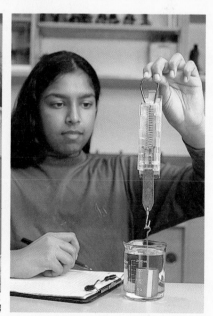

Vegetable oil

Density, Buoyancy, and the Force of Gravity

The students didn't make a mistake—they discovered what Archimedes realized in the bath: **Archimedes' Principle**—*the buoyant force acting on an object equals the weight or force of gravity of the fluid displaced by the object.*

For example, suppose you drop an object into a container such as the one below. When the fluid rises, it will flow into the beaker. You already know that the volume of the displaced fluid equals the volume of the object. You are now discovering that the weight of that overflow fluid equals the buoyant force of the fluid pushing up on the object.

Buoyancy, then, is the force that acts against gravity. **Gravity** is the force trying to pull an object down in a fluid.

In their investigation, the students noticed that the spring scale measured a smaller weight or total force on an object when it was placed in a liquid. The reason was that the buoyant force acting up against the force of gravity reduced the weight.

Archimedes' Principle states that the buoyant force acting on an object in a fluid is *equal* to the weight of the fluid displaced by the object. In the Problem Solver activity, the buoyant force can be calculated by subtracting the weight of the object in air from the weight of the object in the liquid. The difference in the weight between the two is the buoyant force. The students were actually measuring the buoyant force in the same way that Archimedes did.

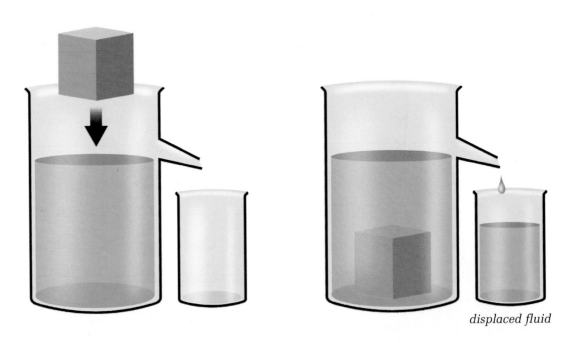

displaced fluid

The buoyant force acting on an object equals the weight (or force of gravity) of the fluid displaced by the object.

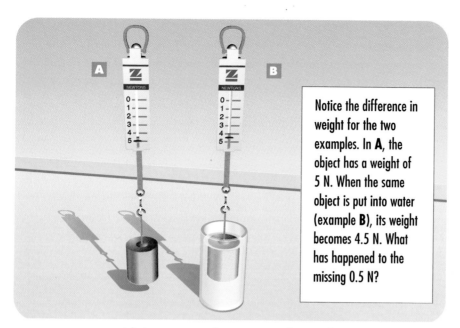

Notice the difference in weight for the two examples. In **A**, the object has a weight of 5 N. When the same object is put into water (example **B**), its weight becomes 4.5 N. What has happened to the missing 0.5 N?

weight in air — weight in water = buoyant force

The Rules of Buoyancy

You have now had an opportunity to investigate situations in which an object floats, sinks, rises, or is suspended in a fluid. Look back at your notes, and think about what you discovered. Can you devise a set of rules that will determine what will happen to an object when it is placed in a fluid? Work with your partner or small group, and share your thoughts with the class.

Look at the following situations and apply your rules to determine if an object will float, sink, or rise in a fluid in each case.

The force of gravity is greater than the buoyant force.

The buoyant force is greater than the force of gravity.

The force of gravity equals the buoyant force. This situation is called *neutral buoyancy*.

1 A 100-g mass is placed on a spring scale and the force of gravity or weight on the mass is measured as 1 N. The mass is then lowered into a liquid and found to weigh 0.6 N. What is the buoyant force?

2 The same mass is lowered into a second liquid. What is the weight of the mass of this liquid to produce a buoyant force of 0.6 N?

3 Would you float better in salt water or fresh water? Explain your answer.

4 Explain why you and some other things float in water. Include examples that you have experienced or observed to support your answer.

3.3 USING THE PROPERTIES OF FLUIDS

So far, in this chapter, you have explored viscosity, density, and buoyancy. Now it's time to use what you've learned.

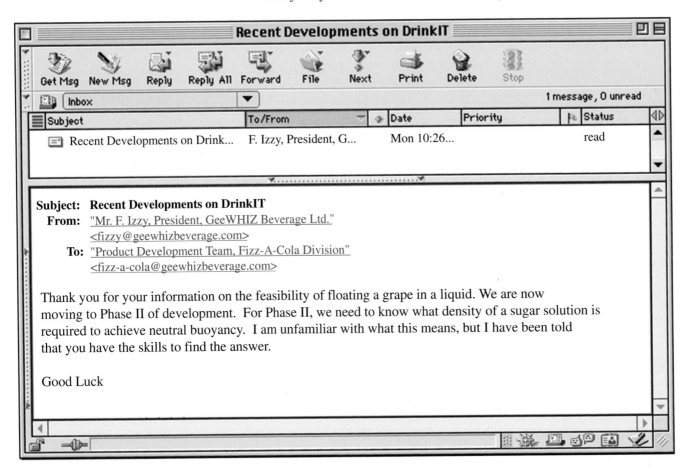

Recent Developments on DrinkIT

Get Msg | New Msg | Reply | Reply All | Forward | File | Next | Print | Delete | Stop

Inbox ▼   1 message, 0 unread

Subject	To/From	Date	Priority	Status
Recent Developments on Drink...	F. Izzy, President, G...	Mon 10:26...		read

Subject: **Recent Developments on DrinkIT**
   From: "Mr. F. Izzy, President, GeeWHIZ Beverage Ltd."
               <fizzy@geewhizbeverage.com>
     To: "Product Development Team, Fizz-A-Cola Division"
               <fizz-a-cola@geewhizbeverage.com>

Thank you for your information on the feasibility of floating a grape in a liquid. We are now moving to Phase II of development. For Phase II, we need to know what density of a sugar solution is required to achieve neutral buoyancy. I am unfamiliar with what this means, but I have been told that you have the skills to find the answer.

Good Luck

Product Development

Develop

Each time you have worked on the DrinkIT problem, you have used a little more of your knowledge of fluids. In the next activity, you get even closer to developing a drink that could be new and different.

PROBLEM SOLVER

WHAT SUGAR SOLUTION WILL WORK?

- Your task is to design and carry out a procedure that will allow you to determine the density of a sugar solution that can float a grape.
- After you design your procedure, show it to your teacher for approval. Then go ahead and solve the problem.
- When you have an answer, prepare a report to Mr. F. Izzy.

Caution!
Do not taste the sugar solutions.

Communicate

1 When you were trying to determine the best sugar solution to use, did you follow a specific procedure or did you just keep trying until you found the answer?

2 If other students had to do this activity, what would you suggest they do differently?

3 Experimental error occurs in all experiments. It can involve measuring a substance incorrectly, spilling something, or making calculation errors. Where could experimental error occur in this activity? Why?

4 What is one new thing you learned in this activity about investigating fluids?

3.4 CHECK YOUR PROGRESS

1. Using your concept map from the end of Big Idea 2.0, add any new words you have learned in this Big Idea.
2. Why does a piece of wood float on water but a steel ball does not?
3. Why do some objects (like a boat) float even though they are made of materials that are denser than water?
4. A rectangular block measures 3 cm × 4 cm × 3 cm. How much water would it displace?
5. Why does an object appear to weigh less in a liquid than in air?
6. What is the buoyant force acting on a 20-N steel ball if it weighs 15 N in water?
7. Why do some objects float in water while others sink?
8. What is neutral buoyancy? Give an example.
9. Describe two things about buoyancy you would like to know more about.

infoBIT

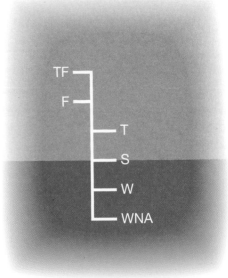

Plimsoll Line

A fully loaded cargo ship sailing across the Atlantic Ocean may sink dangerously low when it enters the fresh water of the St. Lawrence River. Why? Fresh water is lower in density than salt water. The ship floats lower in the less dense water. The same thing happens when a ship sails from cold northern water to warm tropical seas. Warm water is less dense than cold water.

Because of these situations, all cargo ships have what is known as a *Plimsoll line* painted on their hulls. The Plimsoll line shows how heavily a ship can be safely loaded in different water conditions. The marks on the left indicate where the waterline should be in fresh water. The marks on the right indicate where it should be in salt water.

Legend

TF	tropical fresh water
F	fresh water
T	tropical salt water
S	summer salt water
W	winter salt water
WNA	winter North Atlantic

FLUID POWER!

Marla Robinson

Marla Robinson is a fluid power technician, a person who designs, installs, and maintains hydraulic and pneumatic systems. She first became interested in fluid power when the hydraulic brakes on her car needed servicing. To save money, she decided to fix them herself. "I got into the field by accident. I had no idea what fluid power was," claims Robinson. "I took off the front wheels and I saw this thin little tube filled with oil connected to a tiny brake pad. I thought this was the most fascinating thing in the world, how a little squirt of oil from this tube was stopping my car!"

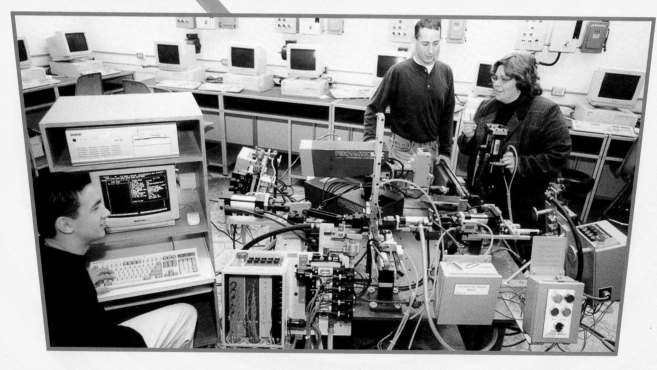

After that day, Robinson never looked back. She studied fluid power for two years at Mohawk College in Hamilton, Ontario. After graduating with Dean's honours, she worked in the industry for 12 years. Now she's back at Mohawk College, teaching the next generation of fluid power technicians.

Robinson's only regret is that there aren't more women in the field. "I think it's because females aren't encouraged to take technical subjects in school. I also think there are no strong female technical role models. It's not a case of women lacking the ability, because the women I do know in the field are very good," says Robinson. "If you're female you don't have to be a secretary or a nurse. It's okay to join the guys in the technical areas. There's nothing wrong with that."

Robinson instructs students at Mohawk College in Hamilton, Ontario. "I don't think people realize how much fluid power affects their daily lives. The drill at your dentist's office, the car hoist at your garage, the brakes on your car—all of these devices are based on fluid power."

BIG IDEA
4.0

Understanding the properties of fluids helps in designing and building useful devices.

You have investigated several properties of fluids: viscosity, density, and buoyancy. Now you will apply your understanding of these properties to the areas known as hydraulics and pneumatics. *Hydraulic* devices use liquids, and *pneumatic* devices use air or other gases.

4.1 COMPRESSION OF FLUIDS

Explore

Another property of fluids is compressibility. When a force pushes on an object, the object is said to be under **compression**. Objects under compression tend to deform in shape. For example, when you kick a soccer ball, the force of your foot compresses the ball and temporarily deforms it.

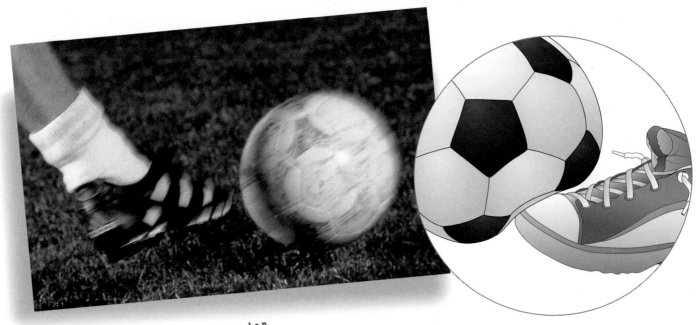

Develop
Fluids and Forces

In the next activity, you will investigate the effects of forces on a fluid.

A COMPRESSING SITUATION

The Question

How can the Particle Theory of Matter explain the compression of fluids?

Materials & Equipment

Part 1

- *50-mL syringe with end plugged with Plasticene*
- *water*
- *sink or bowl*

Part 2

- *2 burette clamps*
- *modified 50-mL syringe with platform and tight-fitting cap*
- *support stand*
- *4 1-kg masses*
- *water*

Procedure

Part 1

1 Place the plunger of the syringe three-quarters of the way up the tube. Seal the end of the syringe with Plasticene.

2 Before you press the plunger down, predict how far the plunger will go. Record your prediction. Test your prediction.

3 Record the change in volume in the syringe.

4 Unseal the end and place the syringe in a sink or bowl of water. Pull up the plunger to draw in water until the syringe is filled to the same level as in step 1. Seal the end of the syringe.

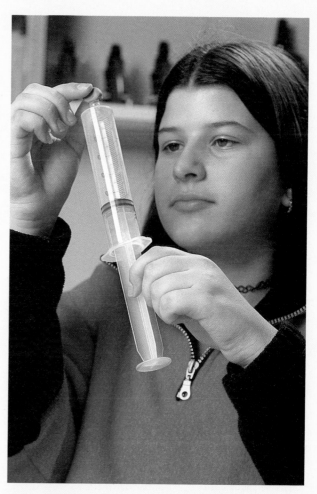

Step 1: the plunger should be three-quarters of the way up the tube.

5 Before you press the plunger down, predict how far you think the plunger will go. Record your prediction. Test your prediction.

6 Record the change in volume in the syringe.

continued on next page ·····➤

Part 2

7 Use the burette clamps to attach a modified syringe (with platform) to a support stand, as shown in the diagram.

Be sure to follow safe work procedures and clamp the syringe tightly and at right angles to the stand.

8 Open the syringe to the 50-mL mark. Seal the end with Plasticene.

9 Place a 1-kg mass on the centre of the platform attached to the syringe. (This is the same as a 10-N force.) Measure and record the volume of air in the syringe.

10 Repeat step 9 by adding another 1-kg mass so that you now have a 2-kg mass (a 20-N force).

11 Repeat step 10 for the following masses (forces): 3 kg (30 N) and 4 kg (40 N).

12 Remove all the masses.

13 Fill the syringe with water and repeat steps 9, 10, and 11.

14 Clean and return your equipment to the appropriate location.

Keeping Records

Part 1

15 Record your predictions in your notebook.

16 Record the volume in the syringe before and after you push down the plunger.

Part 2

17 Record your data in a table like the one shown below.

Force Acting on Fluid in Syringe (N)	Volume of Air (mL)	Volume of Water (mL)
0		
10		
20		
30		
40		

Analyzing and Interpreting

18 How did your predictions compare with your results?

19 Which fluid compressed more? Why do you think this happened?

20 How did the force affect the compression of the air and the water?

21 Plot a line graph of the compression of the air and water from Part 2 using a different colour for each. Put the volume on the vertical axis, and the force on the horizontal axis.

Forming Conclusions

22 Use the Particle Theory to explain what happened when you compressed the air and the water. Focus your explanation on the differences in the amount of space between particles in air and water. Use your observations, and remember to refer to your graph to support your explanation.

1 Compare the compressibility of liquids and gases.
2 Use the Particle Theory to explain the differences in compressibility between liquids and gases.
3 Use your explanation to identify which material in each of the following pairs would compress more than the other. Provide a brief reason for each answer.
   a) a helium balloon or a water balloon
   b) full plastic bottle of juice or the empty plastic bottle
   c) plastic bubble-wrap or a liquid-filled baby teething ring

4.2 HYDRAULIC AND PNEUMATIC SYSTEMS

Explore

Devices That Use Fluids

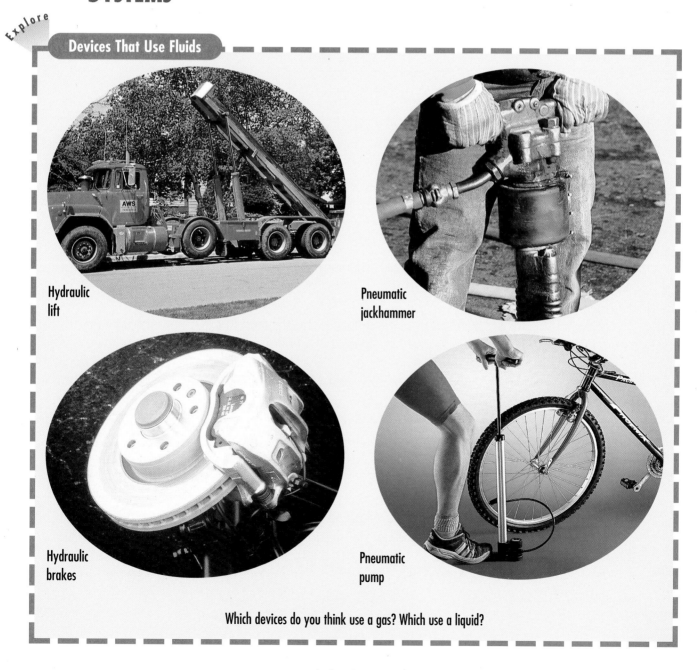

Hydraulic lift

Pneumatic jackhammer

Hydraulic brakes

Pneumatic pump

Which devices do you think use a gas? Which use a liquid?

In the last activity, you found that one of the properties of fluids is that gases can be compressed more than liquids can. The Particle Theory can explain these observations. The illustration below shows that there is much more space between particles in the gas than in the liquid.

As a result, when a force is applied to the particles, there is more room for compression in the gas than in the liquid. In fact, very little compression occurs in liquids. Materials in a liquid state are said to be *incompressible*; that is, they cannot be compressed easily. This property of liquids is very useful. Can you think of any situations where it could be used?

Develop Fluid Technology

Both liquids and gases can be used in devices that help us work. Because they are incompressible, liquids can transfer forces efficiently—but what does this mean?

Suppose you have a liquid in a container, and you apply a force to the liquid at only one place. This is what you did with the syringes in the last Investigator activity. The force you applied over the area of the plunger created pressure on the liquid. This pressure—and force—is exerted *equally* everywhere in the liquid (in the syringe or container). A scientist named Blaise Pascal first made this observation. **Pascal's law** states: When pressure is applied to a confined liquid, that pressure and force are transmitted undiminished (without losing any force) throughout the liquid.

Systems that use liquids in a confined space to transfer forces are called **hydraulic systems**. These systems operate on Pascal's law. The pressure in the hydraulic fluid is the result of the force applied to one surface of the liquid. This pressure is then the same throughout the entire hydraulic system. Because of this, a small input force can be increased by designing an output device that has a larger area than the input device.

For example, look at the diagram of the car lift or hoist on this page. In the diagram, you can see that the input device is a piston with a small area. The output device is another piston, but it has an area 20 times larger than that of the input device.

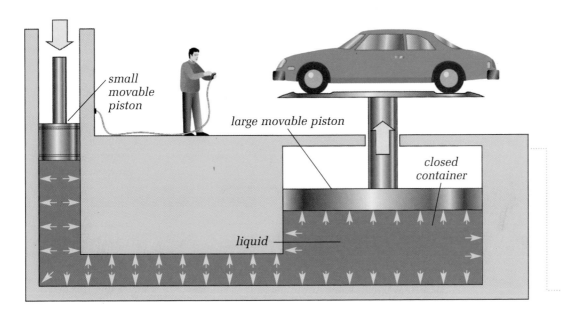

A car hoist is used in a repair garage so that mechanics can work more easily and safely. Each arrow in the picture represents the same amount of force. What conclusion can you make about the forces acting on the two pistons?

The same principle applies for a **pneumatic system**, which uses a gas to transmit forces. But as you saw in the last activity, gases can be compressed quite a bit more than liquids can. For a gas to be used in a system the way hydraulic fluid is, the gas first needs to be compressed. A device called a **compressor** does this as part of a pneumatic system. You may have seen, or heard, air brakes on large trucks. This is an example of a pneumatic system. The diagram on this page explains how air brakes work.

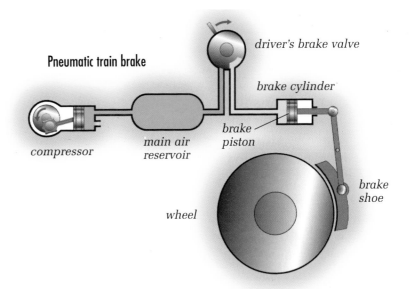

Pneumatic train brake

driver's brake valve

brake cylinder

brake piston

compressor

main air reservoir

wheel

brake shoe

Large trucks use air brakes (pneumatic brakes) because more force is needed to stop the larger wheels. Cars use hydraulic brakes.

In the next activity, you have a chance to apply your understanding of the compressibility of fluids to the construction of a pneumatic or hydraulic toy.

CREATING A HYDRAULIC OR PNEUMATIC TOY

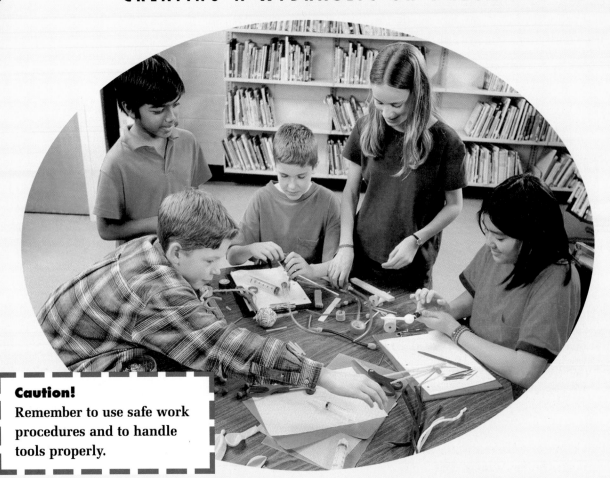

Caution!
Remember to use safe work procedures and to handle tools properly.

Imagine you are working for a small company that makes different kinds of toys. These toys can be used by kids all over the world because they are fun to play with, and they don't require any special equipment like batteries. The toys are for a whole range of ages—from babies to young adults. Before you start, work with your partner or small group to make a list of toys that you think children would enjoy, or that you had fun with when you were younger. The only guide is that the toy must not require any electricity.

- Your task is to create a toy that uses at least one pneumatic or hydraulic device.
- Your toy should not be larger than 30 cm in any direction.
- It must be safe and easy to operate.
- Use Toolbox 3: The Design Process for Technology as a resource in developing your toy.
- Once your teacher approves your plan, construct your toy. Be prepared to demonstrate your toy to the class.

1 How does the Particle Theory explain the fact that gases are more compressible than liquids?

2 What is the difference between a pneumatic system and a hydraulic system?

3 How did you use a hydraulic or pneumatic system in your toy?

4.3 FLUIDS IN ACTION

Water and air can be used for many different things. Working with a partner, look at the pictures below and try to identify which substance is being used and how. Can you think of other examples that could be included with these? Share your ideas with the class.

Examples of Fluids in Action

This device, called a HeartSaverVAD™, helps a sick heart to pump blood.

Submersibles are underwater vehicles designed to dive much deeper than any human could.

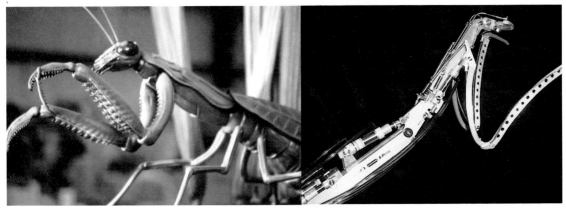

If you think this is a praying mantis, look again! Underneath its body is a miniaturized system of pneumatic cylinders that control its movement.

Hair dryers heat and move volumes of air.

Wind tunnels, which use fast-flowing air, help in designing airplanes, cars, and other vehicles and devices.

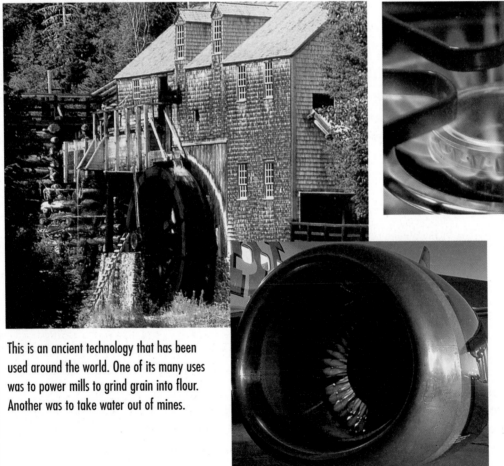

This is an ancient technology that has been used around the world. One of its many uses was to power mills to grind grain into flour. Another was to take water out of mines.

Natural gas is compressed and transported through a system of pipes to home furnaces and stoves.

A jet engine enables an airplane to move much faster than it would with propellers.

Before You Start...

Before you begin this activity, review what you have learned about hydraulics or pneumatics.

The Situation

The situation is serious. A barrel of toxic waste has been left on a loading dock near the sports complex. The mayor has asked for the barrel to be removed immediately in the safest manner possible. No one is allowed to touch the barrel directly. This means a device must be used to grab the barrel, lift it off the loading dock, and place it on a disposal truck. The problem is that no such device is available. What is needed is a hydraulic or pneumatic crane.

The Question

How can you design and build a model of a hydraulic or pneumatic device that will lift the barrel off the loading dock and place it on the disposal truck?

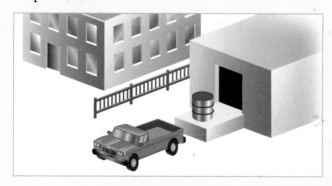

Your Task

1 Your teacher will have set up a model of the situation. You can expect to see a pop can representing the barrel on a model of the loading dock. The model disposal truck should be about 30 cm from the loading dock. You may refer to this model as you plan and build your device.

These machines all use hydraulic or pneumatic systems.

2 Form an Emergency Response Task Force of two to four people. Devise a plan for constructing your device. Make sure the device uses hydraulics or pneumatics to lift the barrel.

3 Make a list of materials that you will need to build your device. Show your plan to your teacher for approval. Then build your device.

4 Test your device once. This will allow you to make any needed modifications before the final demonstration.

5 Each group will demonstrate its device to the rest of the class. After watching the demonstrations, write a paragraph for the following:
   a) how your model worked
   b) what you would do to improve your device the next time
   c) what the most difficult part of the task was.

Pumps and Other Devices

Imagine having to move a fluid from one place to another. Maybe this means just putting air in your basketball. Or maybe you want to filter the water in your fish tank. What would you use?

For both examples, if you thought a pump would be the solution, you're correct. But what exactly is a pump, and how does it work? A pump moves a fluid through or into something. To fill up your basketball, you use a pump to force air into the ball. A water filter draws in and pumps out water to clean and add air to the fish tank. Pumps also exist in nature. The most important one to you is your **heart**—it pumps blood through your body.

Common Types of Pumps

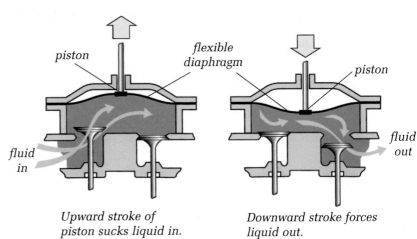

Upward stroke of piston sucks liquid in.

Downward stroke forces liquid out.

Diaphragm pumps are used for both liquids and gases, such as the air pumped into this aquarium.

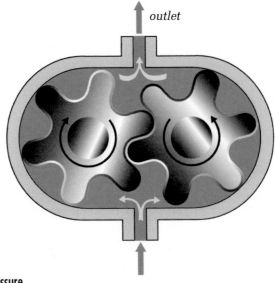

Rotary pumps use gears to pump liquids at a higher than normal pressure. A car's engine uses one to pump oil through its lubricating system.

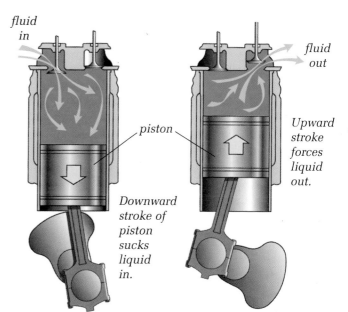

fluid in

piston

fluid out

Upward stroke forces liquid out.

Downward stroke of piston sucks liquid in.

Piston pumps use a cylinder, called a piston, to pump liquids or gases. The internal combustion engine of a car is actually a piston pump. (See on the next page for how a piston pump works.)

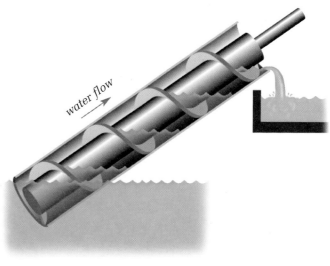

water flow

For raising water, the screw is enclosed in a cylinder. The rotating screw draws water up.

The **Archimedes screw** is a pump supposedly invented by Archimedes to remove water from the hold of a ship. Here it is used as a sand washer on a construction site.

Pressure

A pump functions by raising the pressure of a fluid flowing through it. **Pressure** is the amount of force applied to a particular area.

$$\text{Pressure} = \frac{\text{Force}}{\text{Area}}$$

Pressure is measured in Pascals (P). A Pascal equals the force of one Newton over an area of one square metre ($1 \text{ P} = \frac{1 \text{ N}}{1 \text{ m}^2}$).

Air pressure is measured in kilopascals (kP). The average air pressure at sea level is 101.3 kP.

The more force you can apply to a given area, the greater the pressure. The pressure on a given area can also be changed by making the area smaller (for greater pressure) or larger (for less pressure).

The Bicycle Piston Pump

There are many different kinds of pumps, but one of the most common ones is the bicycle pump. This kind of pump has a piston that moves up and down in a cylinder. At the bottom of the cylinder is an outlet for air. By pushing down on the piston, you decrease the volume of the cylinder, and the pressure of the air increases. You saw a similar situation in an earlier activity when you tried to compress a syringe filled with air. If the vent at the end of the pump is connected to an area of lower pressure, the fluid will move to that area. For example, the area of lower pressure could be a flat bicycle tire or an uninflated soccer ball.

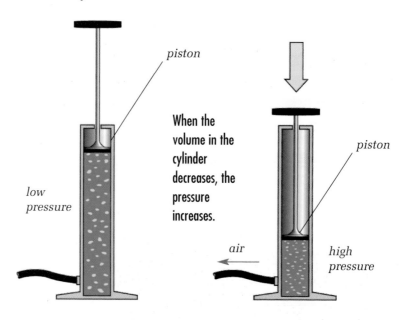

piston

low pressure

When the volume in the cylinder decreases, the pressure increases.

piston

air

high pressure

Let's look at some other examples of hydraulic and pneumatic systems.

The Vascular System

The vascular system is the system of blood vessels that reaches to every part of your body. The most important hydraulic device in our bodies is part of this system—the heart. The **heart** pumps blood to the lungs for oxygen, and then pumps it a second time out into the body.

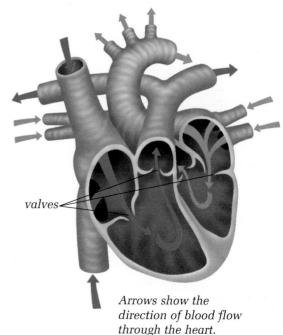

valves

Arrows show the direction of blood flow through the heart.

The direction of blood flow is controlled by valves. **Valves** are devices that control the flow of fluids. The valves in our vascular system are designed to let the blood flow in only one direction. Understanding how the blood flows through the heart can be very important. The heart's pumping creates pressure throughout the vascular system. Doctors can measure a person's blood pressure using a device called a *sphygmomanometer* (sfig mō mi nom i ter). A change in blood pressure can be a sign of a medical problem.

The Bathyscaph

How could an understanding of density help you go to the deepest spot on the planet? This spot is about 11 000 m below sea level in the Marianas Trench in the Pacific Ocean, about 330 km south of Guam. Humans cannot dive this deep because the pressure is too great. To go this deep, you need an underwater ship called a bathyscaph. The name comes from the Greek words *bathos* for "deep" and *scaphos* for "ship." Swiss scientist Auguste Piccard invented the bathyscaph and called his vessel the *Trieste*.

reSEARCH

Heart Valves
Valves are an important part of any system for moving fluids. They are devices to control or regulate the amount of flow, like the valves in your bathroom taps. They can be used to control the level of fluid in a container, like the valve in the toilet tank.
- Find out how heart valves work.
- What can be used to replace human heart valves when they no longer work properly?

2 FLUIDS

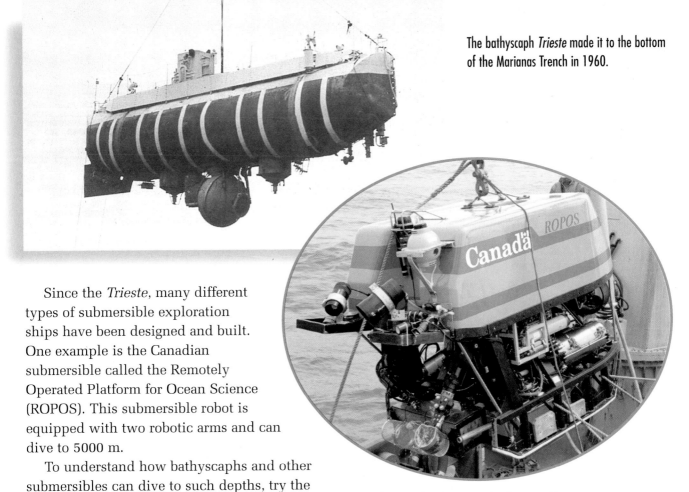

The bathyscaph *Trieste* made it to the bottom of the Marianas Trench in 1960.

Since the *Trieste*, many different types of submersible exploration ships have been designed and built. One example is the Canadian submersible called the Remotely Operated Platform for Ocean Science (ROPOS). This submersible robot is equipped with two robotic arms and can dive to 5000 m.

To understand how bathyscaphs and other submersibles can dive to such depths, try the following activity.

The ROPOS underwater robot has two video cameras, sonar, and a number of digital data transmission channels.

DIVING DEEPLY

Step 2: insert tube.

Step 4: hold jar just below the surface.

In this activity, you will construct a model of a bathyscaph and infer how it works. You will need:

- plastic tubing (about 60 cm)
- small glass jar with a metal lid that seals tightly
- a straw
- deep pan or bucket of water
- latex cement
- safety glasses
- hammer
- nail

Procedure

1 Make two holes in the metal lid of the jar. The tubing should fit in one hole snugly, and the other hole should be much smaller.

2 Insert the tubing into the larger hole and seal it in place with the latex cement. Let the lid dry.

3 Fill the jar half full with water and put the lid back on the jar tightly.

4 Put the jar in the water and hold it just below the surface of the water.

5 Adjust the amount of water in the jar by drawing air out or blowing air into the tube. Continue until the jar floats just below the surface on its own.

Questions

- What do you have to do to make the model bathyscaph go up and down in the water? Use the terms *density* and *buoyancy* to explain your observations and conclusion. (Hint: The buoyancy of an object in a fluid relates to its density and the density of the fluid.)
- What improvements could you add to your model so that it could carry a dry cargo?

4.0 Understanding the Properties of Fluids Helps in Designing and Building Useful Devices

Communicate

1 Give an example of how our understanding of hydraulic systems has helped us understand the human vascular system.
2 Choose one type of pump and explain how it works.
3 How does a bathyscaph work?
4 Identify one industry that uses the properties of fluids.

4.4 CHECK YOUR PROGRESS

1 A gas and a liquid were compressed in two different syringes. The results were graphed, as shown to the right. Which line on the graph was for the gas? Which one was for the liquid?
2 Add any terms you learned in this Big Idea to your concept map. You may also be able to add some examples from this Big Idea to words that are already on your concept map.
3 a) How does the Particle Theory explain why solids cannot be compressed?
   b) How does the Particle Theory explain why gases compress more than liquids do?
4 How can hydraulic or pneumatic systems be used in toys?
5 Give one example of a device that makes use of at least one property of fluids.

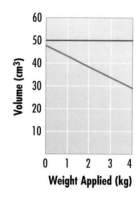

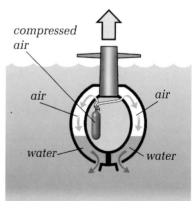

infoBIT

How Does a Submarine Change Its Buoyancy?

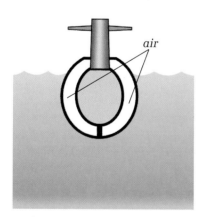

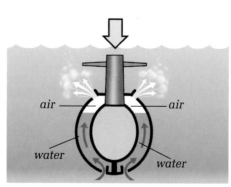

Surfaced
Between the submarine's inner and outer hulls are ballast tanks. When the sub is surfaced, the tanks are filled with air, making the vessel buoyant.

Diving
To dive, the air is released from valves at the top of the ballast tanks and seawater rushes in through valves at the bottom. The seawater is denser than the air it displaces so the submarine sinks.

Re-surfacing
To re-surface, compressed air is forced into the ballast tanks through valves at the top. This forces the seawater out through valves at the bottom. The air is less dense than the water it displaces so the submarine floats.

Fluid Disasters

The Ganges River, India

Hundreds of thousands of "tubewells" were drilled in Bangladesh during the last 40 years.

Technology can vastly improve our quality of life—when it works! Here are two instances of fluid technology to consider. The first example describes a deadly problem that was created by a well-meant technological solution. In the second example, an environmental disaster caused by technology is "cleaned up" using another technology.

Poisoning the Water System

Hand-operated pumps, like the one shown below, were of great benefit to developing countries beginning in the

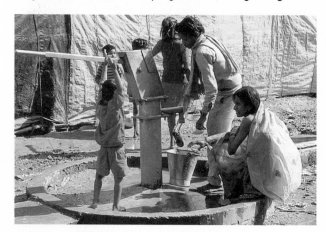

A village pump in India

1960s. (Recall the low-cost pump developed by the University of Waterloo in the Invitation to Explore.) In Bangladesh, for example, hundreds of thousands of wells have been sunk along the watershed of the Ganges River. They provided people with drinking water that was free of surface runoff contamination, as well as water for irrigation.

In the beginning, these wells benefited everyone. People had clean water to drink. Crops could be grown during the dry season, relieving food shortages. Then mysteriously, people began developing skin cancer and severe sores on their bodies. Many died. What was the cause? All the hundreds of thousands of wells were contaminated with arsenic!

Decades of pump use had lowered the level of underground water (the water table). A lower water table meant that air could now reach underground rock containing arsenic. The air reacted with the rock, releasing arsenic into the water. When people drank the water, they also took in the poison, and over time became sick. Technology, which was meant to help the people of Bangladesh, now threatened their existence!

Oil and Water Don't Mix

As you learned in your investigations, liquids differ in their densities. This fact has helped clean-up crews deal with the growing problem of ocean oil spills. Remember, oil has a lower density than water. That means when it hits the water in an oil spill, it *floats*. The spilled oil has nowhere to go but across the water's surface, so it creates a large "slick." Even a tiny spill can rapidly spread out to cover a huge area. One litre of oil, for example, can spread out to cover an area the size of half a football field.

Supertanker ships are used to transport large quantities of oil to ports around the world. Sometimes these tankers have accidents. They break up in storms. They run aground on reefs or rocks. The supertanker *Exxon Valdez*, which ran aground in 1989, spilled 41 million litres of oil. That created an oil slick over 70 km^2 in size.

Because oil floats on water, clean-up crews can use long, floating barriers called *containment booms* to stop the oil slick from spreading. To recover the oil, crews use *skimmers* and *sorbents*. A skimmer works like a giant vacuum cleaner to suck up the oil from the water's surface. A sorbent looks like a giant sponge. It's made of a material that absorbs oil, such as straw, and is placed on top of the slick to soak up the oil.

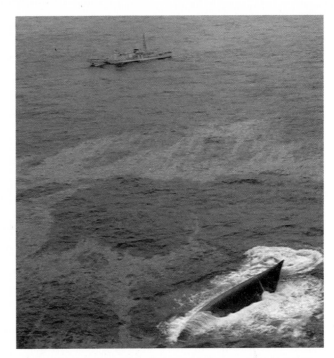

When this oil tanker sank off the coast of Japan, 3700 kL of oil spilled into the ocean.

A typical oil skimmer

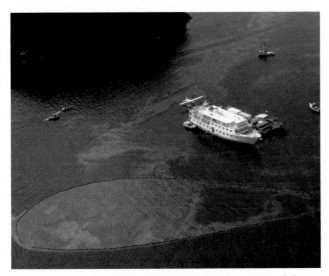

A containment boom is basically a length of buoyant material that extends about 30 cm below the surface of the water. The oil, floating on top of the water, cannot get under the boom and is instead trapped behind it.

In Your Opinion

1 If you were introducing hand pumps to a developing country, what recommendations would you make about their use?

2 Research oil spills and their clean-ups. What other methods of clean-ups are used? What would happen in a fuel spill if the density of the fuel were equal to or greater than water?

PROJECT

Getting Started

Without water, humans cannot survive. Our planet supports life because it is rich in water. But many people on earth do not have access to clean drinking water—and it's killing them. Every year millions of people die from diseases carried by dirty water.

There are many reasons for lack of good drinking water. These include:

- There may not be any water close by.
- The closest water may be polluted by humans or animals.
- People may not have enough money to install pumps or water collection and distribution systems.

Organizations exist to help fix these water problems, but it will take a long time. They have to raise money for people and equipment. They have to find the right kind of technology that will work and is affordable in each situation. Most communities without access to clean drinking water cannot afford the kind of expensive, high-technology systems that we use in our cities and towns.

152

Some people have suggested unusual solutions. One suggestion is to tow icebergs from the Arctic to areas where fresh water is needed. The iceberg would then melt, and the water could be used. While this idea has not yet been proven to work, it is an example of people looking for creative solutions.

Before You Start...

In this chapter, you have learned about some of the properties of fluids and how they can be used. Look through your notes from the activities you did. You will be using your creative thinking abilities and what you have learned about fluids to solve a water problem for the people of Niagao.

The Context

The town of Niagao has a water problem. The town's residents have no easy way of getting water from the river to their homes. Every day they must walk to the river to collect the water they need. As well, they must do this at specific times of day, otherwise the water is slightly salty because of the tide from the nearby ocean.

- The town needs a place to store water.
- They also need a way of detecting when the water is becoming salty, so they can stop it from entering the storage area until it's fresh again.

The town has formed a committee to find possible solutions to their water problem. The committee will use the following criteria when it reviews submissions that describe potential solutions.

Review Criteria

The proposed solution must:
1 function properly
2 use materials that are readily available
3 have some form of pumping mechanism to move the water
4 ensure that water can be transported from the river to the storage tank
5 have a device to detect a change in density and turn the pump off when the water gets too salty

town of Niagao

river

ocean

continued on next page ⟶

The Task

Working as a team, create a solution to Niagao's water problem. Use an illustrated design to show how you would solve the water problem and a working model to simulate the device to detect the change in the water's density.

Procedure

1 With your team, brainstorm features that your design needs to include to solve Niagao's water problem. Make sure to record all your thoughts. You can discard unusable ideas later.

2 Look at the results of your brainstorming. As a team, decide which ideas are worth developing further. Use the following questions to help make your decisions:
a) How will your design take water from the river to the storage tank?
b) How will your design detect the change in density?
c) Which features would be fairly simple to put into practice? Which ones will require further research?
d) What materials will you need to build your density detector?

3 Reach agreement on which features your team will design into your proposed solution. Assign one or more features to individual members or small groups on your team.

4 Describe each feature and provide drawings where appropriate. Remember to make sure that each feature works with all the other features.

5 As a team, review your proposed solution to Niagao's water problem. Once you agree on the design, write your report on the proposed solution.

6 Build a model of your density detector.

7 Before you present your solution, you will need to make sure that your density detector will work. This means your density detector model must be tested. Before you test it, discuss the following questions:

- How will you test your density detector safely?
- How will you test your density detector to make sure it is functioning?
- How might you change your design based on feedback from your group and classmates?

Share and Compare

8 Present your proposal to your class and demonstrate your density detector.

9 As you watch other proposals, fill in the following chart. When it's complete, add it to your report.

Features Other Teams Used That We Used	Features We Should Have Used	Features Used by Others That We Won't Use

Observations and Reflections

10 Include your answers to the following questions in your report:
a) Which design do you think will be the most effective in solving Niagao's water problem?
b) Which design do you think is the most interesting? Explain your answer.
c) If you had a chance to redesign your proposal, what changes would you make? Give reasons for your answer.

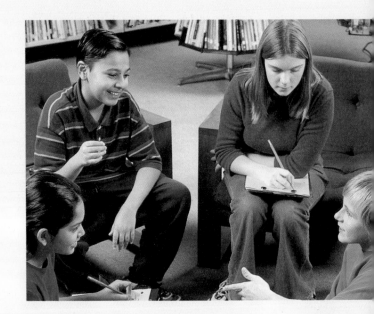

CHAPTER REVIEW

Using Key Terms

1 Create a short story or magazine article about fluids that uses the following terms:

> viscosity
> flow rate
> density
> buoyancy
> gravity
> Particle Theory of Matter
> hydrometer
> compressibility
> hydraulic systems
> pneumatic systems

Reviewing the Big Ideas

2 Describe one factor that can affect the viscosity of a liquid.

3 How are viscosity and density related?

4 What is the difference between mass and weight?

5 Why is it easier to float on salt water than on fresh water?

6 What is the difference in the ability of air and water to be compressed?

7 Describe a situation that uses a hydraulic system and a situation that uses a pneumatic system.

8 Give two examples of industries for which an understanding of fluid dynamics is required.

Connecting the Big Ideas

9 Why do you think the densities of ice, water, and steam are different?

10 Can there be buoyancy without gravity? Explain.

11 You have samples of the same liquid. One is at 50°C and one is at 30°C. What will happen if you poured the same amount of each liquid onto a ramp? Which flow rate would be faster? Explain your answer. If you were to add the same amount of liquid at 70°C to the ramp, what would happen?

12 Use average density to explain why a ship made out of steel can float.

13 If you had to make a device to lift a large mass, would you use a hydraulic fluid or a pneumatic fluid? Explain your answer.

14 A report in British Columbia described a situation in which a fishing boat loaded with fish sank when it entered the Fraser River. Why do you think this happened?

15 The Canadarm on the space shuttle uses hydraulic systems to move large objects. Why is a pneumatic system not used?

The smaller crane is designed to help space-walkers.

16 For each of the substances listed below, describe if the viscosity is likely to be low, average, or high. Give an explanation for each.
  a) oil
  b) salad dressing
  c) cough syrup
  d) carbonated drink
  e) ketchup

17 Describe how you would make and calibrate a hydrometer.

Using the Big Ideas

18 You are given three liquids. Explain what types of tests you could do to determine the properties of each liquid.

19 A student dropped pennies one at a time into a known volume of water and measured the volume displaced. Her results are in the table below.

Mass	Volume
17 g	2 mL
35 g	4 mL
52 g	6 mL
70 g	8 mL
88 g	10 mL

  a) What is the mass-to-volume ratio for the pennies?
  b) What is the density of a copper penny?
  c) Graph this data with mass on the vertical axis and volume on the horizontal axis. Find the slope of the line. How does this slope compare to the density of copper?

20 If you were asked to design a vehicle that could travel through water, what features could you design to take advantage of one or more properties of fluids?

21 A new drink that some people enjoy contains tapioca beads suspended in tea. Describe how you could design an experiment to determine the density of the tapioca beads.

Self Assessment

22 Copy the following diagram into your notebook and answer the questions by filling in the appropriate empty bubbles.

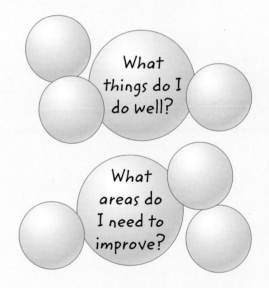

23 a) During this chapter, what was the hardest problem you had to do?
  b) Describe what you did to figure out or solve your problem.

24 During this chapter, what was the most interesting thing you learned?

OPTICS

I t's night. You're ready to fall asleep. You turn off your bedside light, and the room is suddenly thrown into darkness. For a moment, you can't see anything. What happens to the objects in your room? Why can't you see them? Do they disappear? Do their colours turn to black? Do you need light to see them? Do objects have a light of their own?

Optics is the scientific study of the properties of light and the way technology uses these properties. It's a subject that has fascinated and puzzled people for centuries. In this chapter, you will study the properties of visible light as well as those of other types of electromagnetic radiation. By answering the questions above, you will broaden your understanding about the way light is produced, transmitted, and detected. You will also make your own optical devices to further your investigations.

BIG Ideas

1.0 Light travels in straight lines and its intensity decreases with distance from its source.

2.0 Light reflects from a plane mirror according to the law of reflection.

3.0 Light is refracted by transparent materials, and this is what makes lenses so useful.

4.0 The eye and the camera capture images using the properties of light.

5.0 The visible light spectrum is made up of different colours.

6.0 Visible light is only one part of the electromagnetic spectrum.

LIGHT UP YOUR LIFE

Before You Start...

Working in groups, you will experiment with light. There will be eight stations to visit. It doesn't matter in which order you visit the stations.

At each station, answer the following three questions.

1 What do you observe?
2 Explain what you see.
3 What do you want to find out?

The Question

What are the properties of light?

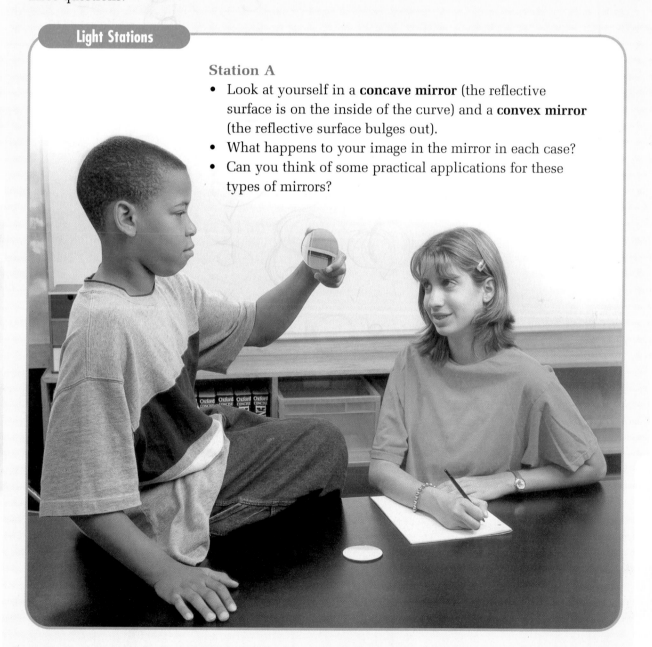

Light Stations

Station A

- Look at yourself in a **concave mirror** (the reflective surface is on the inside of the curve) and a **convex mirror** (the reflective surface bulges out).
- What happens to your image in the mirror in each case?
- Can you think of some practical applications for these types of mirrors?

continued on next page ·······▶

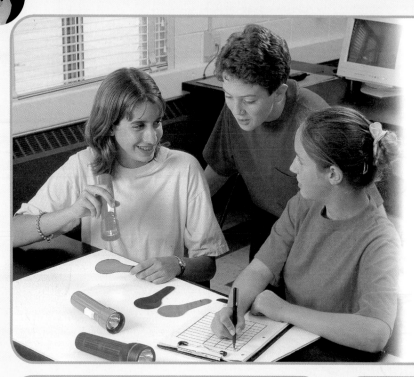

Station B

- Put three coloured filters: blue, red, and green, separately over three light sources of equal brightness (three flashlights or ray boxes). Shine each coloured light source at a white screen.
- Overlap (mix) two different coloured lights together in different combinations. What happens?
- Keep a chart of your combinations and results.
- Lastly, overlap all three coloured lights together on the screen. What do you observe?

Station C

- Look at your image in a plane (flat) mirror. If you step back from the mirror, how does your view change? Can you see *more* or *less* of yourself?

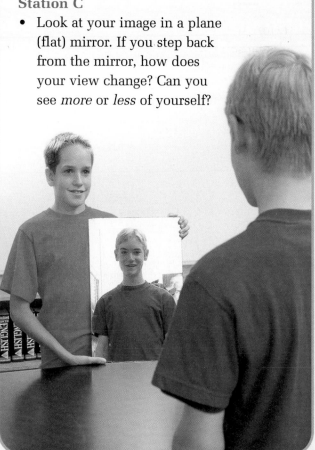

Station D

- Look at a sheet of graph or lined paper using a **convex lens** (thicker in the middle than at the edges) and a **concave lens** (thinner in the middle).
- What happens to the distances between the lines when you move each lens further away from the paper?
- What happens when you move each lens closer to the paper?

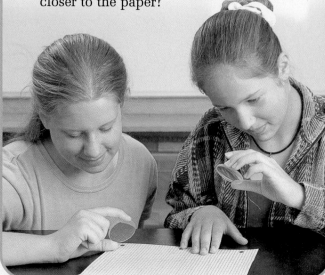

Station E

- Look at a pencil standing in a glass of water. Observe the pencil through the glass at different angles.
- What do you notice?

Station F

- See if you can make a rainbow using a prism and a light source.
- What is a rainbow?

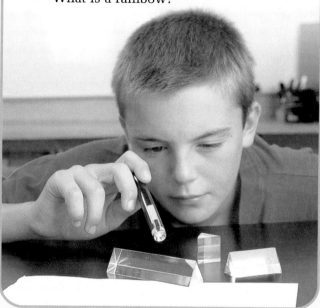

Station G

- Shine a light source through a glass (**transparent**), tissue paper (**translucent**), and a book (**opaque**).
- What happens to the light in each case?
- Shine a light through other materials.
- What do you think the terms transparent, translucent, and opaque mean?

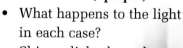

Station H

- Using solar-powered devices, can you show that light is energy?
- Try changing the amount of light that reaches the devices to see how the level of power varies.

Focus Your Thoughts

1 You have had a chance to explore and think about light. In the Invitation to Explore, you investigated some of the properties of light. Compare the photos shown below. How do you think each photo is related to light?

The Hubble Space Telescope allows scientists to see across vast distances of space and time. Each object pictured here (including the tiny points of light) are distant galaxies.

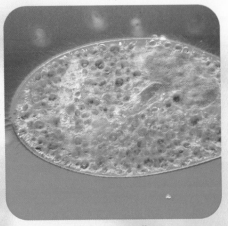

The compound microscope allows scientists to magnify objects hundreds of times. This image shows the one-celled paramecium, magnified 160 times.

2 Look at the four photos at the left and create a title for each. Explain, to the best of your knowledge, how light or the properties of light account for each photo.

3 Below is a list of words whose definitions you may or may not know. Working with a partner, sort the words you know into groups. Predict how each group represents or demonstrates one of the key properties of light that you have explored so far.

brightness	rainbow
colour	reflection
concave mirror or lens	refraction
convex mirror or lens	translucent
energy	transparent
luminous	wavelength

4 Is the advertising flyer *Light, the Amazing Form of Energy!* true or is it misleading?

5 Describe in a paragraph what you think are the properties of light energy. How did you know? How could you find out about any properties of light you didn't know?

1.0 Light travels in straight lines and its intensity decreases with distance from its source.

The people using shadow puppets have something in common with the designers of the lighting for this new theatre. They both need to understand where light comes from and how light travels in order to create the effects they wish. How does light travel from its source? What evidence do you have that this is so?

1.1 HOW DOES LIGHT TRAVEL?

Explore

What source of light are you using to read this page? Put your hand between this source and the page. What happens? Experiment to see how the shadow changes if you change the angle of your hand or its distance from the page. What do you conclude about how light travels from this source to your page?

Where is the sun in this scene? How do you know?

Straight from Here to There

Develop

You probably concluded (or remembered from earlier studies) that light travels in straight lines from its source. Light cannot bend around objects. So when you placed your hand between the light source and this page, it prevented the light from reaching the page and made a shadow. A **shadow** is created whenever light hits an opaque material. Opaque materials, including bricks, books, and people, reflect or absorb all the light that reaches them.

See the chart below for a review of some of the characteristics of objects and materials in relation to light.

A Light Vocabulary

Term	Definition	Examples
luminous	objects that produce light	sun, light bulb, fire
non-luminous	objects that do not produce light but may reflect it	moon, most objects on earth
transparent	materials that allow light to pass through	glass, air, photographic slide film
opaque	materials that do not allow light to pass through	wood, metal, thick plastic
translucent	materials that allow some light to pass through	some types of cloth, stained glass

You can notice how light travels in a straight line when you use a flashlight or see a beam of sunlight coming down through a cloudy sky. You might wonder why, when you turn on the light in a room, the light seems to reach almost everywhere. How is that possible, if light travels in straight lines? One reason is that the light from the light source in your room travels outward in all directions. The lighting in a room is usually designed to allow light to reach all directions. A flashlight is designed to allow light to go in one direction. In either case, light travels in straight lines from its source.

Projecting Images

As you can see in these pictures, light travels in straight lines from its source as well as in all directions. It also travels in straight lines even after being reflected from an object. These characteristics of light should help you understand the next activity.

Before You Start...

The pinhole camera uses a tiny hole to form an image. In one form or another, it has been used for centuries. Photography was invented using a large version of the pinhole camera called the *camera obscura,* which means "dark chamber." This was a small dark room with a tiny pinhole at one end. In 1826, Nicéphore Niépce replaced the pinhole with a lens and projected an image onto a metal plate coated with light-sensitive chemicals. This image was probably the first photograph ever permanently recorded. It took about eight hours to expose the image!

The ancient Chinese and Greeks used the pinhole camera to look at solar eclipses without endangering the viewers' eyes. By the time of Niépce, artists used this early form of camera to trace images onto canvas before beginning a painting.

The Question

How does a pinhole camera record an image?

Niépce's first photograph

Your Task

1 Make your own pinhole camera using two empty chip containers (or any other cylindrical containers that have metal bottoms).
2 Remove the lid and bottom from the first container, leaving a hollow tube.
3 Use a nail to punch a very small hole in the bottom of the second container. Leave the lid on to act as a screen for the image.
4 Use black electrical tape, masking tape, or duct tape to join the hollow tube to the container at the end that has the lid. You now have a long cylinder with a pinhole at one end and a screen (the lid) in the middle. This is your pinhole camera.
5 Point the pinhole of the camera at a bright lamp or a light bulb.
6 Look in the open end. What do you see?
7 What does this show you about how light travels?
8 Share and compare your observations with your classmates.

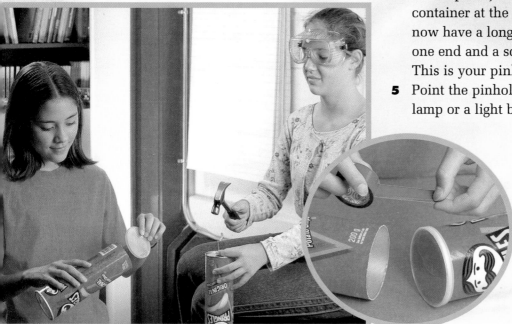

1 a) What causes shadows to occur?

b) How could you make two shadows from the same object at the same time? four shadows?

c) Is there a limit to the number of different shadows you can make at once? Explain.

2 What do you notice about the shape of the beam of light from a flashlight or movie projector as the beam moves farther from its source? Why is this happening?

3 Compare the rabbit's eyes with those of its predator, the hawk. Based on how light travels, which of these animals can see a person approaching from the side or behind? Why do you think this ability is important to this animal's survival?

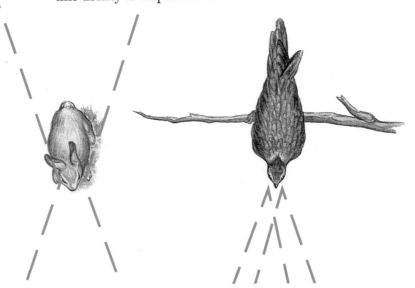

4 Explain why you agree or disagree with this statement: *Once light leaves its source, it will persist and keep going forever.* If you disagreed, under what conditions might this statement be true?

1.2 INTENSITY AND DISTANCE

Imagine there has been a power failure and all the lights in your home go out. You have a test tomorrow and need to study. You find a candle to use as a light source and place it so that you have enough light to be able to read your notes. Your sister shows up and wants to share the light so she can work on a puzzle. You move the candle to the middle of the table. When you look at your notes again, you find the pages are now too dim to be easily read. What happened to the light? How could you provide enough light for both of you?

Intensity

The amount of light arriving at one place per unit area is referred to as the **light intensity**. A person sitting far away from a light source such as a candle will notice the light is dimmer, or less intense, than when she sits closer. In the following activity, you will explore what affects the intensity of light.

PROBLEM SOLVER

LIGHT POWER

You've probably used a flashlight in a darkened room or outside at night. What have you noticed about the light that shines? For instance, suppose you shone a flashlight on the far wall in a darkened gymnasium and then in a darkened small room. Would the light intensity (that is, the brightness of each unit area of wall) be different on the two walls? In which room would it be greater?

- Plan and perform an experiment to show how light intensity is related to the distance it travels before striking an object.
- Predict what you think will happen.
- If possible, compare several types of light sources.
- How did your predictions compare with your results?

Look at the streetlights in this photograph. Where would you find the greatest light intensity if you wanted to read a map?

Telescopes are able to receive light that has travelled from incredibly distant galaxies because that light has moved through the vacuum of space. There is very little matter in space to block or interfere with the movement of light. On the surface of the earth, however, light is constantly being reflected or absorbed by matter.

1 A nebula is a cloud of non-luminous dust and luminous gas in space. Light from nearby stars is reflected by the dust and emitted by the gas to produce these beautiful colours. Some nebulas appear as black shadows. What would you conclude about the black shadows in these nebulas?

info**BIT**

A Light Quiz

Test your knowledge of light in space:

1 What is the most important source of light on earth?
2 What component of the universe moves at the fastest speed?
3 How long does it take for light from the sun to reach earth?
4 How long does it take for light from the next nearest star to reach earth?

Answers
(1) the sun (2) light, travelling 300 000 km/s (3) about 8 min (4) about 4 years

The Orion Nebula, M42

2 Describe how you could use a solar-powered calculator or other device to measure light intensity.

3 An architect designing a building must consider how people will use different rooms in order to plan the best lighting. Explain which intensity of lighting (very bright, medium bright, or dim) you would use in:
a) a bedroom
b) an artist's studio
c) an entrance way
d) a kitchen
e) a family room

1.3 CHECK YOUR PROGRESS

1. Explain, using diagrams, how light travels.
2. How far does the light from a flashlight travel during the day? Is this different from the distance the light from a flashlight travels during the night? Explain.
3. What happens to light when it hits an opaque object?
4. What happens to the light intensity as you move farther from the light source? Why?
5. Is the earth a luminous or non-luminous object? Use evidence from these photographs to support your answer.

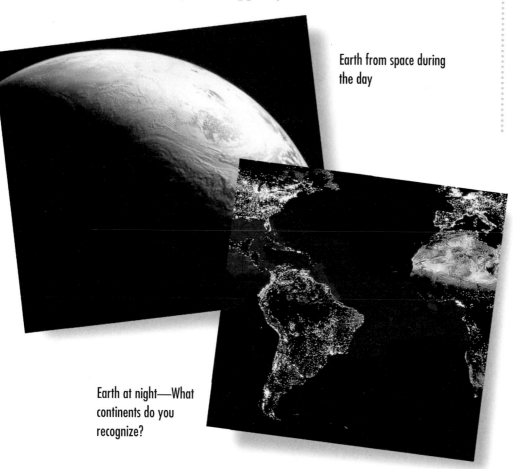

Earth from space during the day

Earth at night—What continents do you recognize?

6. Gardeners and farmers know that some kinds of plants need full sunlight (high intensity light) while others grow best in the shade (lower intensity light).
   a) What is the light source for a plant growing in the shade?
   b) If you want to put a flowering plant that normally grows best in direct sunlight in a shady location, what could you do?

reSEARCH

Looking Back in Time
Historians use ancient records about what people observed in the night sky to help date past events more accurately. According to one historian, "starlight is like seeing back in time."

- What do you think this means?
- Find a star whose light began to travel to earth the year you were born.
- Research the Crab Nebula. Why would historians be interested in this space object?

3 OPTICS

BIG IDEA
2.0

Light reflects from a plane mirror according to the law of reflection.

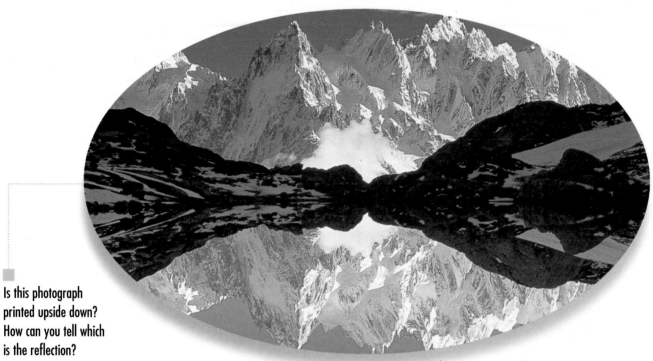

Is this photograph printed upside down? How can you tell which is the reflection?

What does the surface of this lake have in common with the moon? What does it have in common with this page—or your face? You can see these objects because light reflects from their surfaces to your eyes. One of the best ways to learn more about this very useful property of light is to investigate a device you probably use all the time: the mirror.

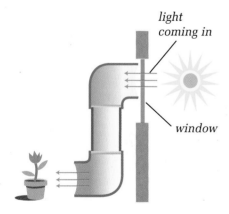

light coming in

window

How would you solve this problem?

2.1 THE REFLECTION OF LIGHT

Explore

The diagram on this page shows a design problem that needs to be solved.
• Copy the diagram.
• Think about how you could use mirrors in the design.
• Draw in any mirrors you would add to this device.
• How did you know where to put them?

^{Develop} **Reflect on This**

As you saw in the photograph on the previous page, a calm body of water can create a clear reflection. The smooth surface of the water acts like a mirror and reflects the light straight into your eyes. But what happens to the reflection if you throw a rock into the water? Let's see how the surfaces of different materials reflect light.

INVESTIGATOR

LIGHT REFLECTION

The Question

Which properties of a material can help predict how well its surface reflects light?

Materials & Equipment

- *sample materials*
- *light source*
- *other apparatus as required*

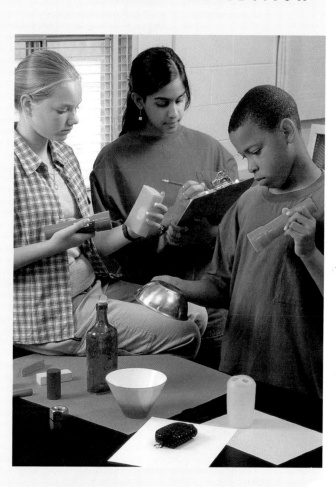

Procedure

1. Plan how you will test your materials for their ability to reflect light. What will you need? What variables will you control? How will you record your observations? For example, do you want to rank the materials from "most reflective" to "least reflective"? Can you make some kind of quantitative measurements?

2. Which properties of materials will you consider? For example, you could investigate colour, texture, shape, and/or softness. Think of as many as you can. Decide if you will work with another group to divide up the tests.

3. Once you have your materials, but before you test their ability to reflect, record their properties and your predictions.

4. Conduct your tests.

Keeping Records

5. Record your findings in a chart.

Analyzing and Interpreting

6. If you took measurements, organize the data into a graph.

continued on next page ······▶

7 Which materials did you predict would be the best reflectors? Which properties of these materials did you think would make them good reflectors?

8 Which material actually reflected light the best? Why did it reflect light so well?

9 Which material reflected light the least? What happened to the light? Did this cause any change in the material itself?

Forming Conclusions

10 List the properties of the material that affect how light reflects from the surface of a material.

11 Based on your findings, what kind of material would you use in each of the following cases? Explain why.
  a) to make a mirror
  b) to cover a container for undeveloped photographic film (this film must not be exposed to light)
  c) to make a table which will be used outdoors in a sunny location

12 If absolutely no light is reflected from an object, can you see the object? Why or why not?

13 If you were going to repeat this experiment, how could you improve the plan of your test? What other properties would you investigate?

You have been investigating how light reflects from objects. But what happens when light hits a mirror? In the next activity, you will find out.

PROBLEM SOLVER

CHECKING OUT THE ANGLES

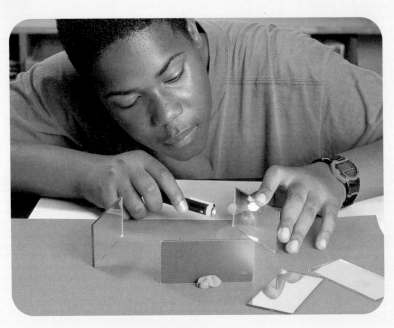

What happens to light when it hits a mirror? Focus a light source (a flashlight, a ray box) that produces a narrow ray of light so that the light ray strikes a flat, or **plane mirror**. What happens to the light ray if it strikes the mirror at a 90° angle or at another angle?

• Can you arrange a group of mirrors together so that the reflected light displays a geometrical shape?

• Can you arrange a group of mirrors so that light could be reflected forever?

The Law of Reflection

When a ray of light hits a mirror straight on, that is, at right angles, it bounces straight back. When a light ray hits the mirror at an angle to the mirror, it bounces back at an angle. If you use straight lines to represent the mirror and rays in a drawing, a line perpendicular to the mirror is called a **normal**. The angle between the incoming ray, the **incident ray**, and the normal is the **angle of incidence**. The angle between the reflected ray and the normal is the **angle of reflection**. How are these angles related? The relationship between these angles is the basis of the **law of reflection**, which you will investigate in the next activity.

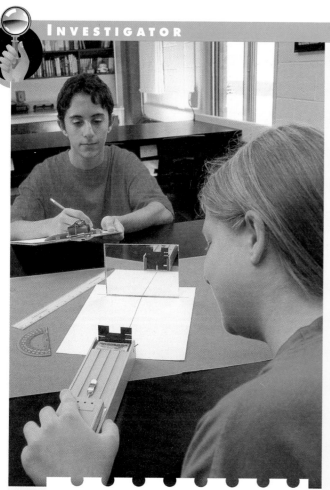

INVESTIGATOR

THE LAW OF REFLECTION

The Question

How does the angle of incidence compare with the angle of reflection?

Procedure

1. Draw a horizontal line. Use a protractor to draw a line perpendicular to it, a normal, to form a "T" on a piece of paper.
2. Using modelling clay, stand the mirror upright with the silvered back of the mirror along the horizontal line.
3. In a darkened room, shine a ray of light at the mirror along the perpendicular line. What do you observe?
4. Move the light source so that the ray of light hits the mirror at an angle. Make sure that your light strikes the point where the normal meets the mirror. What happens to the reflected ray?
5. With your ruler, draw the incident ray and the reflected ray. Show the direction of the light rays using arrows.
6. Repeat the experiment using several different angles of incidence.

Keeping Records

7. Measure the angles of incidence and the angles of reflection using a protractor.

Materials & Equipment

- a light source
- a plane mirror
- paper
- modelling clay
- a pencil
- a ruler
- a protractor

continued on next page ······▶

- Use the letter "i" to stand for the angle of incidence.
- Use the letter "r" to stand for the angle of reflection.
- Write your values as an equation:
  $i = ?°$
  $r = ?°$

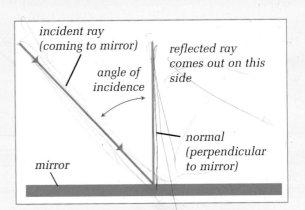

incident ray (coming to mirror)

reflected ray comes out on this side

angle of incidence

normal (perpendicular to mirror)

mirror

Analyzing and Interpreting

8 How does the angle of incidence compare with the angle of reflection?

9 What happens to the angle of reflection when you increase the angle of incidence?

10 How does your drawing compare with the illustration at top right?

Forming Conclusions

11 Why is it helpful to know how light reflects? How could you use this information?

12 How is information about light reflection helpful in designing and creating technology for our use?

Useful Mirrors

There are two basic ways in which people use plane mirrors.

- You can look into them and observe the reflection. Which of these photos shows this type of use?
- The second use is to take light from one source and send it in a different direction. Which of these photos shows this type of use?

1 If you see someone in a mirror, can they see you? Explain why or why not.

2 Use a diagram to illustrate the law of reflection.

3 Why do you think mirrors are a favourite tool for magicians?

4 Two rules you have learned about light are:
   • Light travels in straight lines.
   • Light reflects from a plane mirror according to the law of reflection.
   Using these rules, explain why, when you look in a mirror, everything appears reversed. (Your left hand is in the place of your right hand.)

5 If you move back from a plane mirror, will you see more of yourself in the mirror? Explain why it seems that you can "see into" a mirror.

2.2 THE REFLECTION OF LIGHT USING CURVED MIRRORS

Mirrors make up many common objects. Look at these pictures.

Mirror globe

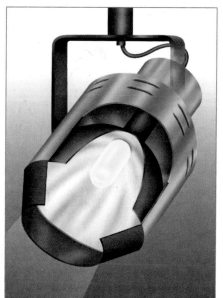

Theatre lights

• What do you think is the function of the mirror in the garden? In your Science Journal, write down your ideas on how this mirror's unusual shape helps it perform this function.

• What do you think is the function of the mirror that forms part of a theatre light? Write down your ideas on how this mirror's shape suits its function.

reSEARCH

Fibre Optics
One technological advance that makes use of reflecting light is **fibre optics**. A fibre-optic cable is a thin flexible tube with an inner surface that reflects light inside the tube extremely well.

• Find out how fibre optics work.

• What technologies and devices use fibre optics?

Which hand is holding the comb?

What You See in a Mirror

When you look at yourself in a plane mirror, does your image depend on the distance between you and the mirror?

- *Consider the size of your image.* As you step back from the mirror, your image stays the same size. It appears smaller only because it's farther away.
- *Consider the orientation of your image,* that is, its position (compared with yourself). Your image in a plane mirror is upright, just like yourself. However, your image is reversed—your left and right sides appear as the right and left sides of your image.

When you look into a curved mirror, you see something quite different from the image produced by a plane mirror. In the next activity, you will investigate the size and orientation of your image in a **concave mirror**, one in which the reflecting surface is curved inward like a bowl.

PROBLEM SOLVER

CONCAVE MIRROR IMAGES

How do you think the image of an object in a concave mirror is different from its image in a plane mirror? To find out, follow these steps:

- Use a concave mirror and any object (your finger, a pencil, etc.).
- Position the object in front of the mirror so the image in the mirror is as clear as possible (in focus).
- Compare the size and orientation (upright or upside down) of the image with the actual object.
- Predict what will happen to the size and orientation of the image when the object is placed at different distances from the mirror.
- Test your prediction and record your observations in your Science Journal.
- What happened to the image in the concave mirror as you moved the object very close to the mirror? far away from the mirror?

As you saw during the activity, a concave mirror produces images different from those that a plane mirror produces. When the object is far away from the concave mirror, the image is upside down and smaller. When the object is very near, the image is upright and enlarged.

Uses of Concave Mirrors

Concave mirrors are used in many devices. The chart below shows some of the common uses.

Concave Mirrors	
Device	**Use of Concave Mirror**
flashlight	• to produce a parallel beam of light leaving the flashlight
telescope	• to collect a large amount of light from a star or other distant source and focus it for viewing
cosmetic or shaving mirror	• to produce an enlarged image of the face
headlights of a car	• to produce a parallel beam of light leaving the car that can be pointed down (low beam) or straight ahead (high beam)

try this at **HOME**

KITCHEN MIRRORS

Find a shiny metal spoon, the rounder the better. Compare the reflection of your face in the inner bowl of the spoon to your reflection in its outer surface. Which surface of the spoon is convex? Which is concave? This will help you remember the difference between a convex mirror and a concave mirror.

Use your spoon as a convex mirror to see your reflection in it at different distances. What can you say about the size and orientation of the image in a convex mirror?

1 What would happen to the reflected light if you shone a flashlight onto:

  a) the outside of a metal bowl?

  b) the concave side of a spoon?

2 Use a labelled diagram to illustrate the "law of reflection" in a plane mirror.

3 A baby can sometimes be fooled into believing a mirror image is the real thing. A young child rarely can. What clues help children learn to tell a mirror image from the real thing?

infoBIT

Catching Some Rays

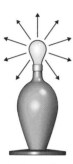

A simple ray diagram

A **ray diagram** is used to represent how light travels. The light travelling from a source is shown as one or more straight lines, called rays. Each ray has an arrow to show the direction of travel. Such a diagram is helpful and easy to make, but it does not show the whole picture. In reality, light travels from its source in *all* directions at once, unless blocked as in a ray box.

2.3 CHECK YOUR PROGRESS

1 How does the reflection of light help explain why you can see non-luminous objects?

2 What types of materials reflect light best?

3 Draw a capital "F" about 2 cm tall at the top of a piece of paper. Below it, draw your predictions of how this letter's image would appear in:

  a) a plane mirror

  b) a second plane mirror placed at an angle to the first plane mirror (that is, the image of the image of the letter)

  c) a concave mirror, with the letter near the mirror

  d) a concave mirror, with the letter very far away from the mirror

  e) a convex mirror

4 Why do car side mirrors that have a convex mirror attached to them carry a warning to drivers that says "Objects seen in the mirror are closer than they appear"?

5 The circled objects in the picture are, or contain, mirrors.

  a) What type of mirror is being shown in each case?

  b) How are the reflections in each mirror of use to the bus driver?

  c) Could a different type of mirror be used in each case? Explain why or why not.

3.0

Light is refracted by transparent materials, and this is what makes lenses so useful.

You have learned how mirrors take advantage of one property of light: reflection. Because light reflects so that the angle of incidence equals the angle of reflection, we can use materials that reflect to collect light and change its path.

What other properties of light can be useful? How about its speed? Light travels at about 300 000 km/s in a vacuum such as space (299 792.5 km/s to be more exact). This means that it takes light from the sun about 8 min to reach the surface of the earth. We use the speed of light to measure very large distances in space, as you can see on this page.

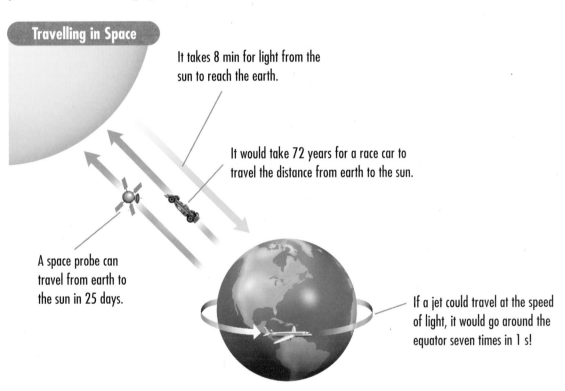

Travelling in Space

It takes 8 min for light from the sun to reach the earth.

It would take 72 years for a race car to travel the distance from earth to the sun.

A space probe can travel from earth to the sun in 25 days.

If a jet could travel at the speed of light, it would go around the equator seven times in 1 s!

Is the speed of light always the same? No, because light slows down when passing through water, air, or other materials. In glass, for example, light travels at a mere 195 000 km/s. That's about 65% of the speed it travels at in the emptiness (or vacuum) of space. But what happens to light when it suddenly changes from 300 000 km/s to 195 000 km/s?

Is this object really bent? How do you know?

3.1 BENDING LIGHT

Explore

Have you ever tried to pick up a pebble or catch a tadpole in your hands when wading in a lake? Think about what that experience was like. Objects underwater look as though they are actually slightly nearer than they really are. Why? What is happening to the light as it reflects from an object underwater to your eye? Look for a clue in the photograph on this page. Write down your ideas in your Science Journal.

Develop

Refraction

The bending of light, called **refraction**, occurs because light travels at different speeds through different materials. As light passes from air to water, it slows down and changes direction. How does this happen? It is because light travels forward much like the line of skaters below. When some of the skaters slow down but the rest continue at the original speed, the result is a bend in the line. When part of a beam of light slows down, and the rest keeps going, the result is a bend in the light. To explore this behaviour for yourself, you will investigate the refraction of light through water and other liquids.

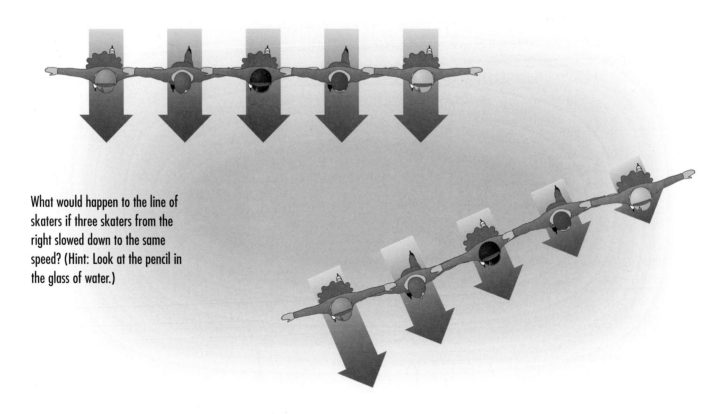

What would happen to the line of skaters if three skaters from the right slowed down to the same speed? (Hint: Look at the pencil in the glass of water.)

Refraction Through Glass

Glass is transparent and easy to shape. Mirrors are made by applying a reflective coating to glass. Is there some property of glass that would make it useful for refraction as well? What happens when light goes from air to glass? Try this activity and find out.

FROM AIR TO GLASS

The Question

What happens to light when it passes from air into glass?

Materials & Equipment

- *a ray box with a single-slit opening*
- *a glass block*
- *paper*
- *a ruler*
- *a protractor*

Procedure

1. Place the glass block on a piece of paper and trace around it. Mark a point near the middle of the front edge of the block. Draw a line on the paper perpendicular to the edge at this point. (As in the case of reflection in mirrors, this line is also called the **normal**.)

2. Darken the room and adjust the **ray box** so the edges of the ray are parallel.

3. Direct a ray of light so that it shines along the line perpendicular to the block. Trace the ray as it enters; this is called the **incident ray**. The point where the ray enters the block is called the **point of incidence**.

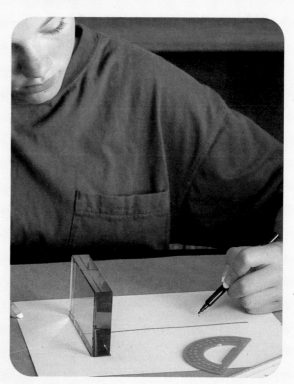

4. Observe the ray through the glass block. On the paper, mark the point where the ray leaves the block. The line joining the points where the ray enters and leaves the block will trace the path of the ray in the glass. This is the **refracted ray**.

continued on next page ·······➤

3.1 Bending Light

5 Move the ray box so that the light strikes the block at the same point of incidence, but at an angle from the normal.

6 Again, trace the incident ray and mark the point where it exits the block. Give matching labels to your incident ray and the exit point.

7 Repeat the last two steps using different angles for the incident ray. Then, remove the glass block.

Keeping Records

8 Complete each refracted ray on the paper by drawing a line from the point of incidence to each exit point. Carefully label each refracted ray to match the incident ray. Add arrows to indicate the direction of the rays.

9 Determine the angle of incidence and the angle of refraction in each case. Note that these angles are measured from the

normal, as in the case of reflection in mirrors.

Analyzing and Interpreting

10 How did the incident ray compare with the refracted ray?

11 What happened to the light when it entered the block at a 90° angle? What happened when it entered at a different angle?

12 What happened to the refracted ray when the angle of incidence was increased?

Forming Conclusions

13 What two factors affect how much light is refracted?

14 Based on your findings, where should you stand to look through the glass of a window?

Refraction Through a Liquid

Glass is a solid substance that easily demonstrates refraction. No wonder it is used in lenses of all sorts. But what about liquids? Do liquids refract light in the same way as solids? The following activity demonstrates just that.

REFRACTION IN WATER AND OTHER LIQUIDS

The Question

What happens to the path of light rays when they pass from air into water or other liquids?

◀ Materials and equipment

continued on next page ·······➤

Materials & Equipment

- *a piece of white paper*
- *tape*
- *pencil and ruler*
- *ray box with 2-slit opening
  (or other light source—see below)*
- *250-mL beaker or jar*
- *water*
- *other liquids to be tested*

If ray box is not available:

- *a piece of cardboard, measuring
  10 cm by 15 cm*
- *scissors*
- *modelling clay to support the cardboard*

Procedure

1. If you do not have a ray box that can produce two parallel rays of light using a 2-slit opening, make your own apparatus as follows:

   a) Cut two parallel slits in the cardboard approximately 2 cm apart, as shown in the picture. Each slit should measure about 5 cm high by 0.5 cm wide.

   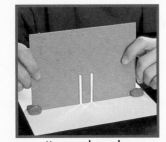

   Homemade ray box

   b) Use modelling clay to stand the cardboard upright in front of your light source.

Step 2

2. Darken the room and move the flashlight in front of the cardboard (or move the ray box) until the two rays of light coming through the slits are parallel.

3. Tape the piece of paper on the table in front of the cardboard or the ray box. Use a pencil and ruler to mark a line perpendicular to the cardboard or the front of the ray box starting between the two slits and extending outward. Now, mark the path of the two rays of light.

4. Put the empty beaker or jar in the path of both rays of light. What do you observe?

5. Fill the beaker with water and place it so that both rays of light pass through it. What do you observe?

6. Move the beaker of water until the rays of light leaving the beaker are as focussed (clear) as possible.

   a) On the piece of paper, mark the path taken by the rays of light leaving the beaker. What do you observe?

   b) Record the distance from the cardboard or the ray box to the beaker. This is where you will put other beakers of liquid during your tests.

Drawing the normal

continued on next page ......➤

7 Repeat steps 5 and 6 using other liquids, as follows:

a) When you select the liquids to test, think about what factors might affect how light passes through them. You may wish to
- compare clear liquids to more opaque (cloudy) ones
- test if viscous (thicker, more dense) liquids such as oils cause light to behave differently than do less viscous liquids such as water.

b) Are there particles present in the liquid? Record these factors before making your tests.

c) When you test each liquid, use a different coloured pencil, or a new piece of paper, to mark any change in the path of light.

Keeping Records

8 Make a chart of your observations about the liquids and how they refracted the two rays of light.

9 How could you use a graph to compare any changes in refraction you observed? For example, on the y-axis you could put the distance from the beaker to the point where the refracted rays came together. What will you put on the x-axis? What type of graph should you use?

Analyzing and Interpreting

10 How did the water affect the path taken by the rays of light? How did you know this change was due to the water and not the glass of the beaker or jar?

11 When you tested different liquids, which factors seemed to make the most difference in how much the light was refracted? Explain.

Forming Conclusions

12 Write your own definition of refraction.

13 What factors affect refraction the most? Why do you think this is so?

---

*info*BIT

Mirages

In this picture, light is playing a trick on you! What looks like a lake is not really there at all—it's a mirage.

Mirages happen when layers of air with different temperatures lie on top of each other. As light passes through one layer of air into the next, it refracts, or changes direction. This can create imaginary pools of water, upside-down images, and even castles in the clouds!

So the next time you're riding in a car, don't worry that the road ahead looks wet even though it's not raining. You're just looking at a "wet road" mirage. Light from the sky changed direction in the hot air over the road, creating the illusion.

Is this a desert lake or a mirage?

Making Use of Refraction

So far, you have learned that light is refracted (or bent) as it passes through different materials, and that this refraction depends on factors such as the angle of incidence and the type of material. What clues do you have about how this property of light could be useful in practical applications? In your Science Journal, write down your ideas about how optical devices might use refraction.

• Think about the shape of the mirrors you investigated in the previous section.

• Predict how you think shape might affect refraction through glass.

Communicate

1 When would it be easier for a bear to catch a fish: as the fish jumps into the air, or as it swims? Explain your reasoning in terms of how light travels through air and through water.

2 Analogies, or comparisons of similar things, can help people communicate ideas. For example, the refraction of light was explained using the analogy of a synchronized skating team. What other analogy can you think of to help explain to someone else the refraction of light as it passes through different materials and slows down?

3 Why do objects at the bottom of an aquarium filled with water look closer than they really are?

4 Imagine you have a waterproof flashlight, and you are underwater in a swimming pool. You point the flashlight perpendicular (at 90°) to the surface of the water. Predict how the light would bend as it came out of the water into the air. What would happen to the light if the flashlight was pointed at 45°?

3.2 USING REFRACTION TO FOCUS LIGHT

Explore

These people are all using the property of refraction to accomplish something. What do you think that is? Think back to the activity in which you shone two parallel rays of light through water. What happened as the rays left the water? How might this be related to what these people are doing?

Looking Through Curves

Develop

When you experimented with mirrors, you found that the shape of the mirror had an effect on the image. For example, the image reflected by a concave mirror was smaller and upside down when the object was far away. The image reflected by a convex mirror was larger and right side up. These characteristics of curved mirrors make them very useful.

In the same way, the shape of a block of glass through which light passes has an effect on the refracted image. A **lens** is a piece of transparent material (glass, plastic) with at least one curved surface. In the following activity, you will explore the effect of different lenses on light.

PROBLEM SOLVER

LOOKING AT CONVEX AND CONCAVE LENSES

There are two main types of lenses: convex and concave. What do you think happens to light as it moves through each? How could you tell?

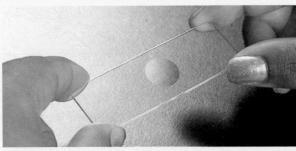

A *depression slide*, or well slide, contains a curved area which you can use as a lens. The slide is acting as a convex lens.

To determine what happens to light passing through a lens, use a depression (well) slide, a piece of graph paper, and a ruler as follows:

• Choose an area on the graph paper that just fits into the depression on the slide. Measure and record the area as the "number of complete squares" you can see.

• Hold the slide so that you are looking through the convex surface. Place it over the graph paper.
  – What happens when you move the convex lens away from the graph paper?

• When you can see the graph paper clearly, measure the distance from the lens to the

paper at intervals as you move the slide upward.
  – Each time, record the apparent size of the graph area you see through the lens by counting the number of complete squares you can see.

• Repeat this procedure using the concave surface.

• Plot a graph of the number of complete squares that were visible in relation to the distance from the lens for both lenses.

• What relationship did you discover?

What do you conclude about convex and concave lenses?

186   3.0   Light Is Refracted by Transparent Materials, and This Is What Makes Lenses So Useful

Types of Lenses

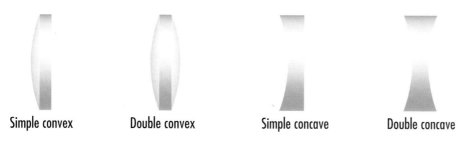

Simple convex   Double convex   Simple concave   Double concave

A **convex lens** curves outward. You can quickly spot a convex lens by noticing it is thicker in the middle than at the edges. A **concave lens** curves inward. You can tell because concave lenses are thicker at the edges than in the middle.

Look around your classroom or home and see how many lenses you can discover. In your Science Journal, make a list noting some of the features of each lens: shape, thickness, whether it magnifies, whether it appears to be double or single, whether it is made of glass or plastic, and any other features you think are interesting. In the next activity, you will look more closely at how light is refracted through convex and concave lenses.

INVESTIGATOR

REFRACTION OF LIGHT USING LENSES

Before You Start...

In this activity, you are going to observe how light passes through two types of lenses: convex and concave. Think about what you've learned about reflection and refraction. In your Science Journal, write a prediction for how light might pass through each type of lens.

continued on next page ·····▶

The Question

How does light refract as it passes through convex and concave lenses?

Materials & Equipment

- *a convex lens*
- *a concave lens*
- *a ray box with a 3- and 5-slit opening*
- *paper*
- *a ruler*
- *a pencil*

Procedure

1. Set up the ray box so that the edges of the beam are parallel and then insert the slit opening. Darken the room.
2. Shine the light rays at the convex lens so that the middle ray goes through the centre of the lens. Observe what happens to the light.
3. Repeat step 2 using the concave lens.

Keeping Records

4. Record your observations in your Science Journal. Draw a diagram noting the incident rays and the refracted rays for both lenses.

Analyzing and Interpreting

5. How do the shapes of the two lenses differ?
6. How did your predictions of the refraction of light for each lens compare with your observations?
7. Compare the refraction of light through a convex lens and concave lens.

Forming Conclusions

8. If all the factors are the same except for the lenses, what influences the way in which light bends after it passes through a lens?
9. What shape is a magnifying lens? Which of your lenses could enlarge things? How did the other lens compare with respect to magnification of things?

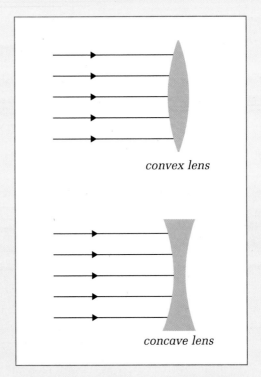

convex lens

concave lens

A convex lens causes light rays to come together, or to *converge*. A concave lens causes light rays to spread out, or to *diverge*. Copy and complete these diagrams to show the rays after passing through the lenses.

1 Many stores sell "reading glasses" to help people see the very small print in newspapers and other publications.
   a) What type of lenses would these glasses contain? Explain.
   b) Would these glasses help people see more clearly at all times? Why or why not?

2 This picture shows the glass bricks builders use to make decorative walls in homes, offices, and stores. How do these bricks preserve privacy while allowing light to pass through?

3 Explain the difference between how a concave lens and a convex lens refract light.

4 A very large aquarium in a zoo has areas where the glass wall is curved outward. Describe the view a fish would have of a person who is looking into the tank through one of these areas.

5 You have a summer job putting homemade candies into an assortment of fancy containers and jars to sell at a local market. The person selling the candies tells you that most people choose the jars which make the candy look larger than it really is, but some of these people come back to complain. How could you stop the complaints while taking advantage of the "selling power" of those jars?

3.3 CHECK YOUR PROGRESS

1 What factors affect how light is refracted through a material?

2 A "magic" trick involves putting a coin in the bottom of a cup, then having the person step back until he or she can no longer see the coin from the top. The magician then makes the coin "reappear" by pouring in water. How does this trick work?

3 Some light fixtures contain a lens through which the light passes before it is used. In each of the following situations, decide whether this lens should be convex or concave. Use a diagram to explain.

a) You are designing an outdoor light that will spread a soft light over a large area.

b) You are designing a reading light that someone could use without the light bothering others in the room.

c) You are designing a store light that will keep the floor well lit, but which will also shine most of its light on the display case directly below.

4 Explain why the newsprint in the drop of water is magnified in the photograph.

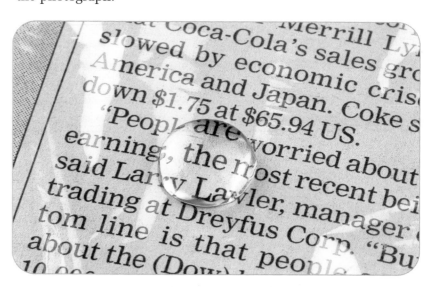

*info*BIT

Light Pollution

Have you ever been on the outskirts of a city at night? If you have, you've probably noticed an unusual glow in the sky. Light rays from street lamps and buildings travel up into the sky. (Do you know why?) There they bounce off clouds and dust particles to form this glow. Ordinarily this light "pollution" wouldn't be a problem, but many large telescopes are located near big cities. Astronomers working with them need a very dark sky in order to observe distant stars and galaxies. Now an international group of astronomers is trying to get large cities to put lamp shades over their lights! That way some of these extra light rays will be directed where they are of the most use, on the ground.

The Hale Telescope, one of the world's largest, is located a few kilometres from Los Angeles.

BIG IDEA

4.0 The eye and the camera capture images using the properties of light.

3 OPTICS

"Buffalo Bulls Fighting" on the North Saskatchewan River (1848–1852) by Paul Kane.

Early explorers either were artists themselves or brought artists with them in order to bring home images of what they saw. Their maps and paintings excited the imaginations of many, helping to encourage further exploration of the world.

How do you record images of what you've seen or experienced? Today, artists still sketch and paint, but a far more common technology used by many people is the camera. Whether you use an instant camera, a videocamera, or one of the new digital cameras, they all rely on the same basic principles as your eye.

At one time, cameras only used film to record an image. Now, they also use videotape and digital media.

4.1 How Does Light Enter Your Eye?

Explore

Make a two-column chart in your Science Journal. Title the first column, Parts of the Eye. List all of the parts of your eye that you know, leaving space to add more. Title the second column, Function, then do the following activities while observing a partner's eyes or using a mirror.

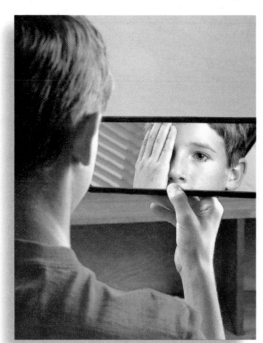

- Blink. What happens? Which parts of the eye are involved? How do you know?
- Hold your head still. Move your eyes from side to side, and up and down. Which parts of the eye move?
- Put one hand over your left eye and keep it there for 30 s. Remove the hand and observe your eyes, comparing the left eye with the right eye. What happened? Why do you think this is so? Which parts of the eye were involved?
- If time permits, stand outside for a few moments. Observe the appearance of your eyes or your partner's eyes. Then go back inside the building and immediately observe what happens.
- Look at something far away for a moment, then look immediately at something very close. What did you notice?

Once you have completed as much of your chart as you can, put question marks beside any parts of the eye whose function you could not figure out. Write down any questions you have about how the eye works.

Develop

The Hole to the World

You have learned that light either travels from a source to your eyes or reflects off an object to your eyes. But how exactly does light enter your eye? If you compare the eye to the camera on the following page, you will see that both have a hole that lets in light.
- In the eye, this hole is called the **pupil**.
- In the camera, it is the **aperture**.

The pupil of your eye is surrounded by a band of muscle, called the **iris**. This band controls the size of the pupil, and so controls the amount of light that can enter your eye. In dim light, the iris opens and the pupil dilates, or becomes wider, so you can gather more light. In bright light, such as outside, your iris closes down so the eye receives just the right amount of light. This happens automatically, without your conscious control.

In the same way, the **diaphragm** changes the size of the aperture of a camera lens to allow in the proper amount of light. The **shutter** of a camera acts like a door. If the shutter is open for a long time, more light enters the camera. Which part of your eye is like a camera's shutter?

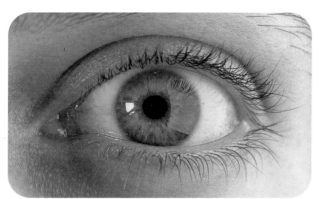

The pupil is *not* dilated.

The aperture is very small.

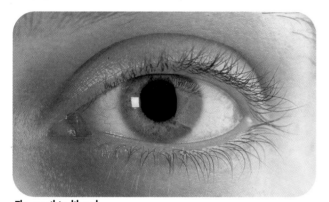

The pupil is dilated.

The aperture is wide open.

What Happens Inside

In order for you to see, something must react to the light entering your eye. The part that accomplishes this for you is the **retina**, a special lining on the back of your eye. When light hits the retina, receptor cells send messages to the brain, which are translated into an image. In a similar way, the light entering a camera hits the **film**. Film, like the retina, contains materials that are sensitive to light.

You have already discovered, when working with mirrors and lenses, that an image is only clear and distinct when it is focussed. Another way of saying this is that the light rays forming the image *converge*, or come together at one point, the focal point. Your eye has a transparent lens, too, just behind the pupil. This lens focusses light on the retina so you can see a clear image. The lens of your eye automatically changes its shape to focus on near or distant objects. In the same way, a camera has one or more lenses to focus incoming light on the film. Some cameras focus automatically while others require the user to manually focus the lens.

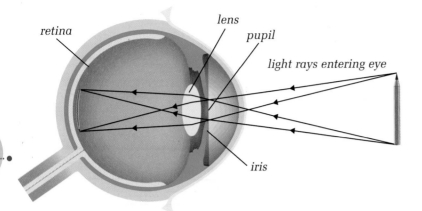
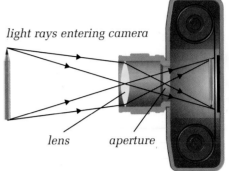

The image formed on the retina is upside down. You don't see things that way because your brain interprets the information sent by the retina and flips it around.

The image formed on the film is also upside down. The information about the image can be recorded as a negative (and used to make a print later), a slide, or it can be stored digitally for use in a computer.

Solving Eye Problems with Lenses

What happens when you look through a concave lens? Light is refracted by that lens, then is refracted by your eye. The combination lets you see a magnified image. There are many ways lenses are used in combinations. Perhaps the most important in everyday life is to help correct vision problems. If you examine a pair of eyeglasses, you'll notice that they are made up of two lenses. Which type are they: concave or convex?

Many people wear glasses or contact lenses because their eyes do not focus images on their retina properly. The additional lenses refract the light entering the eye so that the lens in the eye will produce a good, clear image. The two most common problems are shown below.

In a near-sighted person, the eyeball may be too long or the lens too thick. In this case, light entering the eye is focussed too soon, short of the retina. When a near-sighted person tries to see things at a distance, the image is blurred. In a far-sighted person, the eyeball may be too short or the lens too thin. In this case, the refracted light focusses behind the retina. Objects close to a far-sighted person will be blurred. Lenses can be used to correct both of these problems.

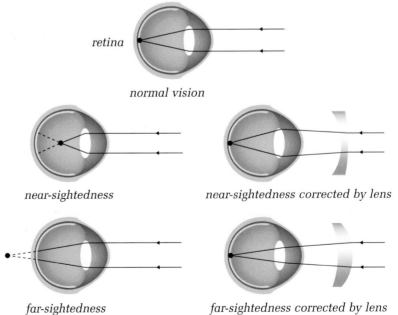

retina

normal vision

near-sightedness

near-sightedness corrected by lens

far-sightedness

far-sightedness corrected by lens

Communicate

1 Return to your chart listing the parts of the eye and their function. Add any new information you have learned. Make a similar chart listing the parts of a camera and their function. How similar is the camera to a human eye? Why do you think this is so? How are they different?

2 Explain the following observations about a camera, based on what you know of its function and how light travels.
   a) The inside of a camera is usually black.
   b) To take a picture in dim light, you must open the aperture wider.
   c) To take a picture in very dim light, you can leave the shutter open for a period of time.
   d) Unexposed film must be carried in a light-proof container.

3 Looking directly into a very bright light can damage the retina. Even a brief exposure can cause discomfort and leave bright after-images that make it hard to see. When there is a solar eclipse, most of the light of the sun is blocked for a few seconds. Knowing that the iris opens to dilate the pupil in dim light, why do you think staring up at an eclipse is so dangerous?

4.2 OTHER OPTICAL INSTRUMENTS

Explore

Human beings have remarkable eyesight. You can read this page, then look up to see who might be coming in the classroom door. You can look out a window at the sky and spot a plane flying overhead. The next moment, you could count the tiny hairs on one finger.

Being human also means being curious. It hasn't been enough to simply duplicate the way the human eye works and record what we see with cameras. People have wanted to see more, so they have designed optical instruments to extend human vision. In your Science Journal, record five things you would like to be able to observe that you can't see with your eyes alone.

Develop

Seeing Things Up Close or Far Away

You now have an understanding of how light can be reflected using mirrors and refracted using lenses. However, lenses and mirrors can be used in combination to create optical instruments. In the next activity, you will design a system of your own.

*info*BIT

Can Cats See in the Dark?

You may have heard that cats and other animals, such as owls, can see in the dark. However, no animal can see in the absence of light. Cats and owls have very large pupils, which allow their eyes to take in as much light as possible. They also have a layer inside their eyes that acts like a mirror to reflect light inside the eye. This also helps them see quite well in dim light.

Telescopes

Telescopes also use lenses and mirrors. There are two types of telescopes: *refracting telescopes*, which use convex lenses to bend light, and *reflecting telescopes*, which use mirrors to collect light and reflect it to form an image. The world's largest telescopes are reflecting telescopes.

Refracting telescope

Reflecting telescope

The **objective lens** or **mirror** of a telescope gathers the light. The greater its diameter, the more light it can collect. More light means more information from a planet or star. The light forms an image, which can be magnified further by another lens, the **eyepiece**. In some telescopes, the image formed by the objective lens can be used to expose film or to activate a CCD (charged coupled device) cell. This cell contains a computer chip that turns the light into a digital signal.

Several factors can make it difficult to achieve a sharp image with a telescope, including the steadiness of the object and the alignment of the object and the telescope.

The stability of the optical system depends on:
- the clarity of the sky
- the balance of the telescope (the telescope must be able to stay in position)
- the ease with which the telescope can be adjusted

Although telescopes are useful for looking at the stars, they are not very easy to carry around. So people who wish to look at other distant objects often use binoculars. **Binoculars** are really two short refracting telescopes fixed together.

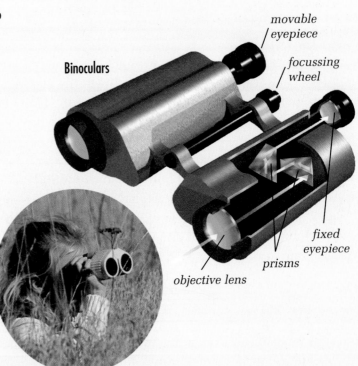

Binoculars

movable eyepiece

focussing wheel

fixed eyepiece

prisms

objective lens

The Microscope

You see the greatest detail when you look at an object about 25 cm from your eye. If you need to see more detail, you use a microscope. **Microscopes** have at least two lenses—the objective lens and the eyepiece lens—as well as a light source. The light passing through the specimen is focussed by the objective lens to form a magnified image. The eyepiece lens magnifies this image so that you see an even larger image. A microscope may have several objective lenses, each magnifying the specimen a different amount. The most powerful light microscope can magnify up to 2000 times.

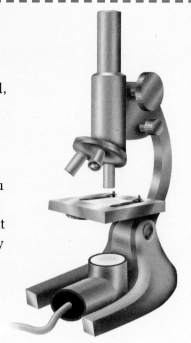

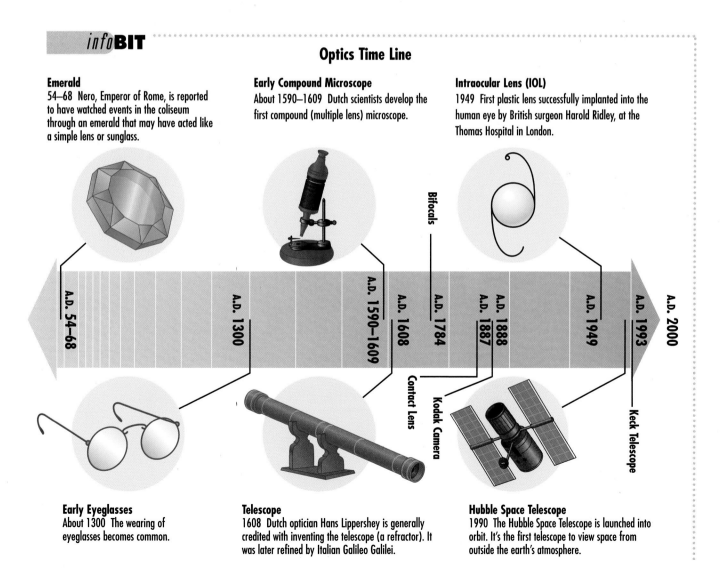

info BIT

Optics Time Line

Emerald
54–68 Nero, Emperor of Rome, is reported to have watched events in the coliseum through an emerald that may have acted like a simple lens or sunglass.

Early Compound Microscope
About 1590–1609 Dutch scientists develop the first compound (multiple lens) microscope.

Intraocular Lens (IOL)
1949 First plastic lens successfully implanted into the human eye by British surgeon Harold Ridley, at the Thomas Hospital in London.

Bifocals

A.D. 54–68   A.D. 1300   A.D. 1590–1609   A.D. 1608   A.D. 1784   A.D. 1887   A.D. 1888   A.D. 1949   A.D. 1993   A.D. 2000

Contact Lens

Kodak Camera

Keck Telescope

Early Eyeglasses
About 1300 The wearing of eyeglasses becomes common.

Telescope
1608 Dutch optician Hans Lippershey is generally credited with inventing the telescope (a refractor). It was later refined by Italian Galileo Galilei.

Hubble Space Telescope
1990 The Hubble Space Telescope is launched into orbit. It's the first telescope to view space from outside the earth's atmosphere.

3
O P T I C S

Before You Start...

Now that you have worked with mirrors and lenses, think about the optical devices you have seen so far in this chapter. Most of these instruments use a combination of lenses (and sometimes mirrors) to magnify and focus an image. For example, look into a camera's lens and you might see as many as six lenses!

The Question

What combination of lenses do you need to use to magnify distant objects? to magnify objects that are near?

> **Caution!**
> Don't look directly at the sun with any magnifying instrument!

Your Task

1 Make two magnifying devices:
   a) one that magnifies distant objects (a telescope)
   b) one that magnifies near objects (a microscope)

2 Decide what materials, other than your lenses, you will need to make your optical devices.

3 Draw a diagram of your two optical devices before you construct them.

4 Test each magnifying device. Does each one work the way you predicted? If not, modify your design until you have the results you want.

5 What did making and using these magnifying devices teach you about the differences between microscopes and telescopes?

6 Demonstrate and explain your devices to the class.

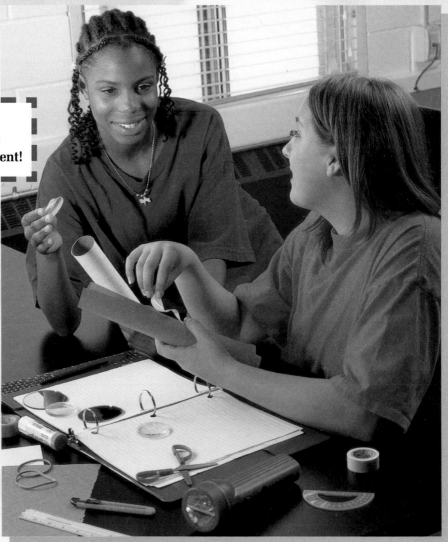

4.0 The Eye and the Camera Capture Images Using the Properties of Light

1 a) Which property of light do mirrors demonstrate?

   b) Which property of light do lenses demonstrate?

   c) How are mirrors and lenses useful in creating optical instruments?

2 You are a member of a group deciding where to build a new telescope. You have considered several locations, each with at least one advantage. Which location will you recommend? Why?

   a) in the city centre, close to the university and other schools

   b) near the local airport, convenient for visiting astronomers

   c) on the top of a tall mountain, where the atmosphere is thinner

   d) on an ocean-going vessel, so it can be moved to different locations to view different parts of the sky

4.3 CHECK YOUR PROGRESS

1 Column A lists the parts of the eye. Column B lists the parts of a camera. Match each part of the eye with the part of a camera that performs the same or a similar function. Describe that function for each.

Column A	Column B
retina	one or more lenses
pupil and iris	aperture
eyelid	film
lens	shutter

2 Brainstorm as many optical instruments as you can that use lenses and mirrors to control light. Choose one. Based on your experiences and observations, use a diagram to describe how the lenses and mirrors may be arranged in the instrument. Be sure to show how light is refracted or reflected and indicate the point of incidence, incident ray(s), and refracted or reflected rays. Show the direction of travel of light using arrows.

3 Which instrument was used to view each of the objects shown on this page?

   a) magnifying glass   b) microscope   c) telescope

   d) binoculars   e) unaided eye

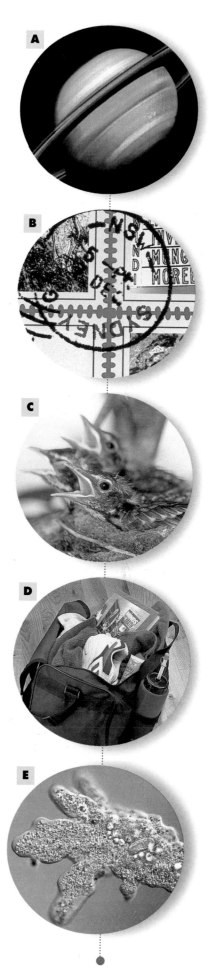

A

B

C

D

E

SAY CHEESE!

Ray Boudreau is a professional photographer. His portfolio includes everything from corporate executives to members of the Royal Canadian Air Farce. In fact, he took many of the photographs that appear in this book.

Q: When did you first become interested in photography?

A: My interest in photography began when I was 11 years old. A friend of the family gave me a little Kodak printing kit. After using it for the first time, I was hooked on it.

Q: What's the most challenging part of your job?

A: Each picture I take has its own photographic problem which I have to solve. It's a problem-solving business. Using my photographic knowledge to solve problems is fun for me.

Ray Boudreau is setting up for a photograph that appears in *Cells and Cell Systems*.

The camera Boudreau uses can be fitted with different lenses.

Each photographic lens uses a combination of convex and concave lenses.

Wide-angle Lens: Objects appear further away than they really are.

Normal Lens: Objects appear as they would to your own eye.

Telephoto Lens: Objects appear closer than they really are.

Q: What was your most challenging photo?

A: I had to photograph the city of Toronto for the cover of a magazine. I rented a wide-angle lens and we went up in a helicopter. I was strapped in and I hung out of the helicopter and photographed the buildings from as close as we could get. The wide-angle lens made the tops of the buildings look really big and the bottoms look really small.

Q: What's your favourite part of the job?

A: The best part of the job is that it's always a little bit different. It changes for me all the time. One day I'm in the studio shooting The Royal Canadian Air Farce, and the next day I'm on location shooting the city of Toronto from a helicopter. The work is varied. That's the most enjoyable part.

BIG IDEA

5.0

The visible light spectrum is made up of different colours.

We live in a world filled with colour. From sunsets to clothing to the images seen in movies and television, colour accents and defines what people see. But what is colour? Why are there different colours? Why do certain lights change the colour of an object? Why are colour television images different from images in photographs and on film?

So far you have learned how light travels, reflects, and refracts. You have been considering the brightness of light and the images it forms. But these properties are only part of the story of light. You need to explore this world in colour.

How many colours can you see in this sunset?

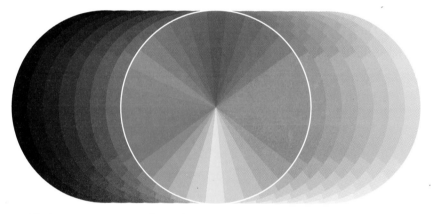

The human eye can see millions of colours.

5.1 THE WORLD IN COLOUR

Explore

Make a list of all of the words you could use to describe a colour to someone else. Compare your list with others, adding any new words. Which words did most people include in their lists? Circle any words that have to do with light. How do you know that the words have anything to do with light?

Light and Colour

Think of what it is like to wake up just before sunrise. There is enough light to see what is around you, but everything appears either grey or black. Then when the sun rises, or you turn on a light, the room is filled with colour. So light is necessary for your eyes to see colour, but why?

To answer this, think about a light source such as the sun. Your eye can detect light either directly from a light source or when this light source is reflected back to your eye by some object. What colour is a beam of sunlight? You probably answered, "White." However, that's not quite the whole picture. In the next activity, you will use refraction to find out for yourself.

THE COLOUR OF LIGHT

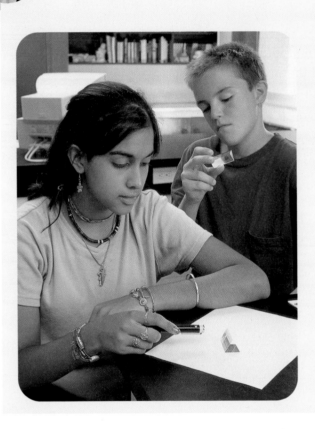

A **prism** is a triangular block of glass. Recall what you have learned about the refraction of light through glass: *light bends in glass.*

- Shine a light ray through a prism. What do you observe?
- Place a second prism in the path of light leaving the first prism. What do you observe?
- Turn the second prism in different ways. Compare the results.

What colours did you find in the light ray? Draw a coloured sketch in your Science Journal. Can you think of a mnemonic to help you remember the order in which the colours appear? What happened when you used two prisms in combination?

infoBIT

Sundogs and Haloes

A *sundog*, or a solar halo, is a glowing, coloured image sometimes seen near the sun. Small ice crystals that are present in the high atmosphere act like prisms and refract light from the sun. This creates two patches of colour on either side of the sun. Sundogs are so named probably because the sun and the patches move together in much the same way as a person walking a dog. Haloes can also be seen around the moon.

Caution: To best see a sundog, you should wear protective glasses (not sunglasses!) to view the sun directly.

The Colour Spectrum

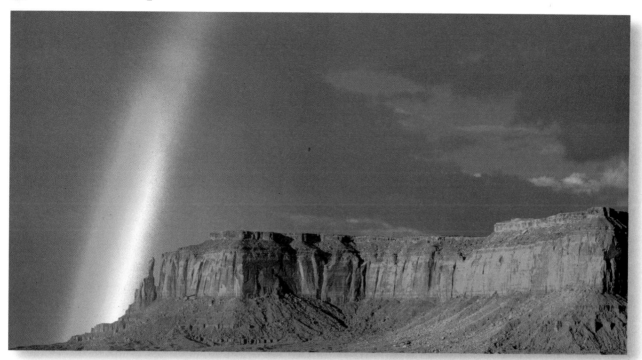

When you used a prism to refract, or bend, a light ray, you were able to split light into its colours. A **rainbow** is created in the same way. Sunlight is bent as it enters each raindrop. Inside the raindrop, the coloured rays are bounced off the inside wall, which acts like a mirror and reflects the rays back out again. As the rays leave the raindrop and return to the air, they are bent further. The result is a band of colours across the sky.

The colours of light together form the **visible light spectrum**. Every colour you see is a mixture of these colours. How can the spectrum produce hundreds of thousands of different colours? In the next activity, you will investigate this for yourself.

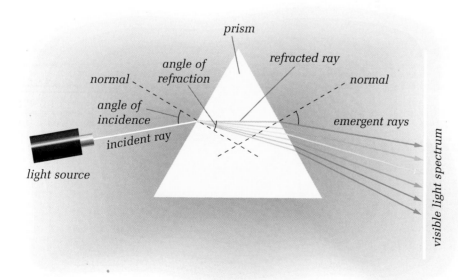

Follow the path taken by light as it moves through this prism. Why were normals included in this diagram? Compare this with what happens when you shine a light along the normal into a glass block and at other angles of incidence.

MIXING COLOURED LIGHTS

Before You Start...

Have you ever mixed coloured paints together to make different colours? For example, when you mix red paint and yellow paint together, you make orange paint. What do you think would happen if you mixed the same coloured lights? Would you get the same results?

Materials & Equipment

- *3 light sources of equal intensity (flashlights or ray boxes)*
- *3 coloured filters of equal thickness (red, green, and blue)*
- *white paper*
- *red, green, and blue coloured pencils*

The Question

What colours can you make using red, green, and blue light?

continued on next page ·······➤

Procedure

1. Predict what colours you would make by combining:
   a) red and green lights
   b) blue and green lights
   c) red and blue lights

   Record your predictions in your Science Journal.

2. Work with two partners. If you are using ray boxes, slide the coloured filter ahead of the one-slit baffle. If you are using flashlights, use coloured tissue paper or coloured plastic film to make filters for each. Experiment with your apparatus until you get the brightest possible light on the white screen.

3. Combine all three coloured lights (red, green, blue) and shine them on the screen so that their beams overlap. What do you observe?

4. Try different combinations of lights. Record your observations in a chart.

Keeping Records

5. Use matching coloured pencils to record your observations.

Analyzing and Interpreting

6. How accurate were your predictions about how coloured lights would combine?

7. What did you need to do in order to make your light more visible?

Forming Conclusions

8. What, if anything, surprised you about some of the results?

9. Make a diagram showing what each combination of colours will produce. How does your diagram explain why sunlight appears white?

Communicate

1. What colours are produced when white light is shone through a prism?

2. What do you think would happen if light of one colour, such as red, was shone through a prism?

3. Imagine you have a choice of using any combination of red, green, or blue spotlights to decorate the front of your home for the holidays. Predict what would happen if you shone each of these combinations against a white wall.
   a) red and green   b) red and blue
   c) green and blue   d) all three

4. Explain why you can see a rainbow. Do you think it is possible to reach the end of a rainbow? Why or why not?

5. Using the list of descriptive words you made at the beginning of this section, write a note describing your favourite colour. In your note, talk about how this colour makes you feel. Where would you use this colour: for clothing, in your room, in some other way? Why?

5.2 SEEING COLOUR

Explore

The technological breakthrough that led to colour television involved making a screen that contained tiny dots of colour. When these dots glow in different combinations, different colours appear on the screen.

If you examine this close-up view of a television picture, you will see that the picture is made up of tiny dots of colour.

Adding Colours of Light Together

Mixing coloured lights together is explained using the **theory of colour addition**. When red, green, and blue lights are put together in various combinations, as you saw in the Investigator activity, your eyes add these colours together and see an average, or secondary, colour.

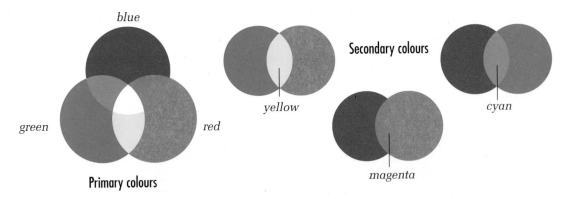

blue

green red

Primary colours

Secondary colours

yellow

magenta

cyan

The **primary colours of light** are red, green, and blue. When you put all the primary colours of light together, you produce white light. **Secondary colours of light** are produced when you mix pairs of primary colours of light together. The secondary colours of light are yellow, cyan, and magenta. Yellow is produced by mixing green and red light. How are cyan and magenta produced?

But how do your eyes see colour? Recall that the retina is the lining at the back of your eye that reacts to light. The retina itself is made up of specialized cells. Some of these cells are called **cones**. There are three types of cones, each sensitive to different ranges of colour: red, green, and blue. When light hits the cones, the cones send messages to your brain. The colour that you see depends on the type and number of cones responding to the light entering your eye.

Communicate

1 The eyes of a colour-blind person can detect some, but not all, colours. For example, a person with red-green colour-blindness cannot distinguish between these colours. Design a test for red-green colour-blindness. What activities might be difficult for a person with this vision problem?

2 If you stare at one colour for a while, then look at a white page, you will see a different coloured after-image. Use the diagram of colour addition on the previous page to predict which colours you would see after staring at each of the following colours for a while. Explain what is happening within your eye in each case.

   a) blue
   b) green
   c) red
   d) yellow (Hint: What colours make up yellow?)

5.3 WHAT COLOUR IS IT?

Explore

Have you ever tried on different pairs of sunglasses? Depending on the colour of their lenses, sunglasses can give the world a coloured tint. Some can make everything look yellowish. Others seem to make greens and blues more intense. What is happening? Is this an effect on your eyes or on the light? In your Science Journal, write down what you think might be happening as light passes through a coloured lens or filter.

*info***BIT**

After-image
Sometimes, after you have stared at a particular colour for a long time, you will see an "after-image." Look at this circle for about 30 s, then immediately look at a piece of white paper. What do you see?

After 30 s, the cones in your retina that are sensitive to red light had become tired. So when you looked at the white paper, which reflects light that contains all the colours, you saw light without any red.

• How does this explain the colour you did see?

Subtracting Colour

Develop

A filter lets some parts through and keeps other parts out. A coffee filter lets water and the flavour of coffee pass into a pot, while keeping out the coffee grains. So coloured sunglasses are like filters that act to take out, or subtract, some part of light.

You know that white light contains all of the colours in the spectrum. But why do objects have colour? For example, why is a tomato red or why is the grass green? What would you see if you looked at a red tomato using a filter that allowed only green light to pass through? if you looked at green grass through a filter that allowed only blue light to pass through? By exploring what happens when you pass light through coloured filters, you will be able to find out for yourself.

INVESTIGATOR

LOOKING THROUGH COLOURED FILTERS

The Question

What effect do coloured filters have on coloured objects?

Procedure

1. Set up your ray box so the beam of light falls on the white screen.
2. Darken the room, and examine the coloured papers in the white light one at a time. Record the colours you see.

Materials & Equipment

- *a ray box with a single-slit opening*
- *coloured filters: red, green, and blue*
- *a prism*
- *white paper to act as a screen*
- *coloured pencils (optional)*
- *coloured paper: red, green, and blue*

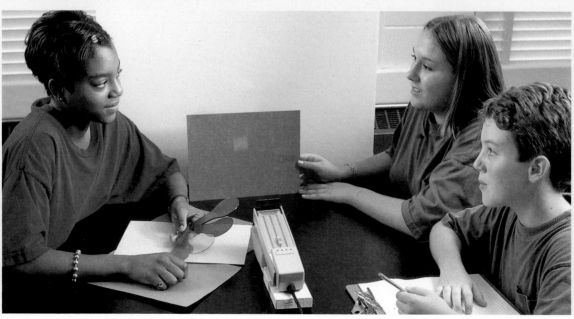

continued on next page ·······➤

3
O
P
T
I
C
S

3 Use the coloured filters one at a time to focus the light ray onto the white screen. Carefully observe the colour that falls on the screen.

4 Select a coloured filter. Predict the effect that the filter will have on each piece of coloured paper.

5 Look at each piece of coloured paper through this filter. Record your observations.

6 Repeat steps 4 and 5 with the remaining filters.

7 Focus a narrow light ray onto the prism to produce a spectrum of colours.

8 Use the coloured filters one at a time to direct a light ray onto the prism. Record what you see.

Keeping Records

9 Make a chart of your observations.

Analyzing and Interpreting

10 When white light passes through a coloured filter, what colour do you see? What happens to the other colours of light?

11 When you looked at the red paper through the green filter, what colour did you see? Why do you think this happens?

12 What effect did each coloured filter have on the light passing through the prism? How do you know?

Forming Conclusions

13 How do coloured filters work?

14 Describe or draw what you would see if you looked at a traffic light through each of the following coloured filters: red, green, yellow.

15 What applications use filters to absorb unwanted light?

The Theory of Colour Subtraction

You have seen what happens when you added different light colours together by projecting coloured light rays on top of each other. When you subtracted light colours by passing light through filters that block, or subtract, certain colours, something quite different was taking place. What determines the colour of something when colour subtraction is used? One way to find out is to ask an artist.

Recall that the primary colours in light are red, blue, and green. If an object appears red, then its surface is reflecting red to your eye, and absorbing (subtracting) the other two primary colours, blue and green. If an object appears blue, which colours have been subtracted?

The primary colours in pigment, however, are different. They are magenta, cyan, and yellow. Look at the illustrations of the theory of colour subtraction on the next page. What do you notice about how the primary colours for light and pigment are related? Can you explain this relationship? In fact, colour photographs in print media (for example, books and magazines) actually use just four colours: magenta, cyan, yellow, and black. Can you guess why black is used?

When white light shines on these colours, the pigments work in the same way a coloured filter works. Each primary colour of pigment absorbs, or *subtracts*, one of the primary colours of light and reflects the other two. This process is called the **theory of colour subtraction**.

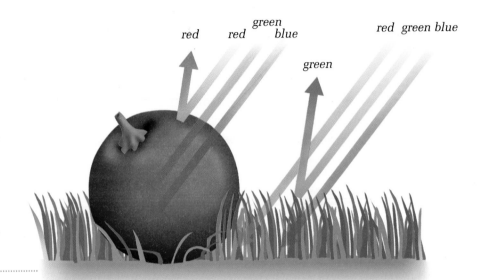

The theory of colour subtraction helps explain why objects are coloured. Pigments in objects absorb (subtract) certain colours and reflect others. You see a tomato as red because the chemicals in the tomato's skin absorb all the colours except for red. Only the red light is reflected to your eyes. Green grass absorbs all light except green, which is reflected.

• Special lights for growing plants look reddish. Why wouldn't they be coloured green?

Colour subtraction applies to the secondary colours as well. Remember that secondary colours are those produced by mixing any two of the primary colours together. For example, yellow light is a mixture of red and green light. A yellow object reflects a mixture of both colours and absorbs, or subtracts, the colour blue, so your eye sees yellow.

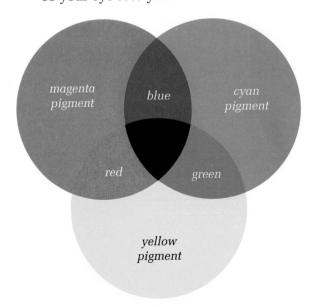

Notice what is happening when the secondary colours are mixed together. Magenta pigments absorb green light and reflect a mix of red and blue light; cyan pigments absorb red light and reflect a mix of green and blue light; yellow pigments absorb blue light and reflect a mix of red and green light.

Communicate

1 What are the primary colours of light? What are the secondary colours of light?

2 a) How does the eye detect colour? Explain using the theory of colour addition.

   b) How does a painting show a colour image? Explain using the theory of colour subtraction.

3 Imagine you are an actor in a horror film. Your costume calls for scary, red contact lenses to change the colour of your eyes. When you examine the lenses, you see that they are clear in the centre, with only a ring of red colour. Why do you think this is so? What would you see if the contacts were completely red? completely yellow? Explain, using the theory of colour subtraction.

4 In photosynthesis, plant cells convert light energy into chemical energy they can store as food. If a plant has green leaves, which colour(s) of light is (are) being absorbed by the plant? What does this suggest about the type of artificial lighting that should be used to grow plants indoors?

5.4 CHECK YOUR PROGRESS

1 Make a chart to show the primary colours of light and how they combine to form the secondary colours of light.

2 With white light, shadows appear black. Describe how shadows would appear if an object were placed between a combination of red and green light, or a combination of blue and green light.

3 Copy these sentences. Complete them using the terms "reflection" or "refraction."

   a) You can see yourself in a mirror because of the _____ of light.

   b) A prism can be used to split light into its colours because it causes _____ of the light.

   c) When an object in water appears to bend, this is due to the _____ of light as it passes through a different medium.

   d) When an object appears red, this is due to the _____ of the red light from the object.

4 You have been asked to talk about the theory of colour subtraction to a Grade 7 art class. Decide how you will present this information, whether as a demonstration, an activity with the students, or in the form of a lecture. Test your presentation with some classmates from your own class before producing your final version.

5 Do you think film strips or slides produce coloured pictures by colour addition or by colour subtraction? Use a diagram to show your reasoning.

6 Based on what you have learned about colour, can you infer why the sky is blue and a sunset is red? You may have to do research to answer this question.

7 Examine the parts of a strawberry plant shown on this page.

a) Copy and complete the following chart.

Plant Colours	
Part of the Plant	**Colour (Explain using the subtractive theory.)**
leaf flower fruit	

b) What is the benefit of the colour of each part to the plant? For each part, make a hypothesis to explain why it is coloured as it is. Plan an experiment that would let you test each hypothesis.

reSEARCH

Spectroscopy

One of the most important applications of the theory of colour subtraction is *spectroscopy*. A device called a *spectrometer* can be used to measure which colours of light are absorbed (subtracted) by a substance. Each substance has its own pattern of light absorption, which can be used as its "fingerprint."

• Investigate how spectroscopy works.
• What are some of the ways it is used in science and industry?

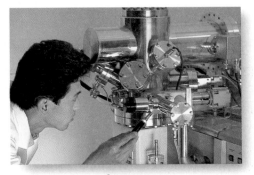

Spectrometer

OPHTHALMOLOGIST

I f you want to be a doctor, but enjoy optics as well, then you might be interested in becoming an ophthalmologist, a medical doctor who specializes in diseases of the eye.

But don't think that because a person wears glasses, she or he has an eye disease! Ophthalmologists treat problems much more serious than poor eyesight. Many older people get a disease that causes a cloudy film to grow over the lens of the eye. This film is called a *cataract*. Using special optical equipment, an ophthalmologist can detect and monitor its progress and decide when it should be removed.

This ophthalmologist is using a refractometer to examine a patient's eye.

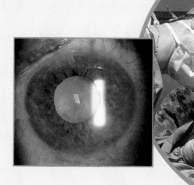

A cataract covers the lens of an eye.

Cataracts once meant certain blindness. Now ophthalmologists use lasers to remove them.

ARTIST

I f you like drawing and creating pictures, you might be interested in becoming a painter or an illustrator.

Computers have changed the way some painters and illustrators create their images.

A painter needs to know about light and how to mix colours. Which theory of colour should a painter understand best?

BIG IDEA

6.0

Visible light is only one part of the electromagnetic spectrum.

What do microwave ovens have in common with radios? How about X-ray machines and cellular telephones? All of this technology makes use of radiation the human eye *cannot* see, sometimes called the **invisible spectrum**. In order to learn more about these other forms of radiation, it helps to take a step back and consider more aspects of light itself.

6.1 THE WAVE MODEL OF LIGHT

Explore

An important part of science is developing models. Models are based on what can be observed about the characteristics and properties of something. They help make it easier to understand complex concepts. What kind of model could be used to help describe light? A model commonly used is the **wave model of light**.

Develop

Developing the Model

On the following pages is an outline of the information and the properties of light on which the wave model of light is based. Like any scientific model, it tries to explain *all* the phenomena that occur.

Wavelength

The distance between the top of one wave and the top of the next is called the **wavelength**. All waves have a wavelength. When the wavelength of light is measured, it turns out that each colour has a slightly different wavelength.

Look at the figure below. Notice that the wavelength is not the same for different colours of the spectrum.

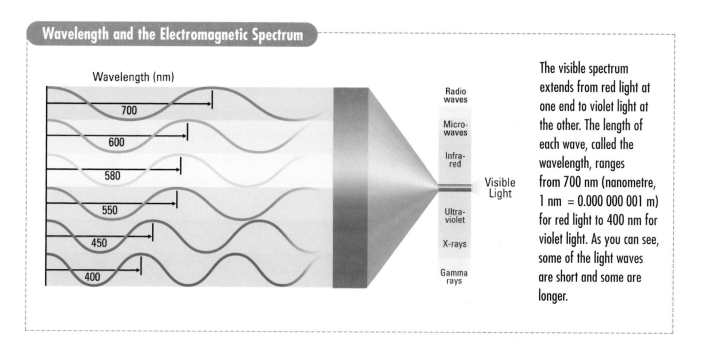

The visible spectrum extends from red light at one end to violet light at the other. The length of each wave, called the wavelength, ranges from 700 nm (nanometre, 1 nm = 0.000 000 001 m) for red light to 400 nm for violet light. As you can see, some of the light waves are short and some are longer.

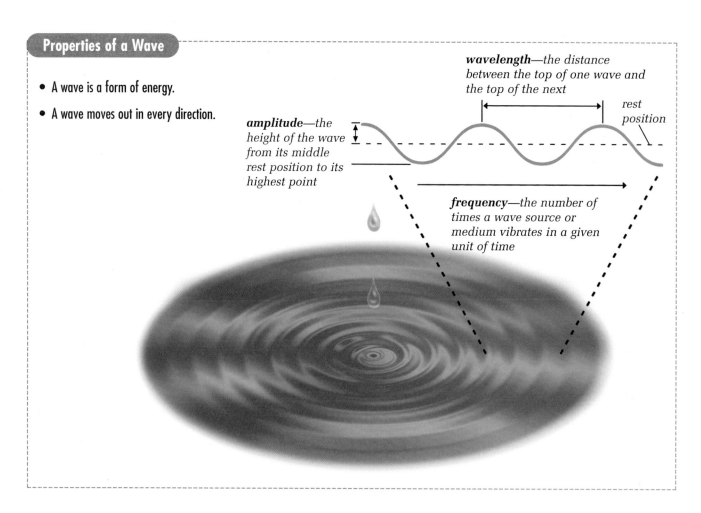

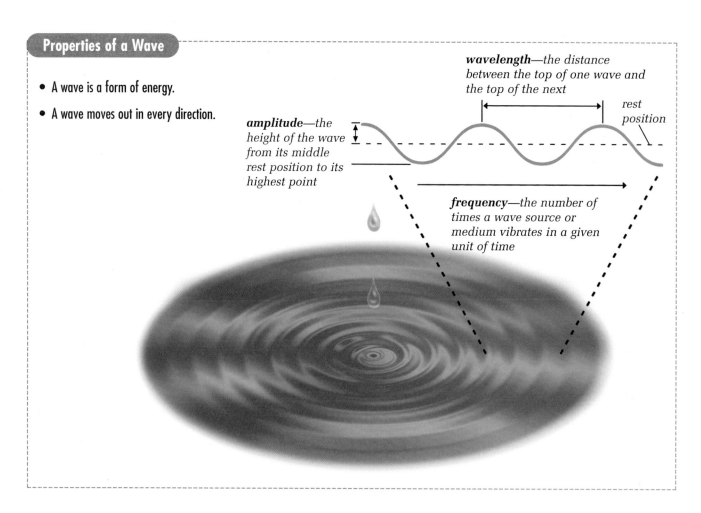

Properties of a Wave

- A wave is a form of energy.
- A wave moves out in every direction.

amplitude—the height of the wave from its middle rest position to its highest point

wavelength—the distance between the top of one wave and the top of the next

rest position

frequency—the number of times a wave source or medium vibrates in a given unit of time

What You Can't See

Does the spectrum end with what our eyes can see? You may have heard the terms *ultraviolet* or *infrared*. What else might be in the electromagnetic spectrum that you can't see? In the next section, you will explore the other components of the electromagnetic spectrum and their importance.

*info*BIT

Laser Light

Lasers produce a fine beam of light that travels long distances without spreading out. **Laser light** is made of waves that have exactly the same wavelength, and each wave is in step with the next. The beam concentrates light energy into a small spot so that lasers can be used to cut metals and perform delicate eye surgery, as well as providing an input module for many electronic devices. (The term laser is an acronym for **L**ight **A**mplification by the **S**timulated **E**mission of **R**adiation.) Arthur Schawlow (1921–1999), who was educated in Toronto, received the Nobel Prize in Physics as its co-inventor.

An argon laser

Communicate

1 How would your life be different if light consisted of only one wavelength? Pick a wavelength from the visible light spectrum and reflect on how your natural surroundings would be affected.

2 What properties of light are like the properties of the waves in A and in B? How do you know?

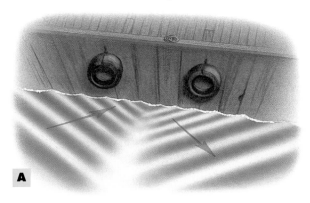

A

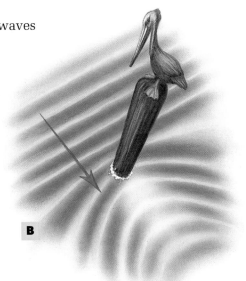

B

3 Draw a diagram of a wave on a piece of graph or grid paper. Your wave should have an amplitude of 4 cm and a wavelength of 10 cm.

6.2 THE INVISIBLE SPECTRUM

Explore

If you were to touch the back of each of these students, which coat would feel the warmest? Can you explain your choice?

What changed the colour of this person's skin?

In a moment, this person will roll over in his sleep so all of his body will be back in the shade. How did he detect the sunlight on his skin while he was sleeping?

Think about the situations shown here. Did they involve seeing colour or forming an image? In your Science Journal, write your own explanations for these events. Add any other observations you may have made about the effect of the invisible components of the electromagnetic spectrum.

Electromagnetic Radiation

The term used to refer to all forms of radiant energy is **electromagnetic radiation**. The electromagnetic radiation spectrum includes visible light, as well as other waves, such as infrared radiation, ultraviolet radiation, radio waves, and X-rays.

The wave model of light is used to explain all electromagnetic radiation. Just as each colour has its own wavelength, so does each of the invisible components of the electromagnetic spectrum. However, you see only visible light. Your eyes are sensitive to the wavelengths from red to violet. You cannot see the other waves because your eyes are not sensitive to their wavelengths.

Uses of Electromagnetic Radiation Spectrum

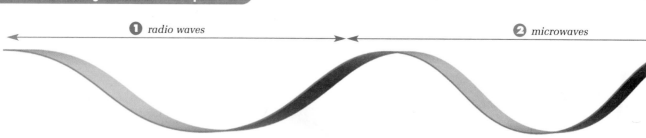

❶ *radio waves*　　❷ *microwaves*

❶ **Radio waves** are used in communications around the world. International agreements assign certain frequencies to different uses, including AM/FM radio, television, cellular phones, short-wave radio, radar, and so on.

❷ **Microwaves** have a shorter wavelength than radio waves. They also carry more energy. When focussed on food, they cause the molecules inside the food to vibrate. This vibration produces heat, so the food cooks from the inside out.

❸ **Infrared waves** are longer than visible light and so have less energy. You can detect infrared waves as heat on your skin.

South-facing windows and skylights allow infrared radiation to help heat homes in northern climates.

FM radio waves are longer and slower than AM radio waves, which are shorter and more energetic.

Devices that detect infrared radiation are used to locate sources of heat.

Electromagnetic radiation strikes the earth in many different forms: radio waves, microwaves, infrared rays, visible light, ultraviolet light, X-rays, and gamma rays.

Useful Radiation Technologies

Although the human eye cannot detect the invisible parts of the electromagnetic spectrum, we have found ways to use the energy they contain. As you examine the uses of the various parts of the spectrum, note which parts have more energy. As a clue, remember that the shorter the wavelength, the higher the frequency of the wave. High-frequency waves carry more energy. Which of the technologies shown here have you or a member of your family used?

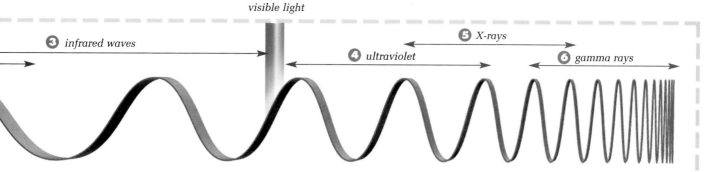

visible light

❸ *infrared waves*

❺ *X-rays*

❹ *ultraviolet*

❻ *gamma rays*

❹ **Ultraviolet waves** have short wavelengths with more energy than visible light. Most ultraviolet radiation is absorbed by the earth's ozone layer.

Ultraviolet waves can penetrate and harm the skin, causing tanning and burning, and increasing the risk of skin cancer. Sun-block creams are opaque and block ultraviolet rays.

❺ **X-rays** and ❻ **Gamma rays** have very short wavelengths and carry a large amount of energy. Even low-energy X-rays can penetrate soft tissues, although they cannot pass easily through bone. High-energy X-rays and gamma rays can pass easily through soft tissues and bones, but cannot penetrate lead 5 cm thick.

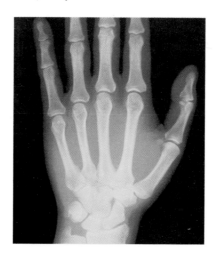

X-rays can be used to make images of the interior of the body, because they will be slowed down by very dense tissues such as bone. Gamma rays and high-energy X-rays are used to destroy cancer cells.

Gamma ray trails in a cloud chamber.

1   Compare X-rays to radio waves and visible light waves to radio waves. How are they different?

2   How do sunscreen lotions protect your skin from the sun's rays? Which part of the electromagnetic spectrum can cause skin damage?

3   Debate this question with your classmates: *Do other forms of electromagnetic radiation, such as microwaves or infrared waves, have the property of reflection?* What support do you have for your opinion?

4   Why do you think X-rays and gamma rays are used to treat cancer?

6.3 SOURCES OF LIGHT AND OTHER FORMS OF ELECTROMAGNETIC RADIATION

Explore

Think of yourself on a sunny day sitting in a classroom. What sources of light are there? Can you think of other sources of light? Look at the photos below and classify each source of light as either *natural* or *artificial*. Share your classification system with others in your class. Is your definition of "natural light" the same as your classmates'?

Natural and Artificial Sources of Electromagnetic Radiation

Do you realize that every day you are bombarded by different forms of electromagnetic radiation from natural and artificial sources? Look at the following picture. Can you identify all the different sources of electromagnetic radiation?

During the day, our primary natural source of light is the sun. Think about being outside in the sunlight. What do you notice as the sun shines on your skin? What effects does the exposure to the sun have on your skin? What about the time you hiked a long distance on a hot cloudy day and were surprised to discover later that you had a sunburn? How could that happen on a cloudy day? Most forms of electromagnetic radiation are produced in space by the sun and other stars.

Artificial Sources

All types of electromagnetic radiation can be artificially produced. You are probably most familiar with devices used to produce visible light, and for good reason. Imagine the moment when your ancestors first used a fire light to push away the darkness. Think about all that you do at night or indoors that you couldn't do without light.

What types of devices are used today to make light? If you look around your classroom, you will probably see either incandescent or fluorescent lights. These are both very common. If you look around your home, which type of lighting is being used in the different rooms? Why do you think this is so?

Fluorescent lamps contain an opaque tube (light cannot pass through from outside) that is coated on the inside with a fluorescent material. When you turn on the electricity, ultraviolet light is produced in the tube. When the ultraviolet light hits the fluorescent material, the ultraviolet waves are absorbed. The material then releases the absorbed energy as visible light.

An **incandescent** light bulb uses electrical energy to heat a thin wire thread, called a *filament*. Because the filament is too thin to carry the electricity easily, it overheats and glows white-hot. You see this glow of the white-hot filament as light.

People make decisions about the technology they buy and use for many different reasons, including convenience, appearance, and cost. Cost involves not just the purchase price but also how much it costs to operate the technology.

Energy can be a major cost in the manufacture and use of any technological system. Count the number of light bulbs in your classroom. How many classrooms are in your school? Estimate the number of bulbs in the building. You can see how quickly the cost of supplying energy to all of these light bulbs would add up. The easiest way to reduce this cost is to use bulbs that are very efficient at transforming electrical energy into light energy, without wasting a lot of energy as heat. In the next activity, you will compare the efficiency of an incandescent light bulb with that of a fluorescent bulb.

DECISION MAKER

WHAT TYPE OF LIGHT BULBS SHOULD I USE?

The Question

How can you demonstrate which is more efficient: an incandescent or a fluorescent light bulb?

Background Information

1 Not all the energy used in a light bulb produces light. Much of it ends up as waste heat. You only have to put your hand near a glowing incandescent bulb to find that out. So, one way you could measure the efficiency of light bulbs is to somehow determine how much waste heat they produce.

continued on next page ······▶

2 Plan and carry out an experiment that compares the waste heat of an incandescent and a fluorescent bulb. Here are some questions you might want to consider.
a) What variables do you need to control (or keep constant) in order to conduct a "fair test"?
b) What materials and equipment will you need?
c) Will you record the results of your data in a chart? in a graph?
d) Why should you repeat your experiment several times?

3 Be sure to compare your results with those of others in your class. Should their results be similar to yours?

In Your Opinion

4 What do the results of your experiment tell you about the efficiency of these types of light sources?
5 What type of lighting would you recommend for your school? for your home? for an office building?

---

try this at **HOME**

THE BETTER TO SEE YOU

What type of lighting do you prefer: incandescent or fluorescent? Try these experiments with your family or friends. You'll need both sources of light as well as some sun! (Hint: How could a camera help you?)

1 *Which light flatters me?*
Ask others to rank how your skin and hair look, on a scale of one to five, in sunlight, in incandescent light, and in fluorescent light.

2 *Which light shows my best look?*
Put on your favourite outfit. Ask others to compare the colours of your clothing under each artificial light source to how they appear outside in the sunlight.

3 *Which light should I use?*
Get a strip of colour samples from a paint store. Compare how these colours appear in sunlight, in incandescent light, and in fluorescent light. Which light gives you the best idea of how the colour would look in your room? Choose a colour you might like for your room.

4 *Based on your results, which type of light makes objects (and you!) look more pleasing?*

Lighting Systems

All lighting is designed as part of a **system** to perform a needed function. As in any system, there must be the following components:

- **Input**—Who decides what is needed? Who plans the system? What type of light source will be used?
- **Output**—What is the desired result? How is the light to be useful?
- **Feedback**—What checks and controls the system?
- **Stability**—How reliable is the system? Does it do the job?

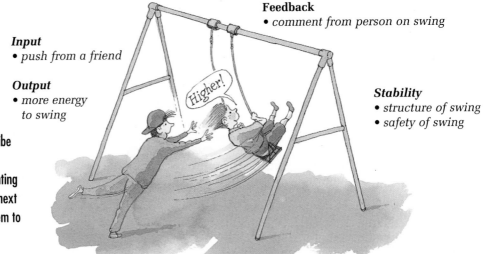

Feedback
• *comment from person on swing*

Input
• *push from a friend*

Output
• *more energy to swing*

Stability
• *structure of swing*
• *safety of swing*

What other systems can you describe that use this model of a system? What are the components in a lighting system? What do they do? In the next activity, you will explore one system to find these answers for yourself.

PROBLEM SOLVER

ANALYZING A SYSTEM

Lighting systems generally follow the model of a simple system. The input comes from something or someone. The output is the action or result of the input. The feedback is a control system that provides a path for data between output and input. Feedback depends on sensors to measure the output to keep it within set limits. The stability of a lighting system helps to maintain the system.

- Read the article on stage lights on the next page. Construct a diagram that identifies the input, output, feedback, and stability of this system.

- Answer these questions:
  - Which part of this system is the most complex? Why?
  - Which part of this system requires the most care? Why?
  - A rock group is doing a series of tours. The lighting technicians must constantly set up, test, operate, then take apart the lighting system. Where does this activity fit into your overall diagram of the system?

continued on next page ┈┈┈┈➤

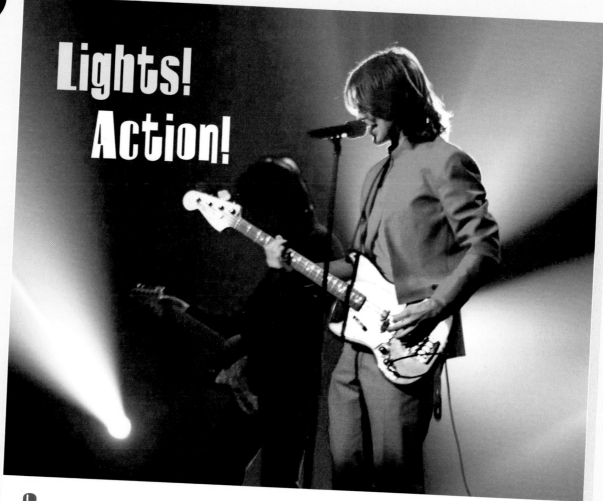

Lights! Action!

Stage lighting systems are at the heart of theatrical performances and rock concerts. They are often what make these events successful. And as any student of biology knows, with every heart, there has to be a brain. When it comes to stage lighting, the "brain" is actually made up of many people. First, a *lighting designer* plans how to light the stage. To make the lighting effective, the designer must understand the behaviour and nature of light and colour. Many lighting designers use computers to help design their stage lighting schemes.

The *lighting technician* uses a console—a computerized board that holds the controls for all the lights—to control the lights. This is a challenging job. The lighting technician must be ready to deal with computers crashing, cables breaking, equipment wearing out, and working at great heights!

A set may have over a hundred lights, many of them hung several metres above the stage. The lights are connected by cables of various sizes and are hooked up to switches (called *dimmers*) that control the brightness of the lights. Coloured filters set the right colour for the scenes.

Besides the designer and the technician, there are a number of people who set adjust the lights

Communicate

1 List four light sources, and identify whether they are natural or artificial. Give a brief description of how each source produces light.

2 Here are two approaches used by the makers of detergents in the unending search for ways to make clothes look cleaner. Explain how each approach uses light to make a white T-shirt look whiter.

   a) Some detergents contain fluorescent materials.

   b) Some detergents contain blue pigment (think back to the theory of colour subtraction).

3 Think about where you like to sit and read. What light source are you using? What, if anything, would you change about this light if you could?

reSEARCH

Sunbathing

Ultraviolet light damages skin. So, why do people go to tanning salons and lie under ultraviolet light or go sunbathing at the beach?

- Conduct a survey to find out how many students know about the risks from ultraviolet light and how many consider a "good tan" to be worth it.

- Do research to find out if tans have always been considered fashionable.

6.4 CHECK YOUR PROGRESS

1 What model is used to help describe and explain the properties of light?

2 The electromagnetic spectrum ranges from low-energy to high-energy waves. Which of the following would you expect in a high-energy wave? Which would indicate a lower-energy wave? Give examples to support your answers.

   a) a long wavelength   b) a short wavelength

3 a) Where does infrared radiation appear on the electromagnetic spectrum?

   b) Can you detect infrared radiation with your body? If so, how?

   c) What is the importance of infrared radiation to you?

   d) Answer parts a)–c) for ultraviolet radiation.

4 How is light being used in this doctor's office? Name as many ways as you can. Add to your list any other ways you can think of in which light plays a role in medicine.

5 Which source would give the greatest amount of light: a 100-W incandescent bulb or a 50-W fluorescent tube? Explain your answer.

Solutions and Problems

Science is the branch of study that tries to explain and define the physical and natural world. Technology uses this knowledge in some practical way. Both areas of learning have dramatically changed the way people live. Both are problem-solving processes. But finding solutions to scientific problems doesn't always produce the desired results. Sometimes the solution creates a new problem. Here is one example.

The Problem

Is Your Refrigerator Out To Get You?

Details on page 12

This headline is not as amazing as it seems. Back in the 1920s, home refrigerators were just beginning to be produced on a large scale. These early refrigerators used chemical coolants that were either highly flammable, toxic, or both. Sometimes the chemicals leaked out, killing people by producing deadly fumes or causing a fire or an explosion. Some people were so afraid of their refrigerators, they kept them on the front porch!

The Solution

One of the first home refrigerators, 1921

Thomas Midgley, Jr., an American scientist, wanted to develop a completely safe substitute for these dangerous coolants. In 1928, he discovered a new group of chemicals known as *chlorofluorocarbons*, or CFCs. They worked well as coolants and were not flammable or toxic. At the time they were hailed as "miracle compounds." In the years that followed, manufacturers found new uses and products for CFCs, for example, in air conditioners, aerosol cans, and foam fast-food cartons.

The New Problem

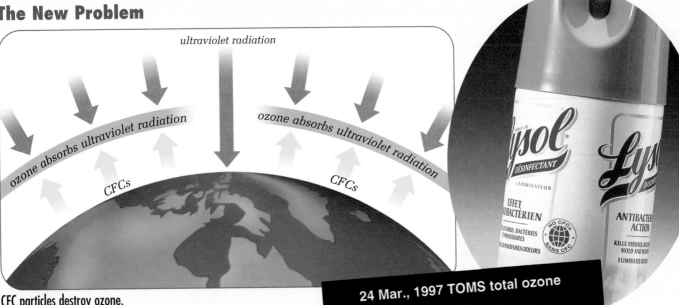

ultraviolet radiation

ozone absorbs ultraviolet radiation

ozone absorbs ultraviolet radiation

CFCs

CFCs

CFC particles destroy ozone.

24 Mar., 1997 TOMS total ozone

Dobson units

220.   500.

As you've learned, the sun emits ultraviolet radiation. You can't see it, but it can harm plants and animals, including humans. Normally, most of the sun's ultraviolet radiation never reaches the earth's surface. It is absorbed by a layer of ozone gas hovering between 10 km and 50 km above the earth. **Ozone** is a form of oxygen. In 1985, scientists discovered that there was a hole in this ozone layer above the Antarctic. More ultraviolet radiation than usual was reaching the ground.

Why did a hole develop in the ozone layer?

The hole in the ozone layer changes from year to year.

The New Solution?

Science went to work on this new problem. Unfortunately, what they found out wasn't good news. The wonder chemical of the last 70 years, chlorofluorocarbons, was at fault. CFCs float up through the atmosphere and, through a series of chemical reactions, cause the ozone particles to break apart.

Now CFCs are or will be banned from use in most countries in the world. New chemicals have been developed to replace these "ozone eaters." And how are these new chemicals doing? Well, first the good news: They don't break down upper atmosphere ozone. Now the bad news: They do, however, add to the earth's greenhouse gases. But that's another problem!

In Your Opinion

1 The ozone story is a perfect example of something that happens often in science: the solution to one problem creates another problem. Another example of this is the discovery of X-rays. Investigate this discovery. What problem did X-rays solve? What new problem did they create?

2 Pick another type of radiation or scientific discovery. Research it and give a specific example of how this discovery has helped us and an example of how it has harmed us.

PROJECT

Getting Started

Since very early times, people have tried to capture energy from the sun to make life more comfortable. One way has been to use fossil fuels, since the source of energy in these materials was sunlight through photosynthesis. However, these are the difficulties connected with depending on fossil fuels:

- They will eventually run out.
- Their use damages the environment.
- Their ability to convert energy isn't very efficient.

So how else could we harness the sun?

Scientists and engineers measure electrical energy in *kilowatt hours* (kWh). In one year, people on earth use more than 50 trillion kilowatt hours of power to run factories, machines, and vehicles, and to heat all our buildings. Does that seem like a lot? It isn't.

Every 40 min or so, the sun delivers this amount of energy free of charge to the earth's surface. So why haven't we made better use of this vast amount of solar energy? A few decades ago, there wasn't much interest. Fossil fuels were cheaper to produce and use than the technology to collect solar energy. Today, interest is growing rapidly, but there remain difficulties to overcome.

An electrical distribution centre

An electrical meter measures how much electricity is used.

For example, the amount of solar energy reaching any one point on the earth at a time depends on several conditions, from weather to the time of year.

One of the ways in which people have tried to capture the sun's energy is through the use of *solar cells* or panels. These are flat plate collectors that use special materials to turn light energy into electrical energy. The efficiency of solar panels ranges from 10–20%. In this project, you will analyze the costs and benefits of producing and using solar panels to power a car.

| Hours of Bright Sunlight Per Year ||
City	Sunshine (hours)
Prince Rupert, British Columbia	1212
Churchill, Manitoba	1821
Charlottetown, Prince Edward Island	1844
Toronto, Ontario	2038
Ottawa, Ontario	1995
Vancouver, British Columbia	1919
Edmonton, Alberta	2303
Kapuskasing, Ontario	1635
Estevan, Saskatchewan	2500

continued on next page ......➤

Before You Start...

You are a member of the "car-of-the-future" research team for a major auto manufacturer. Your team forecasts consumer auto likes and dislikes in the marketplace in order to recommend the type of car the company should plan to build in coming years. You have noticed the growing interest in solar power as an alternative to fossil fuels. Your team wants to recommend the production of a solar-powered family car within five years. Your job is to provide a visual display that compares the benefits and disadvantages of solar-powered cars and gasoline-powered cars. Your company will use your information to determine whether or not to develop a solar-powered car.

To analyze how possible it would be to build a solar-powered car, you can use any information you've gathered as you've worked through this chapter. You will need to collect additional information, however, about solar power from reference books, the Internet, and other resources.

The Question

What are the advantages and disadvantages of a solar-powered car?

Procedure

1 Brainstorm the answers to the following questions with your classmates. Add any other considerations that occur during your discussion.
   a) What are the advantages and disadvantages of a solar-powered car over a gasoline-powered car?
   b) How does the cost of manufacturing a solar-powered car compare with the cost of manufacturing a gasoline-powered car?
   c) How does the cost of running a solar-powered car compare with the gasoline-powered car?
   d) Do you think the production of solar-powered cars is cost effective?
   e) In what products are solar cells or panels used in a cost-effective manner?

2 Determine how you will design and build a display that shows the benefits, advantages, and disadvantages of solar-powered versus gasoline-powered cars. Use the questions that follow to help you with your design.
   a) What are the main points that you want to show in your display?
   b) What other information do you want to include in your display?

To help your thinking, look at these facts and tips.

Solar Facts & Figures
- In Canada, the sun delivers, on average, 150 W/m² energy. Bright overhead sunlight equals 950 W/m².
- A solar panel of photovoltaic cells, measuring 45cm x 50cm, sells for about $313 and will deliver up to 18 W of power.
- A 100-horsepower engine that drives a compact car would be equivalent to a 75 000 W engine.

Design Tips
- Keep car weight down. The lighter the vehicle, the smaller the engine and the fewer solar cells needed to power it.
- Reduce wind resistance (friction) by making the design aerodynamic.
- Be sure the transfer of energy from the engine to the wheels (called "the drive train") is as efficient as possible.

Solar or photovoltaic cells

c) Where will you get the materials you need to build your display?

d) What are all the tasks that need to be done to complete your display?

e) What kind of schedule can you set up to make sure everything gets done by the deadline?

Examples of solar-powered cars

What else do you need to know before designing your display?

3 Design your display and show the design to your teacher for approval. Include these items in your design:

a) a diagram showing how you will display your information

b) a procedure for building your display

c) any safety considerations

4 Build your display according to the design that your teacher approved. If you want to change your display while you're building it, write down the changes you make.

5 Decide how you will present your display to the rest of the class. You may want to have different team members explain sections of the display or present different topics of information.

Share and Compare

6 Present your display to your class. As you watch other teams present their display, write down:

a) what you liked best about their displays or presentations

b) any ideas that you would like to use in future displays of your own

Observations and Reflections

7 Prepare a report so your company has a record of the project and its results. In your report, include a copy of your display, your notes from step 6 above, and the answers to the following questions:

a) Which display was the most interesting? Why?

b) What did you learn about the future of solar-powered cars?

CHAPTER REVIEW

Using Key Terms

1 Write a sentence that defines each of the following terms.

> transparent
> opaque
> reflection
> incidence
> refraction
> concave
> convex
> visible light spectrum
> electromagnetic radiation
> wavelength
> frequency

Reviewing the Big Ideas

2 Describe how you would appear in each of the following types of mirrors. Explain why.
   a) a plane mirror
   b) a concave mirror
   c) a convex mirror

3 a) What is a lens?
   b) What happens to light that passes through a concave lens? Why?
   c) What happens to light that passes through a convex lens? Why?
   d) Which type of lens would you find in a magnifying glass?

4 a) Compare the human eye to a camera using a chart or a diagram. Include the functions of each part.
   b) Use a ray drawing to demonstrate why the image formed on your retina is upside down. Why don't you see the images upside down?
   c) Which way does the image form on camera film?

5 Explain why you agree or disagree with the following statements. For any you disagree with, provide the correct statement.
   a) The normal is a line drawn at a 90° angle to a mirror or lens.
   b) When light is reflected in a plane mirror, the angle of incidence is twice the angle of reflection.
   c) The visible spectrum includes infrared and ultraviolet light.
   d) If you want to see farther into space, build a bigger mirror.

6 What colour do you get when you mix the three primary-colour lights? the three secondary-colour lights?

7 What happens when light passes through a triangular prism?

8 a) List the primary colours of light.
   b) List the secondary colours of light.
   c) How could you produce each of the secondary colours, using only the primary colours?

9 What colour would a green pepper appear to be when viewed in each of the following lights? Explain why.
   a) yellow light
   b) green light
   c) red light
   d) white light

10 How does your eye detect colour?

        Chapter Review

11 a) What is light intensity?

b) How is it affected by distance from the light source?

c) Based on your answers above, explain the arrangement of plant lights and basil plants in the photograph.

12 a) Name three natural sources of electromagnetic radiation.

b) Name three artificial sources of electromagnetic radiation.

13 a) Compare an incandescent light bulb to a fluorescent light bulb.

b) Which bulb would you pick for a bedside lamp? Why?

c) Which bulb would you pick to use in an underground tunnel 5 km long? Why?

Connecting the Big Ideas

14 A reflecting telescope uses a concave mirror to gather light.

a) Why is this mirror better for gathering light than a plane mirror?

b) Why is a telescope able to see more images in outer space than it can on earth?

15 Why do you think stars twinkle when viewed on earth but not in outer space?

16 A two-way mirror is designed to act as a mirror on one side and a transparent piece of glass on the other side. How do you think a two-way mirror works?

17 In colour printing, black is added to the three primary colours. Why do you think this additional colour is needed?

Using the Big Ideas

18 Some people living in the far north experience depression and other symptoms during the winter. Research has shown this is partly due to the very short amount of time the sun shines during the day. Which wavelengths of light would you want to use in artificial lighting where people work and go to school in these areas? Explain your reasoning.

19 A problem with using simple drawings to represent things is that these drawings can be misleading. For example, the ray diagrams you have used for light in this chapter usually included only very few rays. In reality, rays of light travel in all directions from a light source or are reflected in all directions from many parts of an object. Examine the two drawings on this page. (Note: An opaque object is blocking the top half of each lens.) Both were done by students who had learned to use ray diagrams, but only one drawing is correct. Explain which is the correct drawing and why you reached this conclusion.

20 Tucson, Arizona is a city located near Kitt Peak, a mountain with several telescopes on it. Tucson requires all homeowners to install shades above any outdoor lights of more than 150 W, and has banned high-powered mercury-vapour streetlights. Hawaii has passed similar regulations. Why do you think these regulations are necessary? Would you support such regulations in your community?

Self Assessment

21 What are the key ideas of this chapter?

22 Which of the key ideas did you already know before you started this chapter?

23 Which of the key ideas did you learn during the course of this chapter?

24 Which of the key ideas do you still have questions about? How will you find the answers to those questions?

25 What is one idea or thing that amazed you during the course of this chapter?

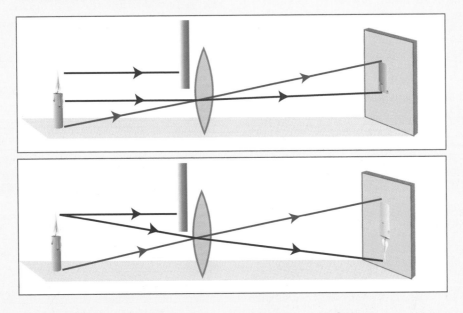

MECHANICAL EFFICIENCY

Chapter 4

I f you've ever dug a hole, walked a long way, or waited for clothes to dry on the line, you've probably realized that there is an easier way to do these tasks. Throughout history, devices have been invented to do work more quickly and efficiently than people can. A backhoe can dig a hole faster and deeper than several people are able to. A bike can easily travel distances five times faster than you can walk. And a clothes dryer can dry a pair of pants in minutes instead of hours.

Devices help us to be more efficient because they take into account the way people use them. In this chapter, you will be looking at a variety of devices that help to improve our lives. Each of these devices uses a scientific principle and is designed to work efficiently. You will also discover how inventors use their creativity to invent or improve devices. And you'll have an opportunity to become an inventor yourself.

BIG Ideas

1.0 Understanding the properties of fluids helps in creating devices that make tasks easier.

2.0 To design new products, you must understand technical drawings and ergonomic factors.

3.0 Gears, levers, and pulleys can help you do a task with mechanical advantage.

4.0 Many factors must be considered in making a new product.

Canadian Inventions

Ontario native, Dr. James Naismith, the inventor of basketball

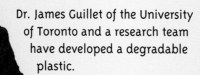

The Imax® motion picture system was invented by Canadians Graeme Ferguson, Robert Kerr, Roman Kroitor, and William Shaw.

Originally from a First Nations reserve in Minnesota, Olivia Poole developed and manufactured the Jolly Jumper® when she moved to British Columbia.

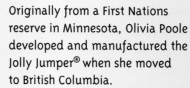

Dr. James Guillet of the University of Toronto and a research team have developed a degradable plastic.

Look at these pictures. You probably know about basketball, IMAX theatres, biodegradable plastics, and the Jolly Jumper. Well, Canadians were involved in creating each of these inventions. Canada is known worldwide for many different inventions and innovations. An **invention** is something new that someone has created. An **innovation** is an improvement to an existing device.

WHAT DOES IT TAKE TO BE AN INVENTOR?

- What do you think it takes to be an inventor? Work in a small group or with a partner to make a list of the qualities you think an inventor should have. Should she know something about science? Should she be curious? Should she be creative?
- For each word in your list, give an example to show why this quality is important.
- Share your list with the class. Add any new qualities to your list that you learn from the discussion.

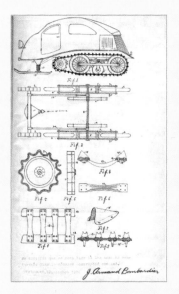

Joseph-Armand Bombardier's early drawing of the Ski-Doo® snowmobile and his patent certificate

Now let's explore the story of one particular Canadian inventor. As you read this story, check off the qualities on your list that this inventor had. If you find a new quality, add it to your list.

The Snowmobile—A Canadian Invention

In the small Québec town of Valcourt, a young boy named Joseph-Armand Bombardier impressed family and friends with his mechanical ability. As he was growing up, he was able to repair clocks and sewing machines, as well as to create new toys from old boxes and motors.

Joseph-Armand Bombardier is best known as the inventor of the Ski-Doo® snowmobile. He began working on his invention at the age of 15 when his father gave him an old, broken-down car. He and his older brother took the motor out of the car and repaired it. Once the car was running, they decided to try to use it to make a vehicle that travelled on the snow. They attached sleigh runners in place of the front wheels and travelled about a kilometre on the snow. They would have gone farther, but the noise bothered their father and the neighbours. Still, Joseph-Armand had made his first successful attempt at designing a snowmobile.

Joseph-Armand Bombardier was fascinated by how things worked.

Over the next 10 years, he worked at his vision of making a vehicle that was able to travel in the snow. Every winter, the need for such a vehicle was confirmed when heavy snowfalls stranded people in their homes. He and his family felt the effects of this problem themselves, when his two-year-old son died of appendicitis one winter because a snowstorm prevented them from getting him to the hospital.

Joseph-Armand worked at many things and was always designing and building something, such as a water-powered turbine to make electricity for his inventions. But he never lost sight of his goal. He wanted to build a commercial snowmobile. Finally in 1937, he realized his dream. His first commercial snowmobile held seven people, so he called it the "B-7" (B for Bombardier and 7 for the number of people it could hold). Orders for the new vehicle began to arrive, and the L'Auto-Neige Bombardier company was born.

The B-7 was the first commercial Bombardier snowmobile.

Soon World War II began, and the company's efforts were focussed on helping with the war effort. Many of the vehicles produced between 1940 and 1945 went to the military. How is the model in the photo to the left different from the B-7? What features of this model suited it for use during World War II?

The Bombardier company developed this snowmobile for the military to use in World War II.

Invitation to Explore

After the war, L'Auto-Neige Bombardier continued to modify and improve its designs. The new models were designed to meet a variety of consumer needs, but they still carried small groups of people. Finally in 1959, Mr. Bombardier designed a new snowmobile for one or two people. This new machine was to be called the "Ski Dog" but because of a printing mistake in the brochure, it became the "Ski-Doo." The Ski-Doo® snowmobile was immediately a bestseller.

Today the Ski-Doo® snowmobile is made by Bombardier Inc., along with other Canadian products such as high-speed metros, jets, Sea-Doo® personal watercraft, and all-terrain vehicles.

Focus Your Thoughts

1 Look at your list of qualities that an inventor should have. Put a star beside the qualities you think you are good at and a circle beside the qualities you would like to improve on.

2 What do you think was the most important quality that made Joseph-Armand Bombardier a successful Canadian inventor?

3 A *design brief* is the starting point for the development of a new design for any object. It's a statement of the aim of the design project and briefly summarizes what must be done. For example, if you were asked to design and build toys for a kindergarten class, your design brief might state: *Design and construct items that are exciting and safe and encourage creative play in the kindergarten classroom.*

   a) What do you think Joseph-Armand Bombardier's design brief would have been when he was 15 years old?

   b) What would his design brief have been when he invented the Ski-Doo® snowmobile in 1959?

4 a) How do you think the design of a Ski-Doo® snowmobile makes it more stable and comfortable to use?

   b) What possible environmental problems might there be in using these land and water craft?

5 Use your library or the Internet to research Canadian inventors. Select one and make a one-page poster summarizing who the inventor is, what the invention does, when it was invented, how he or she invented it, and why it was important. If you need some ideas, look through this chapter on mechanical efficiency. With your class, make some space on your classroom wall for a Canadian Inventors Wall of Fame. Put your posters up on this wall.

6 Canadian Paul Arthur's talent was inventing simple pictures to describe common things. You have seen his work many times. He designed the symbols, or *glyphs*, for the men's and women's washrooms in 1967 for Expo 67 in Montreal. Now these symbols are used all over the world. One idea that is difficult to show as a glyph is whether a door should be pushed or pulled to open it. Design a glyph that you think would convey this message. Remember, a glyph is a picture that doesn't have words, so everyone should be able to understand the picture regardless of the language they speak.

info**BIT**

Some Early Women Inventors

1873 Amanda Jones
(with Leroy Cooley)
Vacuum canning process

1880 Amanda Jones
Oil burner

1886 Carrie Everson
Oil-flotation process for mining

1903 Mary Anderson
Windshield wiper

1910 Sara Josephine Baker
Measured-dose eyedropper

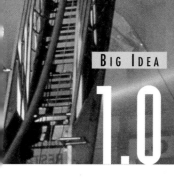
Understanding the properties of fluids helps in creating devices that make tasks easier.

The Laser sailboat is a popular small sailboat with a single sail.

An inventor or innovator has to have an understanding of science. Sometimes this understanding comes from common sense—that is, from your own experience of how things work. Other times, this understanding comes from the knowledge of a particular concept or subject in science. Common sense helped Canadian Ian Bruce when he was working with others to design the Laser sailboat, but an understanding of forces and fluids also helped him. In this section, you will expand your understanding of science as you investigate the properties of fluids and apply them to solving a variety of problems.

1.1 USING SCIENCE AND CREATIVITY TO SOLVE PROBLEMS

Explore

In the Invitation to Explore, you had an opportunity to think about and describe some of the qualities of an inventor. You may have included having an understanding of scientific and technological concepts in your list of qualities. For example, in 1858, James Miller Williams of Hamilton, Ontario, dug the first commercial oil well in North America. Williams was a businessman who quickly

learned about geology and the characteristics of oil. Using the technology of the day, he dug and later drilled dozens of wells, built one of the first oil refineries to produce kerosene for lamps, and in a few years became a multimillionaire. Like many entrepreneurs, he was a problem solver and a good student of science.

In the next activity, you will use your understanding of some science concepts to help you solve a problem.

James Miller Williams dug the first commercial oil well in North America near what is now Oil Springs, Ontario.

Develop Solving Problems

The following scenario is called a "thought experiment." To solve the problem, you will use a paper and pencil. You want to create a solution that would work if you had the right equipment. There is no right or wrong answer. All reasonable answers are correct, but you must be prepared to describe your solution and answer questions about it.

PROBLEM SOLVER

EMERGENCY!

You and your group are part of the emergency robotic environmental response unit at the RoboQuest Company. An accident has just occurred. A robotic explorer has become wedged in a deep drainage pit that you were investigating. The robotic explorer is very heavy—about 100 kg. You have to retrieve it without damaging it. You can see from the diagram of the accident site that this will be a challenge.

Propose a solution to the problem, and include a design that uses the equipment listed below:
- hydraulic arm
- steel beams about 2 m long
- a wide assortment of gears
- a wide assortment of pulleys with rope

Before you start, look at the problem-solving techniques that follow.

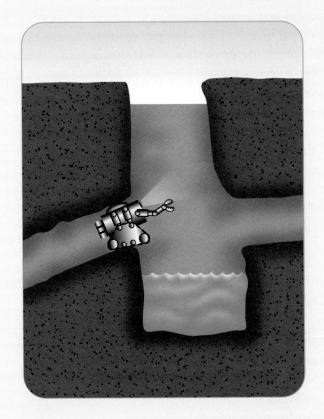

Sometimes when you are presented with a problem, it is difficult to think of solutions. Here are some tips to help you generate ideas.

Brainstorming

You may have done a brainstorming activity before, but it's helpful to review it. Brainstorming enables a group to generate lots of ideas quickly. It works best when everyone in the group uses the following rules:

Bubble Charts

Sometimes answering questions about who, what, where, when, and why can help you better understand your design problem and clarify what you have to do. A bubble chart is one way for you to think about these questions and record your ideas. A **bubble chart** starts with a key word or idea in the centre of a bubble in the middle of a page. Around this centre bubble, write *Who? What? Where? When?* and *Why?* Circle each word and connect it to the centre bubble containing your key word or idea. Now you can generate ideas and answers to your five bubble questions. For each idea or answer, write it on the page, put a bubble around it, and join it to the appropriate question.

Making Connections

Many inventions are not really new—they are created by connecting two or more existing ideas. For example, at some time, you might have seen a pulley used to lift a large object. Another time, you might have seen a device that used a hydraulic system to pick up a rock. By combining these two ideas, you could make a mechanical hand that could pick up the robotic explorer in the Problem Solver activity at the beginning of this section.

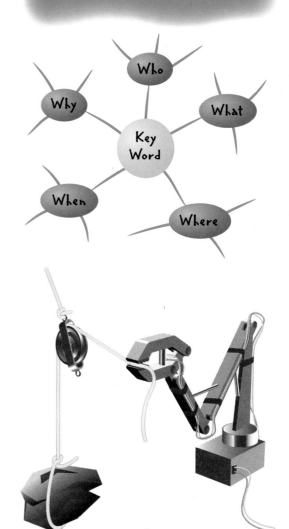

- Ideas are short
- Ideas are creative.
- No idea is criticized.
- No idea is rejected no matter how "far out" it is.
- Group members use earlier ideas to create more ideas.

Connecting existing ideas can help you create a new, useful device.

1 What science concepts do you think James Miller Williams was able to apply when he began extracting oil and producing kerosene?

2 What science concepts did you use when you developed your solution for picking up the robotic explorer?

3 Describe how you came up with your idea for picking up the robotic explorer and what your role was in the activity.

4 If you were to do the Problem Solver activity again, what would you do differently to improve your result?

1.2 PROPERTIES OF FLUIDS

Explore

In the last Problem Solver activity, you used a variety of information to design a solution to a problem. You may have combined what you knew about simple machines, hydraulic systems, and technical drawings.

The hydraulic arm you used in the solution to the Problem Solver works because of the properties of fluids. You may have already studied some of these properties. Recall that a **fluid** is any substance in a gas or liquid state. Before studying fluids in more detail, let's review the Particle Theory of Matter. It can help you better understand the properties of fluids.

You may remember that the **Particle Theory of Matter** provides a way of describing the structure of matter in its three states: solid, liquid, and gas. Below is a magnified view of the particles in each state.

infoBIT

The Origin of the Particle Theory of Matter

Portrait of Democritus, Greek philosopher of the 5th century B.C.

Consider this situation. You cut a copper penny in half with a metal saw. You then take the "half-piece" and cut that in half. You then continue cutting each piece in half. Will there ever be a time when the "half-piece" you've cut *can't* be divided any further?

Leucippus, a Greek philosopher who lived in the 5th century B.C., was the first person we know of to have considered this question. His conclusion? Matter could not be broken down forever. Sooner or later, you would reach a particle so small that it could not be divided.

Democritus, pictured at left, was a pupil of Leucippus. He named these particles *atomos*, which is the Greek word for "unbreakable." According to Democritus, everything in the universe was made of minute, invisible particles. However, for 2000 years no one really believed this theory. It wasn't until the 1600s that scientists began to prove that *atomos*, or atoms as they are now called, really did exist.

The Particle Theory of Matter

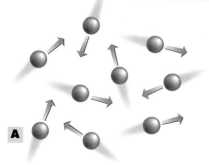
A

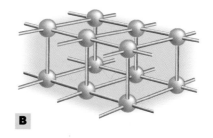
B

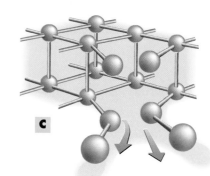
C

Which drawing shows particles in a solid state? in a liquid state? in a gas state?

The Particle Theory of Matter describes matter in the following way:

1   All matter is made up of tiny particles that are too small to see. Different substances are made up of different particles.

2   The tiny particles of matter are always moving and vibrating. In solids, the particles are wiggling in one place. In liquids, the particles are sliding around and over each other. In gases, the particles are moving as far apart as they can in the space they are in.

3   The particles in matter are attracted or bonded to each other.

4   The particles have spaces between them. There is much more space between particles in a gas than there is between particles in a solid or liquid.

From this information, you can determine that in the drawing above, (a) is matter in the gas state, (b) is matter in the solid state, and (c) is matter in the liquid state.

The Particle Theory not only helps to explain the structure of matter. It can also be used to explain the way fluids behave under pressure and when there is a temperature change.

Develop
Volume, Temperature, and Pressure

In the next activity, you will carry out activities at three stations related to volume, temperature, and pressure changes in fluids. From your observations, you will begin to investigate the relationships between volume, temperature, and pressure when a liquid or gas is heated or compressed.

4
M E C H A N I C A L   E F F I C I E N C Y

LOOKING FOR A RELATIONSHIP

The Question

What is the relationship between volume, temperature, and pressure when a liquid or gas is heated or compressed?

Station 1: Volume

Materials & Equipment

- *50-mL syringe*
- *Plasticene to plug end of syringe*
- *access to water*

Procedure

1 At this station, you will compare the effect of pressure on the volume of a liquid and on the volume of a gas. Design a procedure that uses a 50-mL syringe for making this comparison. Make sure to state specifically what data you will need and how you will collect it. Show your design to your teacher for approval.

2 Carry out your investigation. Record your data.

Station 2: Temperature

Materials & Equipment

- *empty 2-L plastic pop bottle with cap*
- *bucket of ice-cold water*
- *bucket of hot tap water*

Procedure

3 If the cap is on the plastic bottle, take it off. Wait several seconds, and then screw the cap tightly back on the bottle.

4 Predict what you think will happen when you place the bottle in the bucket of ice-cold water. Provide an explanation for your prediction. Try to use the Particle Theory in your explanation.

5 Holding onto the cap, place the bottle in the bucket of ice-cold water for 1 min. Remove the bottle from the bucket and record your observations.

Caution!
The water is hot. Use rubber gloves.

COLD   HOT

6 Unscrew the cap from the bottle and let the bottle return to its normal shape. Loosely put the cap back on the bottle.

7 Predict what you think will happen to the bottle when you immerse it in the bucket of hot water. Provide an explanation for your prediction. Try to use the Particle Theory and the word *pressure* in your explanation.

8 Place the bottle in the hot water for 1 min. Remove the bottle from the hot water and tighten cap. Record your observations immediately, at 30-s intervals after removing the bottle from the water, and again at 5 min after removing the bottle from the water.

Station 3: Pressure

Materials & Equipment
- *water*
- *hot plate*
- *ice-cold water*
- *pop can*
- *tray*

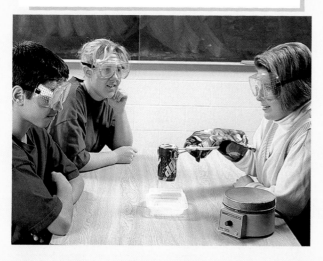

Procedure

9 This activity will be demonstrated by your teacher. Your teacher will put a small amount of water in a pop can and place the can on a hot plate. As soon as the water begins to boil and you see steam coming out of the hole, your teacher will remove the can from the hot plate, invert it, and place it in a tray of ice-cold water.

10 Predict what you think will happen when the can is placed in the cold water. Provide an explanation for your prediction.

11 Observe your teacher carrying out the demonstration. Record your observations.

Keeping Records

12 For each station, record your predictions, drawings, data, and other observations.

Analyzing and Interpreting

13 At Station 1, you pushed on the syringe when it was full of air and then of water. Why did the volume of air in the syringe compress more than the volume of water did? Try to use the Particle Theory to explain this.

14 At Station 2, how did your prediction compare with the actual results?

15 When you cooled and heated the bottle at Station 2, why did you have to remove the bottle cap to get the bottle to return to its original shape?

16 What effect does increasing the temperature have on the volume of a pop bottle full of air?

17 What effect does decreasing the temperature have on the volume of a pop bottle full of air?

18 At Station 3, how did your prediction compare with the actual results?

19 At Station 3, explain what happened to the pop can containing hot water vapour when it was placed in cold water?

Forming Conclusions

20 Use your data and the Particle Theory to describe the relationship between volume, temperature, and pressure when a gas is heated and cooled. Your description should include the following words: *expand*, *contract*, *increase*, *decrease*, *particles moving faster*, and *particles moving slower*. You can use both words and drawings in your description.

Communicate

1 How does the Particle Theory explain an increase in volume when the temperature increases?

2 How does the Particle Theory explain a decrease in pressure when the temperature decreases?

3 When a gas is heated, what happens to the pressure and volume?

4 a) What is the effect of pressure on a liquid as compared with a gas?

   b) What data could you use to support your answer?

1.3 PASCAL'S LAW

Explore

Now let's focus on fluids under pressure. Because of the way they transmit pressure, fluids can be very useful in helping us perform tasks. You may already know something about hydraulics and pneumatics, in which fluids are used in devices. In this section, you'll learn why fluids are useful.

In the mid-1600s, French mathematician Blaise Pascal was curious about how pressure is exerted in a fluid. In one of his first experiments, he investigated the relationship between water pressure and depth. Look at the illustration here, showing water flowing out of two holes at the same level in a can. Working with a partner, develop an explanation for what you observe. Use the following words in your explanation: *pressure*, *sides of the can*, *force*, *equal*, and *depth*. Be prepared to share your explanation with the class.

Blaise Pascal

Born in 1623, Blaise Pascal was noted for his intelligence and inventiveness even as a child. He studied geometry and invented the hydraulic press and the syringe. When he was 31, he was out one evening in his carriage and his horses suddenly went wild. He took this as a sign that he should change his life. For the next eight years, until he died at age 39, he devoted himself to the study of Christianity, philosophy, and mathematics.

*info***BIT**

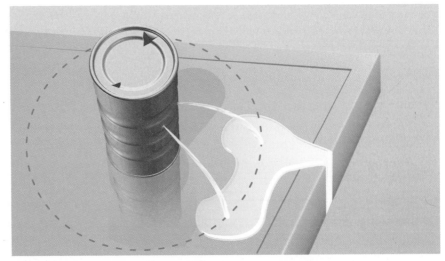

Why does the water flow out of the can in this way? *equal pressure because holes are at the same level*

Develop
Fluids and Pressure

In examining the diagram on the previous page, you and your class may have determined that the **pressure** or **force** of the water on the sides of the can was equal at the same depth. You could infer this because the water that came out of the holes travelled the same distance on each side before hitting the ground. This observation led Pascal to another question. What would happen if you put holes in the can at different depths? Some students tried this activity and their results are presented in the Problem Solver activity below. As you work through this activity, remember to think about Pascal's question: *How does pressure change as the depth of the water changes?*

PROBLEM SOLVER

WHAT PASCAL SAW

A group of students made the following measurements when observing water flowing out of three holes at different depths in a container. Make a graph of the data.

Height of Hole from Bottom	Distance Water Travelled
1.0 cm	3.9 cm
2.3 cm	3.1 cm
3.6 cm	1.1 cm

water volume = 400 mL

Set-up for the students' investigation

• The students then wondered what would happen if they doubled the height of their container and filled it with water, but kept the holes in the same place. What do you think would happen? Discuss your prediction with your partner or group.

continued on next page ·····➤

- Here is the data for the students' second experiment. Graph these results onto the same graph you used for the first set of data. How are the two lines the same? How are they different?

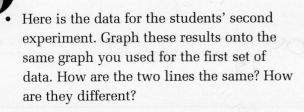

Height of Hole from Bottom	Distance Water Travelled
1.0 cm	6.5 cm
2.3 cm	6.4 cm
3.6 cm	5.9 cm

water volume = 800 mL

- What would happen if another hole were put in the container with 400 mL of water at a height of 3.0 cm?
- How far would another stream of water go if another hole at a height of 1.5 cm was added?
- Using your data, explain which statement below is true.
  a) In a fluid, pressure is transferred in all directions.
  b) In a fluid, pressure is transferred only up and down.
  c) In a fluid, pressure is transferred only back and forth or sideways.

Pressure and Depth

In the Problem Solver activity, you saw that pressure forced water out of holes in a container. The water was exerting pressure on the walls of the container. The amount of water in the upper part of the container acted as a force pressing down on the water in the lower part of the container. The more water above a hole, the greater the pressure, and the farther the water flowed out of the container.

The water exerts pressure in all directions in the container.

Force and Area

Another important part of understanding how to use fluids in devices involves knowing the relationship between **force** and **area**. In the next activity, you will investigate that relationship.

FEELING THE PRESSURE

The Question

What is the relationship between force and area in a liquid?

Materials & Equipment

- *small syringe (about 10 cm³)*
- *large syringe (about 30 cm³)*
- *water*
- *Newton meter (spring scale)*
- *bucket or beaker*
- *masking tape*
- *retort stand and clamp*

Procedure

1 Calculate the inside area of the plunger in each syringe.

2 Make a prediction about which syringe will be easier to push down and empty of water.

3 Half-fill the small syringe with water. Attach it to the stand with the plunger facing up.

4 Attach the hook of the Newton meter (spring scale) to the end of the plunger. Push down the plunger of the small syringe by pulling down with the scale in a smooth, continuous motion. Measure and record the force needed to empty the small syringe into the bucket.

5 Repeat step 4 two more times and calculate the average force used.

6 Repeat steps 4 and 5 with the large syringe.

Keeping Records

7 Copy the following table into your notebook to record your observations.

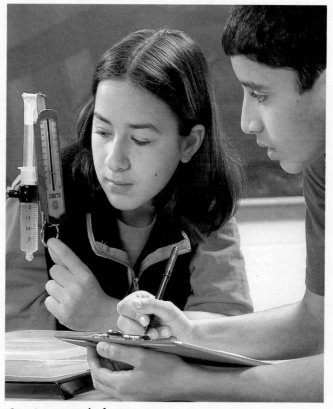

Step 4: measure the force.

Analyzing and Interpreting

8 What was the average force used for the small syringe? for the large syringe?

9 Why do you think there was a difference between the two average forces?

10 Why did you repeat your force measurement three times?

Forming Conclusions

11 Summarize your investigations and describe the relationship between force and area.

Syringe	Area of Plunger	Trial 1: Force Used	Trial 2: Force Used	Trial 3: Force Used	Average Force Used
small					
large					

4 MECHANICAL EFFICIENCY

infoBIT

Measuring Pressure

The unit for recording pressure is the Pascal (Pa). When you calculate pressure, you are dividing force, which is measured in Newtons, by area, which is measured in square units (e.g., m^2). So your answer would come out as N/m^2.

A pressure of 1 N/m^2 is equal to 1 Pa. But a pressure of 1 Pa is very small, so scientists usually use kilopascals (1 kPa = 1000 Pa). The average air pressure at sea level is 101.3 kPa. A pressure of 1 Pa is only about the amount of pressure that a small sheet of paper on your desk exerts on the desk! (Note that pressure can also be measured in N/cm^2.)

Understanding Pascal's Law

In the Investigator activity on the previous page, you discovered that as the surface area of the plunger in the syringe increased, the greater was the force needed to push the plunger down. Through his investigations, Pascal determined, as you may have, that pressure was the result of a force applied over a given area. He also determined that pressure was transmitted equally throughout the whole liquid. From these observations, Pascal developed a law to describe the relationship between pressure, force, and area.

Pascal's law states that *an enclosed liquid transmits pressure equally in all directions.* You can also write Pascal's law as an equation: $p = F/A$, where p is pressure, F is force, and A is area. The next illustration shows an example of this equation.

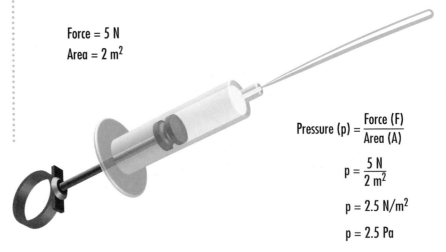

Force = 5 N
Area = 2 m^2

$$\text{Pressure (p)} = \frac{\text{Force (F)}}{\text{Area (A)}}$$

$$p = \frac{5\ N}{2\ m^2}$$

$$p = 2.5\ N/m^2$$

$$p = 2.5\ Pa$$

Pascal's law explains the relationship between pressure, force, and area in a fluid.

Using Pascal's Law

An understanding of Pascal's law has led to the invention of many different devices, such as pneumatic and hydraulic equipment. Pneumatic devices use compressed air to do tasks. A dentist's drill and the mechanism for opening and closing bus doors are examples of pneumatic devices. Hydraulic devices use compressed fluids. Backhoes for digging or lifting or a car's braking system are examples of hydraulic devices.

Hydraulic and pneumatic systems work well because fluids are good transmitters of force. As you saw in your earlier investigations, liquids tend to transmit force better than gases do.

A backhoe uses hydraulics to help it lift and dig.

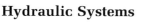

A dentist's drill uses compressed air or a pneumatic system.

Hydraulic Systems

Hydraulic systems work because they contain a liquid. This liquid is able to transmit pressure equally throughout the whole container. But how can these hydraulic devices lift objects much heavier than a person could ever lift?

By examining a hydraulic system, you can get a better understanding of how it lifts or moves heavy objects. The picture below is of a flight simulator machine. The first flight simulator machine was invented by the Canadian company CAE Electronics Limited in 1947. This device allows pilots to practise flying a plane without having to take a real plane off the ground. The result saves time and money. It is also an opportunity for pilots to practise handling a variety of dangerous situations without risking themselves or a plane.

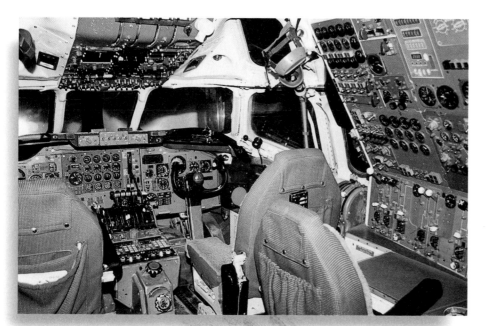

Flight simulators use hydraulics to give pilots the feeling that they are really flying an airplane.

When you look at the picture of the flight simulator, you'll notice the large hydraulic pistons on the sides. The input that causes the pistons to move comes from the pilot moving the flight stick. The resulting output causes the flight simulator to move up, down, and even sideways.

The input piston is smaller and generates a force that is transferred through the whole liquid. This force moves the output piston. The output piston has a larger surface area, so it generates a larger force.

Early examples of flight simulators have been in use since 1929. All have used some kind of mechanical or hydraulic devices to simulate flight movement.

Let's look more closely at how hydraulics work. If the pilot uses the input piston to put in 10 N of force, the flight simulator piston generates 1000 N of force. Does that seem as though we are getting something for nothing? We aren't really. Although the amount of force transferred is much greater, the input piston also has to move much farther than the output piston.

Communicate

1 Describe how forces are transferred in a fluid.
2 How does the hydraulic part of a flight simulator operate?
3 If 10 N of force is applied to an area of 1 m², what is the pressure? If the same force is applied to an area of 1.5 m², what is the pressure?
4 A hydraulic lift has 1000 N applied to an input piston that has an area of 30 cm².
   a) What is the pressure in N/cm² (Pa) exerted on the liquid by the input piston?
   b) If the force were doubled, what would be the pressure?
   c) If the area were reduced to 15 cm², what would be the pressure in N/cm² (Pa)?

try this at HOME

SHAKE IT UP

Procedure

1 Put a can of pop in a large Ziploc-type bag.
2 Shake the can. Now, tap the can several times with your finger.
3 Before you open the can, make a prediction about what will happen when you open it.
4 Holding it through the bag, open the pop can.
5 What happened when you opened the pop can in the bag? Were you surprised?

DESIGN AND BUILD A HYDRAULIC OR PNEUMATIC ELEVATOR

Before You Start...

One of the most common ways to move people or things up and down is an elevator. There were simple elevators as early as the 3rd century B.C., but elevators were put into buildings only in the 1800s. These devices were powered by steam engines or operated with a hydraulic system. Their use was limited because of safety concerns. The main concern was that the rope or cable lifting the elevator could snap and send the passengers plunging to the bottom of the shaft.

This changed when an inventor named Elisha Graves Otis developed a "safety elevator" in 1852. This elevator had ratchets along the side of the shaft and two cogs attached to the elevator cable. If the cable broke, the cogs would swing out and get "caught" in the ratchet. Otis demonstrated his device by going up three floors and then having someone cut the cable. The elevator fell a short distance and then the cogs caught the nearest ratchet. He was stuck in the elevator, but he was safe!

By the late 1800s, elevator motors began to replace hydraulic systems. Today, the limitations of an elevator are more human than technological. If an elevator moves too fast, people feel sick from the speed.

A modern, glass-enclosed elevator running up the side of a building.

continued on next page ······→

Other types of elevators or lifts include hydraulic ladders, such as those on firetrucks, and hydraulic cherry pickers on repair vehicles.

The hydraulic system on the truck lifts the ladder so firefighters can reach trapped people or animals quickly.

A cherry picker makes it easier for workers to do tasks in high places where they need to be able to use both hands.

Now you'll have an opportunity to design your own hydraulic or pneumatic elevator.

Design Brief

Design and build a hydraulic or pneumatic elevator to lift a golf ball 30 cm.

Your Task

1 Working by yourself or in a small group, generate possible ideas on how you could design your device.
2 Create a plan for how you will build your device. Include a detailed sketch of your device and a list of equipment you will need. Show your plan to your teacher for approval.
3 Build your device. Be prepared to demonstrate how your device works to the class.
4 Compare your device with those of others in the class. How successful were the other devices?

1.0 Understanding the Properties of Fluids Helps in Creating Devices That Make Tasks Easier

1.4 CHECK YOUR PROGRESS

1 Why is it important to be able to apply your understanding of science concepts when you are inventing something?

2 What are three ways to help a group generate ideas?

3 When groups are brainstorming ideas, what rules should they follow to be successful?

4 A can of pop is sitting on a burner. By accident, the burner is turned on. About 10 min later, the can explodes. Why did this happen?

5 Why is it easier to compress a syringe full of air than a syringe full of water?

6 A syringe plunger has an area of 4 cm². A force of 8 N is applied to the plunger. What is the pressure on the liquid medicine in the syringe?

7 What is the relationship between area and pressure in a fluid if the force is constant?

8 Knowing the relationship between pressure, volume, and temperature for compressed and heated liquids or gases can help you in designing fluid-related devices. Fill in the blank cells with increases or decreases in the table below to summarize your understanding of the relationship between pressure, volume, and temperature.

	Pressure	Volume	Temperature
compressing the liquid			
heating the liquid			
compressing the gas			
heating the gas			

9 What did Pascal discover about fluids?

10 Review the list of inventor's qualities that you started in the Invitation to Explore.
   a) Are there any new qualities you can add to the list?
   b) You also identified qualities of your own that you needed to improve. Which ones have you improved? How did you do this?

MECHANICAL DRAFTING TECHNICIAN

Drafting technicians use computers to prepare detailed scale drawings of mechanical devices and their various parts. The use of computers in the design process is known as computer-aided design (CAD). Using CAD, drafting technicians can manipulate and test their drawings on video display screens until the best balance of features has been incorporated. Many community colleges offer courses in CAD design and drafting.

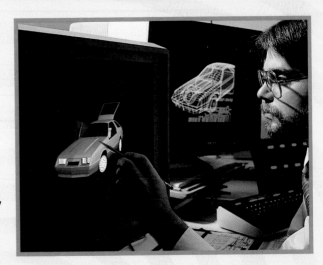

Drafting technician working at a CAD terminal. For a car, airliner, or spacecraft, tens of thousands of individual drawings are often needed to convey all of the details.

INVENTOR

Most successful inventors will tell you they started by developing their natural curiosity at an early age: they took things apart to see what made them tick; they constructed gadgets using erector sets; they participated in science fairs; and in school they took a variety of science, math, and engineering courses. Have you ever thought about inventing something?

While riding on a streetcar in New York City in 1903, Mary Anderson noticed that the shivering driver had to continuously get out and wipe snow and ice off the front windshield. She thought long and hard about how to solve this problem until she eventually came up with the idea of a hand-operated windshield wiper. Within 10 years, her invention was standard equipment on most vehicles. Above is a copy of the drawing she submitted to the U.S. Patent and Trademark Office.

Canadian Peter L. Robertson (1879–1951) invented the Robertson square-headed screw in Milton, Ontario. The new square design prevented screwdrivers from slipping off the screw head as easily as was the case with other screws. In 1908, he set up a factory, Recess Screws Limited, in Milton, to manufacture the new screw. Now known as Robertson Inc., the plant is still busy turning out Robertson screws.

2.0

To design new products, you must understand technical drawings and ergonomic factors.

Not all inventions and innovations require a brand new idea. Many times, people are able to combine existing ideas to make something new and useful. For example, in the 1920s, Dr. Archibald Huntsman wanted to find a way for everyone in Canada to enjoy fish. People who lived far from the oceans or lakes didn't eat very much fish. He thought if fish could be frozen, it would be possible to transport it to areas far from where it was caught, and people in those areas would buy and eat it. After much experimenting, he figured out a way to freeze fish and ship it to stores for sale. The frozen food industry had begun.

2.1 TECHNICAL DRAWINGS

Explore

Part of inventing or creating a product or device is illustrating what it will look like and how it will be built. There are many different kinds of drawings that can be used depending on what you want to show. For example, if you get an idea, you may quickly sketch a small, rough diagram on a piece of paper. This type of drawing is called a **thumbnail sketch**. When you make a thumbnail sketch, remember these points:

- Make the drawing quickly and simply.
- Draw your product or device as though it were flat, just using outlines without shading or colour.
- Use only stick figures for people.
- If you need to show movement, use arrows to show the direction.
- Use labels to help explain what you're showing.

Try making a thumbnail sketch of a toy for a young child. Your toy must use at least one wheel and a syringe. Be prepared to explain how it works.

How many frozen fish products does your family eat?

Types of Drawings

*info***BIT**

For more information about making drawings, please see Toolbox 7.

There are many other types of drawings besides thumbnail sketches. These other types can show hidden details, magnified details, cut-away views, or exploded views. The type of drawing you choose depends on your needs. Read through the following overview of the four types of drawings. After that, you will have an opportunity to practise them.

Hidden Details

Sometimes an object has details that you cannot see. A lock on a door, the inside of a toy, or the inside of a human body are all examples of things that have covers hiding their inner workings. A **hidden details drawing** shows what's inside the object. There are three ways to make a hidden details drawing:

1 Make a **see-through drawing** that shows what you would see if the outside casing of the object were transparent.

2 Make a **sectional drawing** that shows what you would see if you cut a slice through the object.

The gears connected to the crank are inside the box.

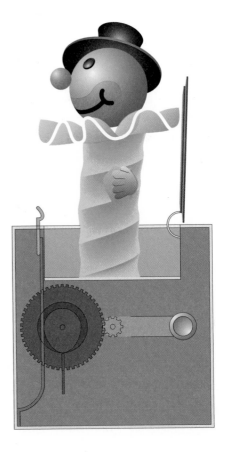

The sectional view shows the accurate placement of the gears and crank mechanisms.

3 Use dotted lines to outline the **hidden details** within the object.

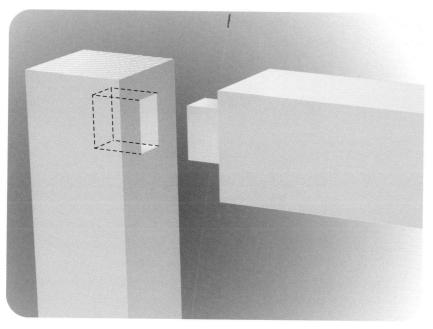

The dotted lines show a cutout in a piece of wood called a *mortise.*

Magnified Details

Sometimes a picture of a whole object isn't the right size to allow you to see the fine detail in some parts of the object. A **magnified drawing** of part of an object shows an enlarged detailed view. Look at the diagram below. The section of the waist pack is magnified to show the detail of the zipper.

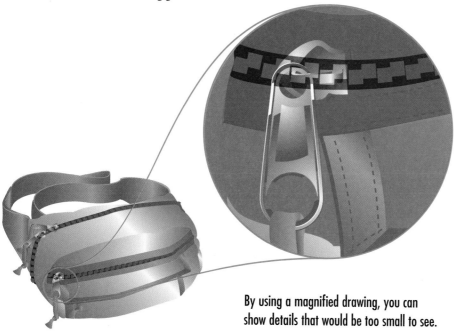

By using a magnified drawing, you can show details that would be too small to see.

Cut-away View

A **cut-away view** has part of the device removed so that hidden details can be shown. How is this diagram similar to the see-through drawing?

You can use a cut-away view to "remove" a piece of an object wherever you want to show hidden details.

Exploded View

Sometimes a device has many connected parts that are hard to show in an ordinary drawing. An **exploded view** shows all the parts of the device pulled or exploded apart. Readers see the device presented in a way that shows how all the parts fit together. This allows them to figure out how the device is made and how it works. The diagram below is an exploded view of a clock.

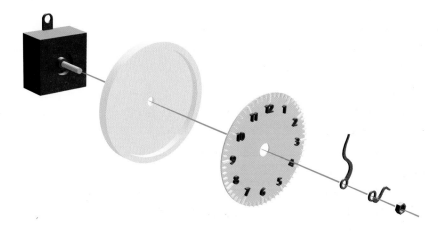

This diagram shows how the parts of a clock fit together.

CREATING TECHNICAL DRAWINGS

- Your teacher will have a box of devices including toys, and small electrical and kitchen appliances.
- With your partner or in small groups, select one device from the box.

- Each of you will do two drawings of the device you selected. The first drawing should be a thumbnail sketch. The second drawing can be any one of the four different views described on the previous pages.

infoBIT

Drawing to Scale

Most objects are too large or in some cases too small to be drawn accurately on ordinary paper. That's why designers use what is called scale drawings. In a **scale drawing**, a certain measurement on paper is equivalent to a real-world measurement. For example, in the drawing to the right, 1 cm (or one square) would be equivalent to 10 cm on the actual shelving unit. That means it is drawn using a 1:10 scale.

Look at the types of drawings your classmates used in the above Problem Solver. They probably were not all the same.

- What was the most common type of drawing used? What type of drawing did you use?
- Did you make your drawing to scale? If so, what scale did you use?

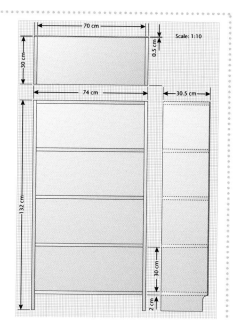

Orthographic drawing of a shelving unit using a 1:10 scale.

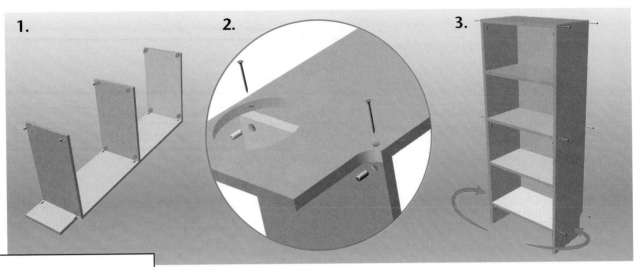

1 You have just bought all the parts of a bookshelf at a local furniture store. It came with the directions shown in the diagram to show you how it should be assembled.

Construction Steps

Assembling the support

1. Locate the holes for **insert A**.
2. Screw **connector B** into **insert A**. There are 2 for each side.
3. Do the same for the other side.

a) Copy the following table into your notebook, and use it to record your evaluation of the directions. Rate the directions given for the bookshelf's assembly in the following way:

4 = very good
3 = good
2 = satisfactory
1 = unsatisfactory

In the Comments column, provide a reason for your rating. Include at least two suggestions for improving the directions.

Category	4	3	2	1	Comments
Clarity of directions					
Thoroughness					
User-friendliness					
Suggestions for improvement					

2 a) Find one of the following: (1) a manual on how to use a product that you own, such as a VCR or calculator, or (2) a Help screen for a computer program.
b) Copy the table above into your notebook. Record your evaluation of the manual or the Help screen in the table.

3 a) If you were asked to provide a drawing of your classroom, what kind of drawing would you do?
b) Why would you choose that kind?

4 Draw your desk, locker, or backpack and show what is inside it.

2.2 MAKING THINGS EASIER FOR PEOPLE

Explore

Drawings are usually the first step in developing a new product or in designing buildings, bridges, and other structures. The next step is to make a model. A **model** allows you to create a smaller version of your object so you can see how the pieces fit together. If it's a device, you can try out the model to see if your device works. You can make changes easily to the model to improve it and try it again.

This model of a new car design is being tested in a wind tunnel to see how well it is streamlined.

Sometimes the model can be done on a computer. The use of the computer allows for a "virtual" environment to be created. For example, a new house design could be modelled on the computer to allow decisions to be made about the sizes and shapes of rooms, the placement of windows, and the colours of paint.

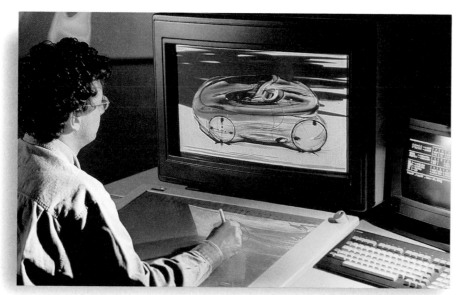

infoBIT

The Boeing 777 was the first commercial airplane to be completely designed and tested on the computer before its construction began. It has three million individual parts!

This designer is using a digital drawing tablet to create a 3-D computer model of a car.

4

M E C H A N I C A L   E F F I C I E N C Y

What elements in this computer work station make it ergonomic?

Ergonomic Factors

Any device or appliance for human use should be designed with the human body in mind. As you know, humans come in many shapes and sizes, with a wide variety of likes and dislikes. Anyone who produces a product of any kind must consider the needs of the people who will use it.

Ergonomics is the study of how people use devices in their environment in order to make these devices more efficient. For example, manufacturers of car seats use ergonomics to design seats that provide comfort and safety for your body. Bicycle manufacturers use ergonomics to design handlebars that are shaped to fit your hands in a comfortable way. Can you think of other examples?

For the ergonomic modelling of products, designers use a variety of measurements, such as human weight, height, age, sex, and physical abilities. They also consider the symmetry of the human body. **Symmetry** occurs when an object has the same features on both sides, as mirror images of one another. The human body is symmetrical because it has a right side and a left side that match each other. Sometimes symmetry can be very important in the design of an object, such as a chair or a keyboard.

Ergonomic modelling is very important to a special group of Canadian inventors and engineers who belong to the Workshop Solutions organization. These men and women design and build devices to help people with disabilities. For example, Tom Jeary, founder of Workshop Solutions, designed and built a skiing device for people who must use crutches to walk. He called the device the Ashmobile in honour of the first student to use it—her name was Ashley. Mr. Jeary also developed a drink holder for wheelchairs and an automatic dice tosser. All of his devices make it possible for people with certain disabilities to do tasks that they normally could not.

The Ashmobile—What ergonomic factors do you think the designer had to consider to create this device?

2.0 To Design New Products, You Must Understand Technical Drawings and Ergonomic Factors

In the next activity, you will create an ergonomic model called an *ergonome*. You will use this model to help you find answers to design questions.

USING AN ERGONOME

- Trace separate body parts from the handout your teacher gives you or from the diagram in this book. Notice that some parts of the diagram show hidden details.
- Construct your ergonome. Make sure you have all the correct body parts as shown in the second diagram. Each grey dot represents a paper fastener that attaches two or more paper body parts together.
- You will need to calculate the scale of your ergonome. Here's an example of how to do it. Your ergonome is 15 cm tall. Suppose the height you want it to represent is 45 cm. That means the scale of your ergonome is 1 to 3. So 1 cm on your ergonome would equal 3 cm in real life.

- For this activity, the height you want the ergonome to represent is 150 cm. Calculate the scale of your ergonome. You will need this scale to answer the following questions. Be prepared to explain how you derived your answers.
  - You are asked to design a worktable for a person who is 150 cm tall. What would be the best height for the worktable?
  - What would be the best height for door handles on a door used by a person who is 150 cm tall?
    - Design and make a small-scale model of the worktable and door, using paper or cardboard. Be sure to include measurements on your design.

Material and Design

One important element that influences design and eventually ergonomics is a product's materials. For example, a concrete garden chair will have a very different look and feel compared with a plush recliner in a living room.

4

M
E
C
H
A
N
I
C
A
L

E
F
F
I
C
I
E
N
C
Y

PLASTIC OR METAL—CHOOSING THE RIGHT MATERIAL

The Issue

A new company has been formed to produce and manufacture soft drinks and juice. Today, most drinks come in one of two types of containers—plastic or metal. Before production can begin, the company must first decide which type of container they should use. Their product development team has come up with a number of questions that need to be answered before making their choice of container.

• Is one material better than the other?
• How do you define a better material?
• Should you consider the cost of making the material, customer preferences, or material disposal methods?

Each of these questions is important to consider when determining what material they should use to make the containers.

The Task

Your teacher will divide you into groups and assign a container type to your group. In this activity, you will be part of an information forum on the Use of Materials in Drink Packages. Your task is to provide information to the product development team so they can make an educated decision. However, you are not there to convince or persuade people to your point of view. You're there only to provide information.

You will work in small groups to put together a multimedia presentation on the benefits of either plastic containers or metal containers for soft drinks and juice.

USE OF MATERIALS IN DRINK PACKAGES

Background Information

1 Your presentation should contain information on the following areas:
   a) what your material is and how it is made
   b) different uses of the material besides soft drink and juice containers
   c) design considerations based on the material
   d) the benefits and costs of reusing and recycling the waste material
   e) the costs of using this material

2 Use at least two different types of media in your presentation.

3 Include an informational pamphlet to hand out to the product development team.

4 To find your information, you will need to use your library resources and the Internet. (The most current information may be found at environmental or government Web sites.) Refer to Toolbox 10, Researching Topics, for information on gathering facts and data.

In Your Opinion

1 After hearing the different presentations, write a paragraph that starts with the prompt:

   I think all soft drink containers should be made of _____ because _____.

2 Your answer should contain at least four different reasons for your opinion. Reference your reasons to the different groups that gave presentations.

3 Briefly explain why a product's design is related to its choice of materials.

1 If you were designing a new type of chair, what kinds of human factors would you have to consider? Explain your answer.

2 Below are two proposed designs for a computer mouse. Which one do you think would be better? Explain your answer.

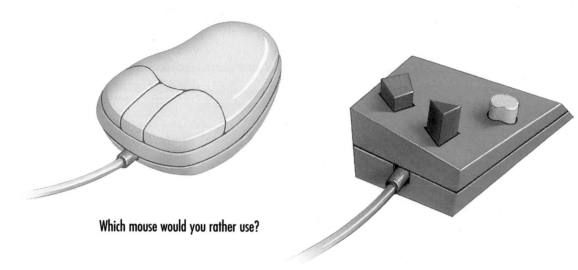

Which mouse would you rather use?

3 Why is symmetry important in the ergonomic design of many objects, such as a chair or a computer mouse?

4 The letters on a keyboard are *not* in alphabetical order. Explain why you think they are arranged the way they are—from an ergonomic point of view.

5 Review your solutions to the questions in the Problem Solver activity. What could you modify to improve the quality of the symmetrical item you designed?

2.3 CHECK YOUR PROGRESS

1 What four different types of technical drawings have you studied? Give an example of a situation in which you would use each type of drawing.

2 What type of drawing would you use for illustrating how a Walkman works?

3 Why is ergonomic modelling important?

4 Give an example of an ergonomically designed object. Explain how it meets the needs of humans.

3.0

Gears, levers, and pulleys can help you do a task with mechanical advantage.

So far in this chapter, you've developed some of the skills and tools needed to design an object or device. Now you will have an opportunity to use these skills when you investigate gears, levers, and pulleys. Learning about these devices and how they operate will help you to invent products to meet a variety of needs.

What simple machines do you see here?

3.1 MAKING THINGS EASIER BY USING MECHANISMS

Explore

Inventors and innovators look for ways to create devices that are more efficient than ones we use now. What does *efficient* mean to you? Work with your partner or a small group and think of the many different ways you can use the word *efficient*. Record your responses on chart paper and be prepared to share them with the class.

Develop

Mechanical Advantage

In technology, the term *advantage* can be used in more than one way. Advantage describes how much easier it is to do something with a mechanism or device, compared with not using that mechanism or device. For example, lifting a box up onto a loading dock by yourself takes more force than using a pulley system to do it. So using the pulley system gives you more of an advantage. Later in this Big Idea, you'll learn another word that describes mechanisms, *efficiency*.

A ramp uses less force to lift an object than lifting it straight up. The ramp gives you more advantage and efficiency.

Mechanical Advantage = 2.0

But how much easier are tasks that use such devices? To get a better understanding of what this means, you need to know about mechanical advantage and velocity ratio. **Mechanical advantage** is a way of comparing the amount of force needed when you don't use a device for a task with the amount needed when you do use one. Usually a mechanism has a mechanical advantage greater than 1. For example, a pulley may have a mechanical advantage of 2. This means that using the pulley to lift a load takes half the force than you would need to use if you were lifting the load by yourself. In other words, the pulley can lift *twice* the load that you could by yourself.

To calculate mechanical advantage, you need to know the input force and the output force. The force applied to the mechanism is called the **input force**. The force produced from using the mechanism is called the **output force**. Both input and output forces are measured in Newtons.

Here is an example, which is also shown in the diagram below. It takes 6 N to lift a box with a pulley (or block and tackle). If you lifted it by yourself, you would have to use 18 N. So the pulley has a mechanical advantage of 3 *(18 ÷ 6)*. The mechanical advantage of the pulley is calculated by dividing the output force by the input force.

$$\text{Mechanical Advantage} = \frac{\text{Output Force}}{\text{Input Force}}$$

or

$$\text{M.A.} = \frac{F_{output}}{F_{input}} = \frac{18 \text{ N}}{6 \text{ N}} = 3$$

Where F = Force in Newtons (N)

$F_{in} = 6 \text{ N}$

$F_{out} = 18 \text{ N}$

Velocity ratio is another important concept of machines. You may have heard the terms velocity and speed before. **Speed** describes how fast something is moving: A car is moving at 100 km/h. **Velocity** describes how fast something is moving and in what direction it is travelling: A car is moving at 100 km/h in the direction of north. The velocity ratio represents the *Ideal Mechanical Advantage* of a machine if friction did not exist.

You calculate the velocity ratio by dividing the *input distance* by the *output distance*. In the example on the previous page, the 5-N force would have used 4 m of rope to lift the box 1 m into the air.

4 m

1 m

Velocity Ratio = $\dfrac{\text{Input Distance}}{\text{Output Distance}}$

$\text{V.R.} = \dfrac{d_{input}}{d_{output}}$

Where d = distance

$\text{V.R.} = \dfrac{4\text{ m}}{1\text{ m}}$

$\text{V.R.} = 4$

This shows that you are not "getting something for nothing" when you use a simple machine like a pulley to help you. The pulley makes it easier for you to lift the box, but you need to move much more rope in order to move the box a short distance (4 m of rope to lift the box 1 m).

Using the formulas, you can calculate the mechanical advantage and velocity ratio for any device. Try these examples before going any further.

Calculating Mechanical Advantage and Velocity Ratio

1

A gear moves a conveyor belt with 30 N of force when 5 N of force is put into the gear. What is the mechanical advantage of the gear?

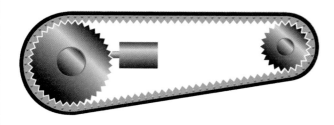

$\text{M.A.} = \dfrac{F_{output}}{F_{input}} = \dfrac{30\text{ N}}{5\text{ N}} = 6$

2

A pulley system lifts a load 5 m when the rope is pulled 10 m by two people. What is the velocity ratio of the pulley system?

$\text{V.R.} = \dfrac{d_{input}}{d_{output}} = \dfrac{10\text{ m}}{5\text{ m}} = 2$

Now that you have begun to understand mechanical advantage and velocity ratio, try the following problem.

SCIENCE OLYMPICS

You are part of the Science Olympics team representing your school at the provincial championships. Your final task is to determine which of the four mechanism set-ups below would work best for the following three tasks. Calculate the mechanical advantage and velocity ratio for each mechanism.

Tasks

1 Help a human-powered vehicle to go uphill

2 Help a human-powered vehicle to go downhill

3 Lower a large load down a cliff

Mechanism Set-ups

Set-up 1

Input Force = 7.0 N
Output Force = 10.0 N
Input Distance = 1.0 m
Output Distance = 0.5 m

Set-up 2

Input Force = 5.0 N
Output Force = 4.0 N
Input Distance = 1.2 m
Output Distance = 1.2 m

Set-up 3

Input Force = 14.0 N
Output Force = 20 N
Input Distance = 30 cm
Output Distance = 10 cm

Set-up 4

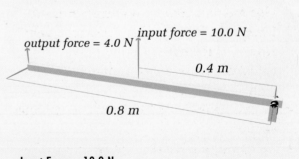

output force = 4.0 N   input force = 10.0 N

0.4 m

0.8 m

Input Force = 10.0 N
Output Force = 4.0 N
Input Distance = 0.4 m
Output Distance = 0.8 m

Efficiency

In the last section, you learned about mechanical advantage. Here's another factor that influences machines: efficiency. **Efficiency** can be used to describe how well a mechanism runs. Any mechanism, such as a pulley lifting an object, loses some energy. Usually the energy is lost as heat because of friction. The more energy that is lost, the less efficient the mechanism is. So a mechanism that is 40% efficient loses more energy than another mechanism that is 70% efficient. The mechanism with 40% efficiency loses 60% of its energy to heat and other forms of energy. The mechanism with 70% efficiency loses only 30% of its energy to heat and other forms of energy.

You can calculate the percent efficiency of a mechanism by dividing the mechanical advantage you calculated by its velocity ratio and multiplying the result by 100. Suppose a pulley has a velocity ratio of 3 and a mechanical advantage of 2. Its efficiency is $66\frac{2}{3}$%. Look back at the last Problem Solver activity. What is the efficiency of each mechanism set-up in the Problem Solver activity?

One force that can affect the efficiency of a device is friction. **Friction** is a force that opposes motion. The more friction a device meets, the less efficient it is. Try this activity to investigate and measure the effects of friction.

$$\text{Efficiency} = \frac{\text{Mechanical Advantage}}{\text{Velocity Ratio}} \times 100$$

or

$$\text{Efficiency (\%)} = \frac{\text{M.A.}}{\text{V.R.}} \times 100$$

$$\text{Efficiency (\%)} = \frac{2}{3} \times 100 = 66\frac{2}{3}\%$$

PROBLEM SOLVER

A FORCE THAT AFFECTS MOVEMENT AND EFFICIENCY

- (1) Take an object with at least one flat surface and attach a force meter (spring scale). (2) In a smooth motion, drag the object across your desk and measure the force required to pull it. (3) Record your result. (4) Repeat three times and calculate the average force required to drag your object.
- Repeat steps 2, 3, and 4 with two different surfaces.
- Compare your results: Which surface required the most force? Which required the least? If friction is a force that opposes motion, which surface had the most friction? Describe how the force of friction affects the movement of an object.
- A wheel on a bicycle is hard to ride because of the friction between the chain, gears, and pedals. It seems the chain is very dirty and dry. What could you do to reduce the friction on the chain and make the bicycle easier, or more efficient, to ride?

Input Force = 25.0 N
Output Force = 62.5 N
Input Distance = 75 cm
Output Distance = 25 cm

Communicate

1 What is the difference between velocity and speed? Give examples to support your answer.

2 Explain the difference between the mechanical advantage and the velocity ratio. Why is there a difference?

3 a) What is the velocity ratio of the pulley system shown in the illustration to the left?

 b) What is the mechanical advantage of the systems?

 c) What is the efficiency of the pulley systems?

3.2 LEVERS

Explore

An inventor looks at things differently. Montreal Canadiens goalie Jacques Plante was an inventor. Until 1960, he was like all goalies— he didn't wear a face mask. But he grew tired of risking serious face injuries, so he developed a fibreglass mask. During the 1960 Stanley Cup playoffs, he changed goaltending forever by wearing his protective mask. Jacques Plante's invention was entirely new for hockey, but face masks had already existed in other activities, such as welding. Lacrosse, Football, Fencing, Jausting

Many new inventions or innovations improve or change a specific quality of an existing device. Often, they use simple machines such as levers, gears, and linkages to achieve one or more of the following effects:

The Effects of Simple Machines

1

Changing the type of movement (for example, the gears on an eggbeater)

The gears on an eggbeater change the vertical motion of your cranking to the horizontal motion of the beaters.

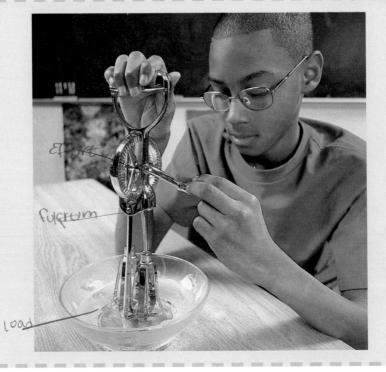

2

Changing the direction of movement (for example, the gears used to move a CD tray in and out)

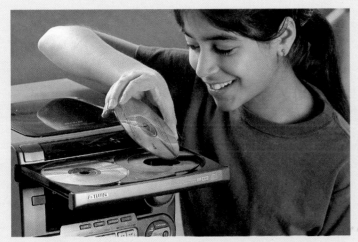

Gears allow the tray in a CD player to move in and out easily.

3

Increasing the speed and reducing the output force (for example, scissors)

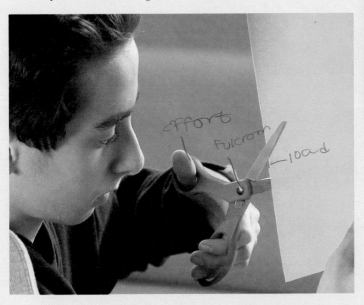

When you cut, you move the handles of the scissors together. The scissors are able to cut the paper more quickly than you can move the handles together. And they cut farther than the distance that you moved the handles. Try it and see!

4

Reducing the speed and increasing the output force (for example, the low gears in a bike)

5

Transmitting force and motion (for example, the linkage between the bike pedal and the bike chain)

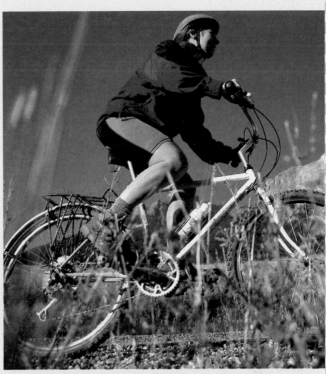

Low gears on a bike reduce the speed and increase the output force so you can ride up hills more easily. Your bicycle's chain transmits force and motion from the pedals to the wheels.

Remember: **Speed** describes how fast something is moving. **Velocity** describes how fast and in what direction something is moving. Also recall that for each type of mechanism you use, the force applied to the mechanism is called the **input force**. The force produced from using the mechanism is called the **output force**. Both input and output forces are measured in Newtons.

In the next activity, you will invent a new device that uses one or more of the mechanism effects listed above.

Lever Innovations

Most mechanical devices use a variety of simple machines. In the next activity, you will use a simple machine called a lever to model a new innovation in television channel changers.

MECHANICAL CHANNEL CHANGER

Your television probably has a button to change channels. Design and build a device that uses at least one syringe and a lever mechanism that will allow you to sit in your chair and change channels. For this activity, use only 30 cm of tubing rather than enough tubing for the normal viewing distance of 2 to 3 m.

- Once your design is complete, show it to your teacher for approval.
- Build your device.

- Be prepared to demonstrate your device. Also be prepared to explain how the levers and the syringe system make changing the channel easier than having to get up and do it manually.
- Now that you've had an opportunity to invent a device that uses levers and syringes, take a look at the picture below. Some students have modified a lever-type hole punch to work using syringes.

Below are two pictures. The first picture shows a hole punch that uses levers to punch holes in paper. The second picture shows a modification to the hole punch designed by some students. What have the students done to change the hole punch?

This is a standard hole punch. It can punch a hole in up to 7 pieces of paper at one time.

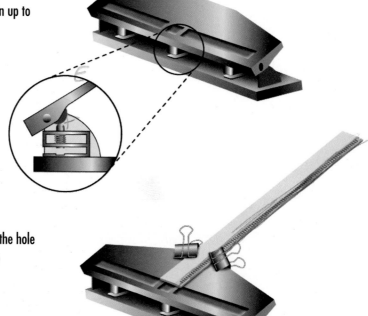

This picture shows what the students did to modify the hole punch. This "new" device can punch a hole in up to 15 pieces of paper at a time.

1 a) How did the use of symmetry affect the ergonomic design of your mechanical channel changer?

  b) How did the use of symmetry affect the modification of the hole punch?

2 a) What human factors did you have to consider when designing your channel changer?

  b) How did your design address these factors?

3 Explain how using levers, gears, or other ways of linking components improves the performance of the following devices:

  a) scissors

  b) bicycle

  c) eggbeater

4 Here is a picture of the inside of a newly invented machine. Using your understanding of levers and gears, describe what this device is supposed to do. Once you figure this out, design a use for this machine.

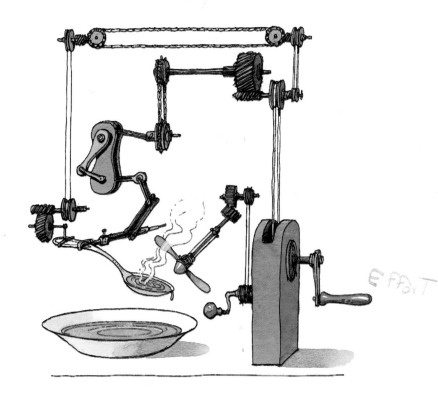

infoBIT

The History of the Lever

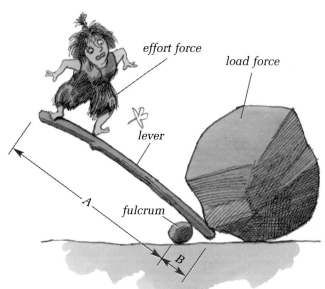

effort force

load force

lever

fulcrum

A

B

The lever is one of the simplest and oldest tools ever used by humans. Prehistoric people used long sticks or strong tree branches as levers to move heavy objects.

Around 2500 B.C., the ancient Egyptians used levers to move large 100-t blocks of rock into position to form the pyramids.

In the 3rd century B.C., the Greek mathematician, Archimedes, was the first to apply the laws of mathematics to understanding the lever. According to Archimedes' calculations, if part A (see illustration to the left) is seven times longer than part B, the force required to lift an object will be one-seventh that required to lift the object without a lever. After figuring out the science of levers, Archimedes reportedly uttered the famous line, "Give me a place to stand, and I will move the earth!"

3.3 COMPLEX MACHINES AND EFFICIENCY

Explore

Of course, most machines and devices people use aren't just made up of levers or pulleys. They are usually constructed with a variety of **simple** and **compound machines**, often incorporating electrical or electronic elements. All work together as a system to enable the device to function.

Common Machines and Devices

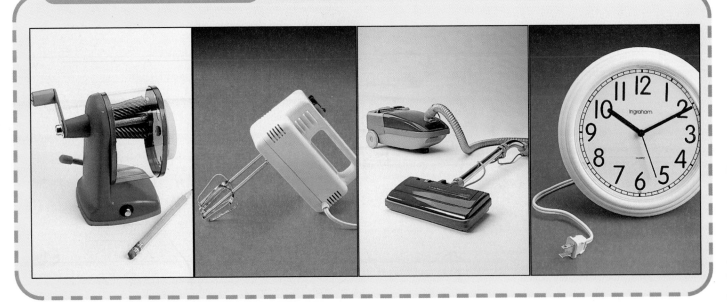

Think about the machines you might encounter at school and at home. A few are pictured above. Brainstorm a list of these machines. Choose one example and list all the simple and compound machines as well as electrical parts that might be part of its construction. In a paragraph, describe how you think all these elements work together to make the device function.

Develop

How Efficient Are Machines?

Not all devices of a similar kind operate at the same efficiency or are as easy to use. Consider the common can opener in the next activity. How would you determine which is the best can opener to buy?

CHOOSING THE RIGHT CAN OPENER

The Question

How can you determine what is the best can opener to use?

Materials & Equipment

- *various mechanical and electric can openers*
- *a variety of can lids to open (for example, clean cans from the recycling bin)*

Caution!

If you use cans from your recycling bin, wash them and be careful of the sharp edges of the previously opened lids.

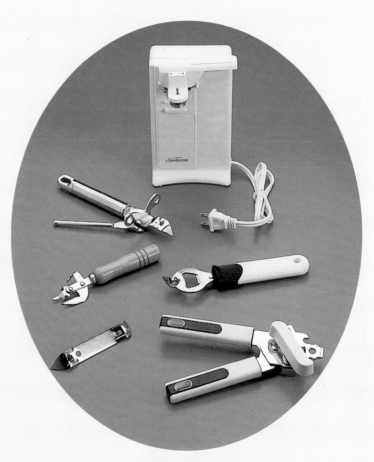

Common can openers

Procedure

1. With a group, examine a number of different kinds of can openers. Briefly explain how each one works.

2. Discuss the different ways that you could use to determine the efficiency of these can openers.

3. Develop a list of criteria based on your discussion that would help you rank the can openers from worst to best (for example, ease of use, cost, speed of operation).

4. Plan, design, and carry out an experiment that will test your criteria.
   a) What variables will you need to hold constant?

   b) How will you determine if your test has successfully proved your criteria? How will you rank the importance of each of your criteria?
   c) If your test is too complicated, how will you revise and simplify your criteria?

Keeping Records

5. Consider how you will record your data: in a table? in the form of a graph?

continued on next page ┈┈┈➤

Analyzing and Interpreting

6 Which can opener did you rank best. What made it best? Which ranked last? Explain how you decided on your ranking.

7 Did you include cost and portability in your criteria? Did you consider any environmental factors? If not, how might these factors influence your ranking?

Forming Conclusions

8 Based on your experiment and results, list some general criteria that could be used to rank other consumer products. If it applies, add criteria that you did not use in this investigation.

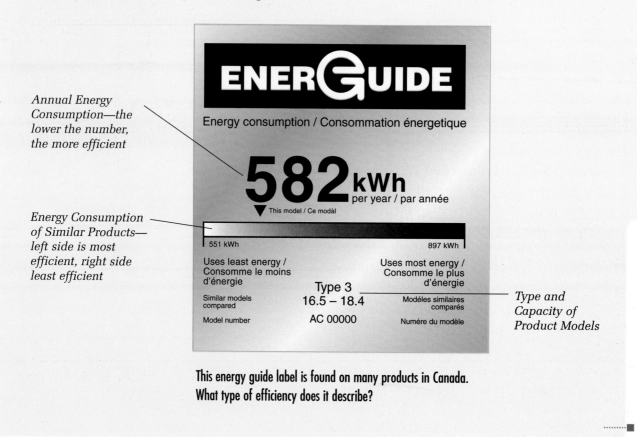

Annual Energy Consumption—the lower the number, the more efficient

Energy Consumption of Similar Products— left side is most efficient, right side least efficient

ENERGUIDE

Energy consumption / Consommation énergetique

582kWh
per year / par année

▼ This model / Ce modàl

551 kWh   897 kWh

Uses least energy / Consomme le moins d'énergie

Uses most energy / Consomme le plus d'énergie

Similar models compared

Type 3
16.5 – 18.4

Modéles similaires comparés

Model number   AC 00000   Numére du modèle

Type and Capacity of Product Models

This energy guide label is found on many products in Canada. What type of efficiency does it describe?

Communicate

1 What factors make machines efficient?

2 Think of a device your family uses, for example, refrigerator, telephone, or car. Use consumer magazines and books to find out what criteria are used to rank and evaluate these products. For example, is energy efficiency considered when ranking refrigerators? fuel efficiency when ranking cars?

3.4 ROBOTS: MASTERS OF MECHANICAL EFFICIENCY

Explore

How would you like to have a robot that could clean your room, do all of your chores, and complete your homework every day? Ever since the first machines were invented, people have dreamed of making mechanical humans that could perform all sorts of boring or dangerous work. Made of metal, wire, springs, tubes, and cables, with some kind of brain or controlling mechanism, these mechanical creatures would be able to work faster and lift heavier loads than any human. They would never complain or need a break to eat lunch or to sleep. They would be the ultimate in mechanical efficiency!

Develop

The History of Robots

Early steam-powered robot built in the 19th century

R.U.R. was produced in Prague, Czech Republic, in 1921. These pictures are reproductions of a publicity photo and the play's poster.

The first person to actually use the word robot to describe an artificial person was the Czechoslovakian playwright, Karel Capek. In 1920, Capek wrote a play called *R.U.R.*, the name of an imaginary robot company, "Rossum's Universal Robots." In the play, human-like creatures were manufactured by the millions to work as slaves in factories. Capek named the fictional creatures **robots** from the Czech word, *robotnik*, "serfs" or "workers."

Some movie robots

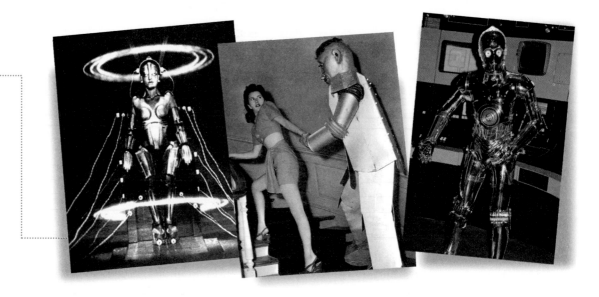

The human-like creatures in Capek's play were just the first of many fictional robots. Since the 1920s, films, television series, novels, magazines, and short stories have been filled with stories and images of shiny, metallic, walking, talking, and thinking robots. All these creatures, though, were imaginary. It would take decades for science to catch up with science fiction writers.

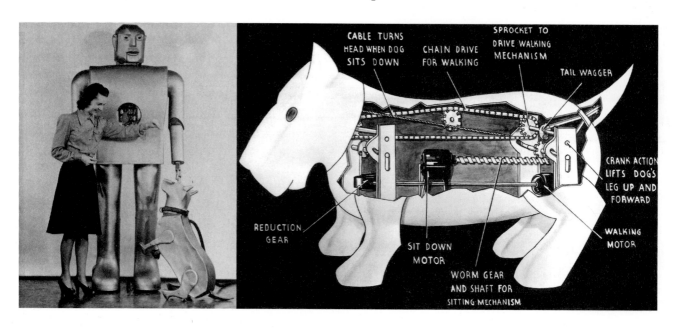

In 1939, a big robot named "Elektro" and his robot dog "Sparko" were the sensation of the New York World's Fair. Elektro could move backward, forward, and speak over 70 different words. Sparko could walk, sit, and bark on command. But these were not real robots. They could not do any useful work. They were simply novelty items whose only purpose was to entertain. The world had to wait another 20 years for the real thing.

Assembly-line robots weld car bodies together in an automobile factory.

Bomb squad robot investigating a suspicious package

Robotic explorer investigating the surface of Mars

While movie makers and writers were busy creating fictional robots, scientists and engineers were trying to build real ones. The first practical examples were developed in the 1960s. Today, robots perform tasks far more efficiently and quickly than humans are able to do, although these robots don't look like their science fiction sisters and brothers. There are robots that weld car bodies together, diffuse bombs, perform surgery, help the handicapped, and even explore other planets.

While fictional robots usually resemble their human creators (having arms, legs, and heads), making a robot in the form of a human is extremely difficult. Certain basic talents that we take for granted, like vision, intelligence, and walking on two feet, have proved difficult to duplicate in robotic form. So, a robot that will do your homework or all of your chores is still many years away.

A human form is actually not necessary or even desirable for most robots. An industrial robot that welds car parts together, for example, works faster and more efficiently than any human. And it doesn't need a head, torso, or legs to do its job. All it needs is an arm. In fact, most industrial robots today are nothing more than "smart" arms.

People once thought that robots could be used as servants. This still is from *Forbidden Planet,* produced by MGM in 1956.

Anatomy of a Robot

Robots are extremely complex devices and vary widely in appearance depending on the job they're designed to do. However, a very simple robot contains some or all of the following basic parts:

1. **Body:** steel, aluminum, or plastic frame or box. Metal rods are used for arms. Simple grippers that open and close are used for hands. Wheels, rather than legs, are used for movement.
2. **Motor Devices:** electric motors and hydraulic or pneumatic cylinders move the robot's arms and wheels.
3. **Power Source:** batteries or solar cells.
4. **Sensors:** detect light, sound, pressure, and heat. They tell the robot about the outside world.
5. **Output Devices:** buzzers, flashing lights, or synthesized speech. They are used by robots to communicate with the outside world.
6. **Microprocessor:** minicomputer that acts as the robot's brain. It receives signals from the robot's sensors, decides what action to take, and sends instructions to the robot's output devices or motor devices.

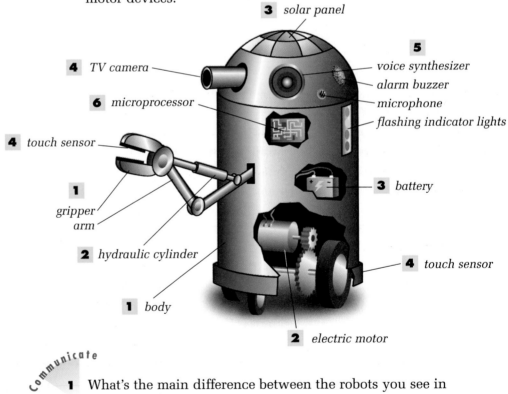

3 *solar panel*

4 *TV camera*

5

voice synthesizer

alarm buzzer

6 *microprocessor*

microphone

flashing indicator lights

4 *touch sensor*

1

gripper arm

3 *battery*

2 *hydraulic cylinder*

4 *touch sensor*

1 *body*

2 *electric motor*

Communicate

1. What's the main difference between the robots you see in movies and real robots?
2. Where did the term "robot" come from?
3. List the main parts of a simple robot and explain what they do.
4. What qualities make robots more efficient than humans?

Before You Start...

You've had a chance to investigate the world of robots. Now is your chance to learn how to design your own robot. Using the Internet and resource books in your library, research how to build a robot.

The Question

Can you design a model of a robot that would perform a simple task in your classroom or home?

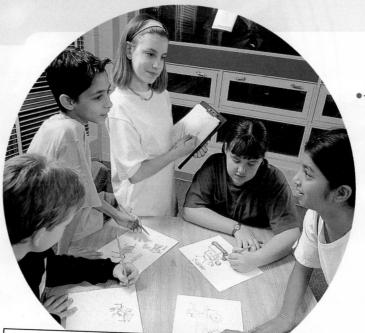

Your Task

1 With a group, brainstorm as many tasks or jobs you think a robot could do for you. The tasks should be simple: vacuuming your living room or patrolling your school at night for intruders.

2 Select one of these tasks.

3 Create a design brief that outlines the task your robot should complete. Your design brief should contain the following information:

- diagram of your robot with all the main parts labelled. Remember, your robot does not have to look human.
- description of what your robot can do. Be sure to explain what each part does.
- signatures of each group member

You may use the sample design brief to the right as a guide.

4 When you're done, share and compare your design brief with other groups. After you have seen their briefs, make *one* modification to your design using the ideas from others in your class.

The robot's job is to patrol the school hallways at night and sound an alarm if an intruder is detected. An electric motor connected to the wheels moves the robot forward. Pressure sensors around the robot's base send signals to the microprocessor if the robot bangs into an object. The microprocessor then sends signals to the robot's wheels instructing them to turn around and proceed in the opposite direction. A sound sensor sends a signal to the microprocessor if any sound from an intruder is detected. The microprocessor then switches on a set of bright spotlights and a loud alarm to scare away the intruder.

3.5 CHECK YOUR PROGRESS

1 Calculate the actual mechanical advantage of each mechanism in the following picture.

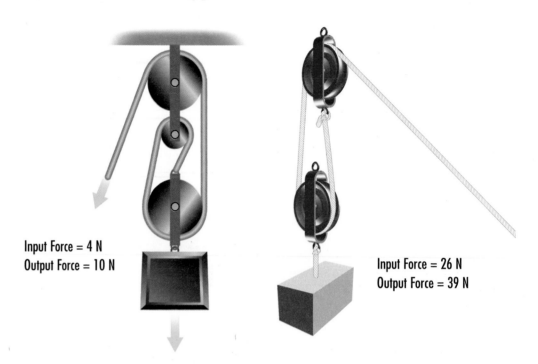

Input Force = 4 N
Output Force = 10 N

Input Force = 26 N
Output Force = 39 N

2 What is the velocity ratio of each of the following mechanisms:
   a) a mechanism that has an input distance of 4 m and an output distance of 2 m?
   b) a mechanism that has an input distance of 20 cm and an output distance of 40 cm?

3 How do you calculate efficiency?

4 What are the five ways a mechanism can affect motion?

5 For each mechanism below, describe how it affects motion:
   a) stapler
   b) pencil sharpener
   c) bicycle
   d) can opener
   e) skateboard wheel

6 Review the list you made of inventor's qualities in the Invitation to Explore.
   a) Are there any new qualities you can add to the list?
   b) Are there any qualities that you needed to work on that have improved? If so, what are they, and how did you improve them?

BIG IDEA 4.0 Many factors must be considered in making a new product.

When we use a device, we expect it to work the way it's supposed to. What we don't realize is that the device has probably had many failures during its development. Most inventions and innovations don't work the first time the inventor builds them. The final, successful product is the result of many mistakes and corrections. What is important in this process is that inventors learn from their mistakes.

In 1952, this IBM 701 mainframe computer occupied a large room. The laptop computer pictured here is not only smaller (and, of course, portable), it is *many* times more powerful.

4.1 THE ALUMINUM CAN

Explore

In this chapter, you have spent some time developing a variety of skills related to inventing and innovating devices. By now you know that anyone can create an invention. If you are willing to pursue an idea, there's a chance you may be successful. Canadian James Gosling successfully pursued his own idea when he worked with a team to invent Java, the computer language of the Internet. He likes to quote Thomas Edison's saying, "Genius is 1% inspiration and 99% perspiration."

Many things in your life are the result of a lot of perspiration by many different people. One of these is the aluminum can. When you hold a can in your hand, think about the amount of work that has gone into designing, building, and modifying this product. Let's take some time to study in detail the evolution of the aluminum can.

Develop

What Kind of Can?

Before you begin your investigation, make a T-chart in your notebook similar to the one below.

The Problem	The Solution

As you investigate the history of the aluminum can, note in the first column of your table every problem or failure that you read about. When you determine its solution, note that in the second column.

Imagine that you have been given the following design brief:

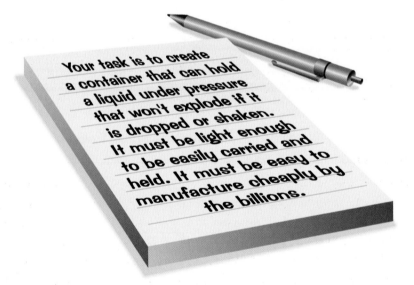

Your task is to create a container that can hold a liquid under pressure that won't explode if it is dropped or shaken. It must be light enough to be easily carried and held. It must be easy to manufacture cheaply by the billions.

This is not a simple challenge. But you have probably held the solution to it in your hands many times: *the aluminum pop can.*

The first solution to the problem of storing drinks and food was an iron can. Unfortunately, iron is heavy, and the iron can was often heavier than the food it contained. As well, it was difficult to open. The can came with instructions explaining how to open it with a hammer and chisel! A better solution was needed.

Steel was another possible solution. A steel can could be made thinner than an iron one, so it was lighter. Steel cans were also strong enough to withstand denting when dropped. But opening the can was still a problem. A special can opener had to be designed.

iron can

steel can

Steel cans were lighter and stronger than iron cans, but still difficult to open.

PROBLEM SOLVER

DESIGN AN OPENER

Imagine you have a steel can in front of you full of your favourite drink.

- How could you open it without spilling any liquid?

- Draw a thumbnail sketch of a design for a device that would open the can. Hint: Your device could be a modified lever.

Why Aluminum Was Chosen

Using steel cans containing solid food was practical. Drinking out of a steel can was still a problem, because opening it left rough edges. A material was needed that could be made into strong but easy-to-open containers. But the can couldn't be so easy to open that it would split open by accident. Aluminum was the material selected.

Aluminum is strong enough to store carbonated drinks. The pressure created by a carbonated drink gives the can added strength. You may have noticed that it's easier to crush an empty can than a full one. As well, if you stand on a full can, it can probably support your weight. But if you stand on an empty one, and a friend lightly touches the sides, the can will collapse.

Aluminum cans are also easy to manufacture. Aluminum is easier to bend than steel because it is a ductile metal. Recall that a *ductile* metal is one that can be easily moulded. So after steel cans, aluminum cans were a new solution for storing carbonated drinks. But one problem, which you will read about later, still remained: How do you open them?

Filling coffee cans during the 1930s

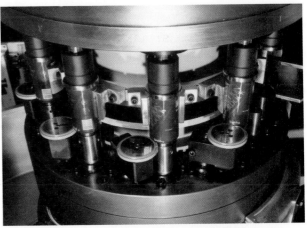

Aluminum cans are made from sheets of metal. The body of the can is formed and then the top is added after the can is filled.

Communicate

1 There are many types of containers to hold hot and cold drinks. Create a questionnaire so you can survey your friends and family to determine their favourite type of containers for hot and cold drinks and why they prefer the containers they chose. Carry out your survey and then answer the following questions.
   a) From the data collected, summarize the reasons for people's choices.
   b) Review the data from your survey. Do you think there is a situation in which people might change their preferred type of container?

2 Research the advantages and disadvantages of aluminum and other types of containers that can hold soft drinks. Create a poster to show the costs and benefits of each type of container.

3 Review the sketch you made of the device for opening a can in the Problem Solver activity. What modifications could you make to your device to improve it?

---

*info*BIT

Aluminum Can Facts
- Aluminum cans today use 43% less aluminum than they did in 1972.
- Canadians recycle 2.25 billion aluminum cans a year.
- The electrical energy saved from recycling 1 aluminum can is equal to the amount of energy you use to watch 3 hours of television.

- Soft drinks in aluminum cans can keep their carbonation for about two years.
- It takes 95% *less* energy to produce cans using recycled aluminum cans. For example, the energy needed to produce 1 can from raw aluminum ore could make 20 recycled cans.

4.2 LEARNING FROM MISTAKES

Explore

Another important part of the invention process is learning even when you don't succeed in your task. Sometimes inventions and designs just don't work the way they were expected to. The Tacoma Bridge is a good example. This bridge worked exactly as planned except for one thing. The engineers forgot to account for the effect of high winds on the bridge. When the wind blew, the bridge vibrated. Eventually, the vibrations were strong enough to destroy the bridge.

In 1940, this bridge in Tacoma, Washington, failed because of its poor design. The engineers didn't realize that the bridge's design would cause it to vibrate so much when the wind blew.

In such situations, it would be easy to say the object was a complete failure and forget about it. This is not what happened. By learning how and why the bridge failed, engineers have been able to design new bridges that don't have the problems that caused the Tacoma Bridge to fail. The failure became a learning experience. Stories like that of the Tacoma Bridge are common whenever someone is designing a new product, building, or device.

Let's find out how a series of failures led to the solution of the problem of how to open the aluminum pop can.

Develop The Evolution of an Opener

The development of an opening mechanism for the aluminum can went through four distinct designs:
- the church key
- the removable pull tab
- the buttons
- the non-removable tab

Each new design was the result of the previous model having some problem. As you investigate this development, remember to fill in your problem-solution T-chart.

History of Sealing Food in Containers

Glass bottle **1809**

Iron can **1810**

Steel can **Late 1850s**

Aluminum can **1958**

Removable pull tab **1963**

Plastic bottle **Mid 1970s**

Push button tabs **Mid 1970s**

Non-removable pull tab **1980**

Lighter aluminum can with tapered top **Late 1980s**

4.0 Many Factors Must Be Considered in Making a New Product

Church Key

To pour a liquid out of a flat top container, you need two holes. The first hole allows the air into the can; the second hole lets the liquid out. The air flowing into the can replaces the liquid that is leaving the can. In fact, the air helps to create a smooth flow of liquid out of the second hole. An opening device was needed to make two holes in the top of the can. This device was called a church key, because it resembled an old-fashioned key. A common church key was a piece of metal with a triangle end designed to hook onto the can and open it. The picture here shows a church key being used to make the two holes in the top of a can.

The church key worked well, but it did have some drawbacks. Can you think of at least one problem with using a church key? Add this to your chart.

The church key was the first practical design for a pop-can opener.

Removable Tab Top

One sunny summer day in the early 1960s, Ermal Fraze of Ohio was picnicking at the local lake. Unfortunately, he forgot the church key he needed to open his cans of pop. It was clear that this was a failure of the church-key can. If you didn't have a church key with you, you couldn't open the can. Fraze was determined to find a better solution. Making thumbnail sketches, the metal engineer devised his solution on paper.

The paper solution was the easy part. Fraze had a problem when constructing his new can-opening device. For his device to work, it had to fail! He had to make a device that would fail to keep the can sealed, but would only fail when the person wanted to open the can. So the mechanism couldn't unseal the can when someone was carrying it, only when someone wanted to drink.

Fraze solved the problem by having a ringed tab that could be pulled off the top of the can. After much trial and error, he found the right design. When you wanted a drink, you would put a finger in the ring part of the mechanism and pull back the ring like a lever. The tab would "fail" and rip from the lid. Now you could have your drink.

Not needing a church key was a big improvement, but an environmental problem arose from the new pull-tab design. What do you think that was?

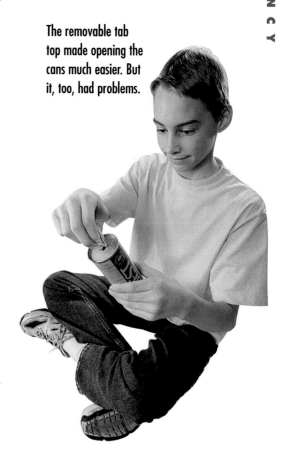

The removable tab top made opening the cans much easier. But it, too, had problems.

Buttons

With billions of cans being used every year in North America, an environmental problem arose with the removable pull tab. What do you do with the tab after you take it off the can? Some people would put the tab into the can before they began drinking, and then

The buttons eliminated the litter problem, but consumers didn't like using them.

would accidentally swallow it or choke on it. Many people just threw their tabs onto the ground. The result was a litter problem and a safety hazard. People were cutting their feet on the metal edges of the tab. A new solution was needed.

One solution was to have two holes with buttons pre-formed in the can's lid. One hole was smaller than the other. The directions on the can had the user open the small hole first. This released the pressure. It was also easier to open the small hole first. Recall that pressure is the result of force over an area. Because the area of the small hole was less than that of the larger hole, it required less force to open. Once you opened this small button, you then opened the larger button for drinking or pouring the liquid.

While this solution solved the litter solution, people found the device inconvenient. They didn't like having to press two buttons, and pressing the small button was difficult for some people. A better solution was once again needed.

Non-Removable Tab Top

In 1976, inventor Daniel F. Cudzik designed the current easy-to-open aluminum can top with an attached tab. Because it eliminated the environmental problems of the earlier pull tabs, this design was called the "environmental can end" or "ecology top."

The company Cudzik worked for was not sure if consumers would accept this new design on their drink cans. To find out, the company's researchers designed a survey. They stocked 10 supermarkets with cans that had the new opening mechanisms. Then, to ensure that the test was not biased, they also stocked one other store with the old-style cans having removable pull tabs. The consumers who shopped in that store were the control group. After several months, consumers who shopped at all the stores in the study were interviewed about the can-opening mechanisms. The company's researchers analyzed the results from the interviews. They compared the interviews from the two groups: the shoppers who bought cans that had the new opening mechanism and the control group. It was clear that consumers liked the new environmental can and felt that it would be accepted by everyone.

The research was well worth the time and investment. Today over one trillion non-removable pull-tab aluminum cans have been manufactured.

Today's aluminum cans are easy to open. Because the pull tabs stay attached to the can, they don't contribute to litter.

Communicate

1 a) What personal factors influenced the changes in devices used to open aluminum cans?

   b) What societal factors influenced these changes?

   c) Briefly explain what is meant by personal and societal factors.

2 Why do you think the new non-removable pull tab was tested with consumers before it became widely used by can manufacturers?

3 How do you think the company's researchers made sure they had an unbiased control group that used the removable pull tabs?

4 Do you think the design of the non-removable pull tab will change again or is this the final design? Explain your answer.

4.3 OTHER SUCCESSES AND FAILURES OF THE ALUMINUM CAN

Explore

The problems with the aluminum can appear to be solved, but other successes and failures are still associated with this design. The two main areas of concern are the environmental impact of aluminum cans and the amount of aluminum in each can. Solutions exist for both problems, but these solutions are continually being modified.

With your partner or in a small group, discuss the possible environmental impacts of using aluminum cans. Continue filling in your T-chart while you go through this section. As you read, identify the possible impacts and suggest a possible solution for each one.

Environmental Concerns

Develop

Earlier you learned about a variety of environmental concerns connected with different aluminum can designs. People would throw the removable pull tabs on the ground, causing a major litter problem and potentially injuring others. Some governments considered banning the production of aluminum cans. The new non-removable pull tab solved this problem.

Another environmental concern with aluminum cans is the amount of resources and energy that are used to produce them. Aluminum comes from the mineral bauxite, which is a non-renewable resource. As well, the process to produce aluminum from bauxite requires large amounts of electricity.

To help reduce the environmental impact of producing all these cans, most provinces have a recycling program for aluminum cans. In some instances, a recycled can is made into a new can in about 60 days. But there is still room for improvement. Only about six out of every ten cans are recycled. That means four cans are dumped in landfills rather than being recycled.

reSEARCH

Drink Containers

- Using your library or the Internet, determine the environmental impact of other types of drink containers, such as glass, plastic, and Tetra Paks.

Production of Cans

Engineers are constantly looking for ways to reduce the amount of aluminum in cans. Sometimes their ideas are successful, sometimes they are not. For example, it is possible to make the top of the aluminum can smaller. This reduces the amount of aluminum needed to make the can. However, the top can't be too small. If the shape of the can is changed too dramatically, consumers will have trouble drinking from it or even holding the can.

Another example of a modification to the shape of aluminum cans occurred in the mid-1990s, when some cans were made in a fluted shape. This design reduced the amount of aluminum needed without reducing the can's strength. In pictures of Greek or Roman ruins, you can see how the columns of their buildings took advantage of this design.

Unfortunately, consumers did not like to hold and drink from a fluted can. So it was a good idea for both the environment and the production cost, but most consumers didn't like to use it. As a result, very few drink cans have this shape.

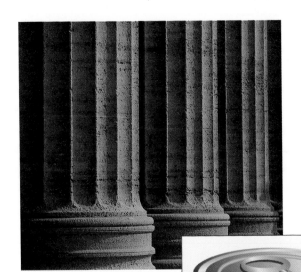

These columns are fluted in shape so they use less stone than straight, rounded columns but are still very strong.

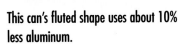

This can's fluted shape uses about 10% less aluminum.

Think about the evolution of the aluminum can that you have just studied. This story has helped you begin to understand the challenges that inventors, designers, engineers, and marketers face when producing a new or modified product. Look at the problem-and-solution chart that you have been keeping. Compare your list with those of your classmates. Which problem were you most surprised by? Which one do you think was the biggest problem that had to be overcome? Share your thoughts with your classmates.

Communicate

1 What environmental factors have influenced the design of the aluminum can?

2 What economic factors have influenced the design of the aluminum can?

3 What personal or human factors restricted the design of the aluminum can?

4 a) Assess the impact that the use and disposal of aluminum cans has on the environment.

   b) What role can humans play in reducing the impact? What can you do?

4.4 Check Your Progress

1 a) What types of materials have been used to store food and drinks?

   b) Describe one problem with each material.

2 a) What are the advantages of using an aluminum can to hold a carbonated drink?

   b) What are the disadvantages?

3 How can you collect information on the preferences of consumers?

4 In your opinion, is failure a good or a bad thing when you are designing and building a new device?

5 Review the list of inventor's qualities that you started in the Invitation to Explore.

   a) Are there any new qualities that you can add to the list?

   b) Are there any qualities you needed to work on that have improved? What were they and how did you improve them?

   c) Write a paragraph that describes what makes a good inventor.

infoBIT

Plastic Pop Bottles
In 1966, as an alternative to aluminum cans, Gustave Côté developed a rotary blow-moulding machine for making hollow plastic containers. This device made it possible to manufacture the plastic pop bottles you see in stores today. Besides being an inventor, Mr. Côté was the Member of Parliament for Montreal.

PRACTICAL DESIGNERS

Mechanical engineers design engines and machines that extend our physical capabilities. These machines include automobiles, aircraft, ships, trains, spacecraft, robots, earth-moving equipment, harvesting machines, nuclear power plants—basically any object or device that moves. Colette E. Taylor is a mechanical engineer. Since 1988, she has worked at Chalk River Laboratories in Chalk River, Ontario. Here, she does research, along with other scientists and engineers, that supports and advances the development of CANDU nuclear reactor technology.

"If you want a job that challenges you each and every day, and provides you with a wide variety of career opportunities, mechanical engineering is an excellent choice."

Colette E. Taylor conducts research at the CANDU nuclear generating station in Chalk River, Ontario.

Q: Why did you choose to become a mechanical engineer?

A: When I was in high school, I had no idea what a mechanical engineer was, but I really enjoyed taking a wide range of science courses. I didn't want to specialize in any one thing. I wanted to use all of my science background. When I looked at the options for university, I discovered that mechanical engineering was one of the few career choices that required you to use a wide range of sciences. It was perfect!

Q: Are there many women mechanical engineers?

A: There were nine women in my graduating class of 135 students. And that was considered high! I think women have a distorted idea about what engineers really do. They think that you have to work with big, dirty, noisy equipment. Well, that's just not part of the job. I spend most of my day in meetings and working on new designs in my office.

Q: What does it take to be a good mechanical engineer?

A: Strong technical ability, communication skills, and high motivation are important characteristics for a successful engineer in today's competitive and demanding workplace.

How Efficient Do We Want to Be?

The benefits of mechanical efficiency are many: giant drilling rigs extract vast quantities of oil from the ground; powerful construction cranes erect taller skyscrapers and longer bridges; trucks, planes, and trains transport goods all over the world. The direct result of increasing mechanical efficiency in machines has been a higher standard of living. But these new machines are not without their problems. In the quest for greater mechanical efficiency, the health and safety of the people who must use these devices have not always been considered.

Accidents

Each year about 45 000 people in North America die in automobile and truck accidents. Do efficient and powerful cars save lives?

Modern mechanical devices are increasingly complex. That means there are more things that can go wrong with them. When a malfunction does happen, the results can be deadly. Large industrial machines in the workplace, cars and trucks on the nation's highways, and small power tools and appliances in the home claim thousands of lives each year.

Work Environments

Mechanical devices can create an unhealthy work environment by exposing the user to loud noise, toxic chemicals, and fumes, dust, and excessive heat. These factors are a major cause of illness and death in modern industrial countries.

Would you consider this a healthy work environment?

Assembly Lines

Would you be bored working on an assembly line?

On the assembly lines in many factories, workers are expected to perform a single repetitive task at a pace dictated by machines with little or no thinking or creativity required. Rarely do the workers have a say in how a product is made. As a result, workers become bored, sleepy, and inefficient. This "dehumanizing" condition of mechanical efficiency has been linked to alcoholism, drug addiction, low productivity, and high absenteeism.

Repetitive Work

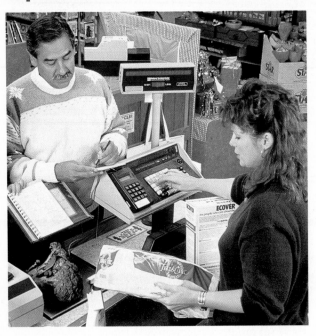

Repetitive strain injury (RSI) is a disorder that results from performing a seemingly insignificant motion—such as pressing a button, pulling a lever, or flipping a switch—hundreds of times every day. The repetitive action causes damage to muscles, nerves, and tendons resulting in pain in the hands, wrists, arms, shoulders, or neck. The effects can range from slightly painful to completely crippling. It is common among assembly-line workers and heavy users of computer keyboards and cash registers.

The Cost of Efficiency

Mechanical efficiency often comes with an environmental price tag attached. Cars and trucks consume huge amounts of petroleum. They also produce a tremendous amount of waste that is harmful to the environment. Factories and power stations pump thousands of tons of pollutants into the atmosphere. Giant excavators in open-pit mines strip thousands of hectares of foliage from the land each year. A bucket wheel excavator, for example, like the one shown above, can remove up to 12 000 m^3 of earth per hour. But do we really want to remove and use our non-renewable resources this quickly?

This excavator has replaced the work of dozens of people. It quickly damages the environment, but it also saves many workers from injury.

Engineering with Humans in Mind

In response to the above problems, an increasing number of engineers and designers are trying to design machines to take into account the safety, comfort, and productiveness of their human users. This may include the best placement of hand controls, the installation of soundproof material, or giving assembly-line workers more control and input concerning the products they make.

In Your Opinion

1 Discuss whether you think the added mechanical advantage we get from using mechanical devices is worth the economic, social, and environmental problems that some devices cause.

2 If you were a designer of mechanical devices, what would you consider when designing machines with the health and safety of the human user in mind?

3 Analyze a common mechanical device in your home. Do you feel the designers have done a good or a bad job? If you were the designer, what would you do to improve the product?

BUILDING A MECHANICAL HAND

Getting Started

Earlier in this chapter, you drew a design for a device to solve the problem of retrieving a robotic explorer that had become wedged in a drainage pit. After you designed the device, you studied some of the properties of hydraulic and pneumatic systems, levers, gears, and pulleys. Now it's time to put all that information to use.

Before You Start...

If you did not design a mechanical device earlier in this chapter to remove a robotic explorer from a drainage pit, you should do that activity now. If you have completed that activity, collect your notes and designs and organize them in a manner that makes sense to you.

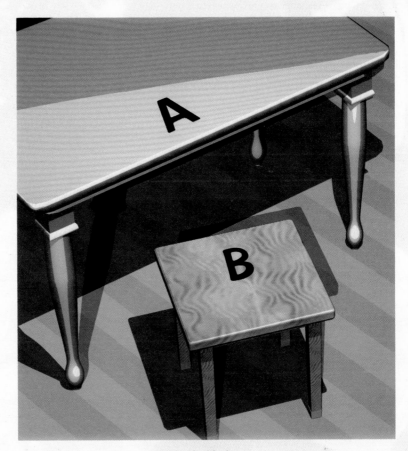

Place gripper device at A and load to be lifted at B.

The Task

Redesign the gripper device you designed earlier, and construct a working model of it.

The Context

Take out your original drawings from the Problem Solver activity in which you designed a gripper device. Review your results with your partner or group. Your task now is to construct this device. Your teacher will show you the model of the drainage pit where the robotic explorer is located. It will look something like the picture on page 242. Note that in the earlier activity you assumed that the robotic explorer had a mass of 100 kg. For this activity, you can decide what the mass of the load will be.

continued on next page ·······➤

Procedure

1. Review your original design drawings and make modifications to improve your design.
2. Create a plan that describes how you will build your gripper device. Include in your plan a list of the materials you will need.
3. Show your plan to your teacher for approval. Revise your plan based on your teacher's comments.
4. Build your device and test it.

Share and Compare

5. Demonstrate your device to the class.
6. Observe how your classmates' devices work and record any ideas you think you could incorporate into your device.

Observations and Reflections

7. What worked well in your gripper device?
8. What would you modify so your gripper device would work better next time?
9. What were some of the limitations you faced when you built your device? For example, did you have enough time? Could you have made a better device with different equipment?
10. Which device out of all of those made by your class do you think worked best? Explain your answer.
11. Go back to your list of inventor's qualities. Which qualities did you use during this activity? Write a paragraph explaining how you used these qualities to design and build your gripper device.

1 Using the following list of key terms below, create a story about an invention using each of these terms in the appropriate context:

> brainstorming
> Particle Theory of Matter
> pressure
> force
> Pascal's law
> thumbnail sketch
> design brief
> symmetry
> efficiency
> velocity ratio
> mechanical advantage

Reviewing the Big Ideas

2 What are some of the ways you can brainstorm ideas to solve a problem?

3 What are the four key points in the Particle Theory of Matter?

4 Describe the difference between pressure and force.

5 What evidence have you observed during this chapter that would answer Pascal's question: "How does pressure change as the depth of the water changes?"

6 Describe Pascal's law and give one example where a device uses this law in order to function.

7 What is the pressure exerted on the bottom of a can filled with fluid if the surface area of the can is 0.2 m² and the force is 10 N?

8 What are the different types of technical drawings?

9 What are the ergonomic factors a designer must consider when making a chair?

10 What is the difference between mechanical advantage and velocity ratio?

11 What is the mechanical advantage of the following situations?

	Output Force	**Input Force**
a)	25 N	5 N
b)	100 N	10 N
c)	10 N	20 N
d)	0.5 N	0.1 N

12 What is the velocity ratio of the following situations?

	Input Distance	**Output Distance**
a)	0.8 m	0.4 m
b)	1.0 m	2 m
c)	50 cm	10 cm
d)	75 cm	25 cm

13 What are the five different effects of a simple machine? Give an example of each effect.

14 Outline the major events or inventions in the history of robots.

15 Describe the key stages of the evolution of the opener for a can.

16 What are the environmental factors to consider when designing a container to hold a soft drink?

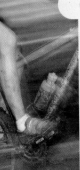

Connecting the Big Ideas

17 How can the Particle Theory of Matter help you describe the differences between when a gas is compressed and when a liquid is compressed?

18 How can the Particle Theory of Matter help you describe how a change in temperature in a closed container affects the pressure in the container?

19 Describe a Canadian invention that requires knowledge of levers and Pascal's law.

20 Make two technical drawings of your choice showing the outside and inside of a symmetrical object in your classroom or home.

21 Can a mistake be a good thing? Explain your answer and provide an example.

Using the Big Ideas

22 If you bought a bag of chips at the store during a hot, sunny summer day and then left them in a car for a couple of hours, what would happen to the bag? Explain your answer using the Particle Theory of Matter.

23 What do you think will happen to a car's hydraulic system if a puncture in one of the brake lines allows brake fluid to leak out? Explain your answer.

24 How can a 2000-kg vehicle be lifted with a small force?

25 Create a User Manual for an activity you like to do (for example, how to kick a soccer ball, how to paint a picture, or how to play your favourite video game). After you have completed your manual, have someone try to follow your directions. Modify your manual based on the person's suggestions.

26 There are two ways you could deliver a large box of erasers to a store. You could lift the box with a force of 10 N a distance of 1 m onto the loading dock, or, carry the box up a ramp of 4 m using a force of 2.5 N. Which way is better? Explain your choice.

27 What would be the efficiency in each of the following situations?
a) A pulley has a mechanical advantage of 4 and a velocity ratio of 2.
b) A lever moves 0.75 m with an input force of 14 N. The resulting output force is 42 N and the other end of the lever moves 0.25 m.

28 Describe a situation where you could invent a robot that used levers and hydraulics to complete a task for your school.

Self Assessment

29 During this chapter, you have read about a variety of inventors and investigated the characteristics of an inventor. Your class may have even made a wall of fame to highlight some of these inventions. Take a few minutes and think about what you consider are the three most important characteristics of an inventor. List these three and explain why you chose them. Then for each one, describe something you did in this chapter that reflects that characteristic.

Chapter 5

WATER SYSTEMS

Water covers about 74% of the earth. It's found in every living thing, from one-celled organisms and plants to insects and mammals. You drink it, wash in it, and play in it. In fact, water makes up 70% of you. So clean, fresh water is extremely important to living things.

Water is called the universal solvent because it can dissolve many substances. It's an incompressible fluid and that makes it useful in many technological devices. Because it's a part of most manufacturing processes, industries often need great amounts of it.

In this chapter, you will explore water's important role on earth. You will discover how the rain that falls on you today could end up in the ocean or frozen in an ice cap some time in the future. You will investigate how water moves in winds, tides, and currents. You will discover its effect on climate. And you will learn what effect you and your way of life have on the earth's water supply.

BIG Ideas

1.0 Water exists naturally in all three states on the earth's surface.

2.0 The different characteristics of salt and fresh water support a diversity of living things.

3.0 Bodies of fresh and salt water are created by geological processes.

4.0 Waves, tides, and currents are powerful forces that interact with the environment.

5.0 Large bodies of water and glaciers affect the environment.

6.0 People's use of water can affect the earth's water supply and the environment.

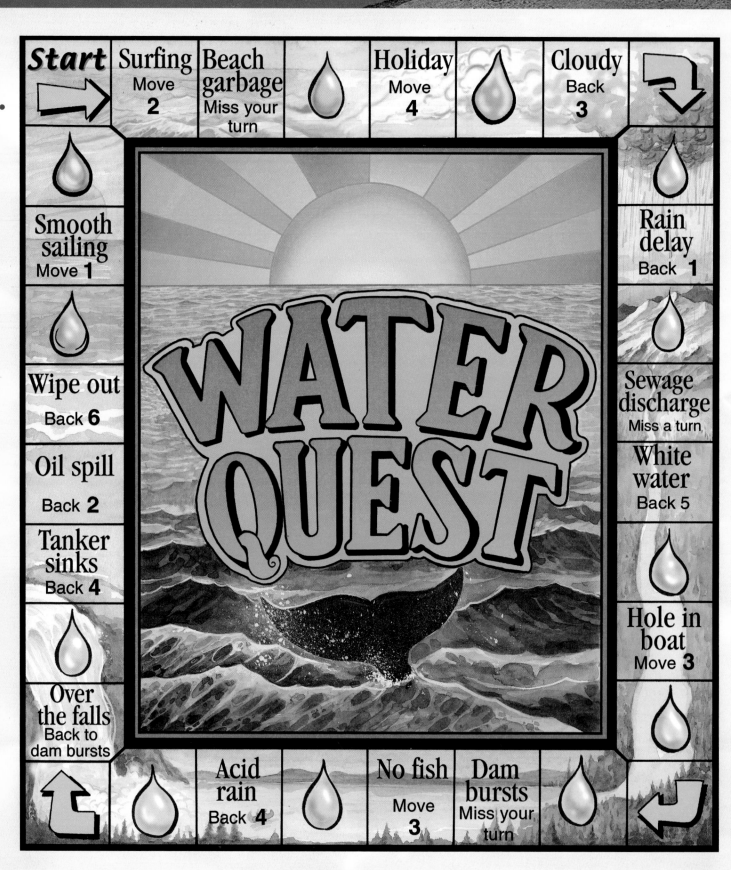

How to Play

1 Play this game with a partner. All players begin at START. To move around the board, throw one die and move that number of squares.

2 If you land on a raindrop, choose a question that hasn't been answered from below. If you answer incorrectly, *go back to the closest corner square.*

3 You must choose a different question each time you land on a raindrop.

4 You lose a turn if you land on a water problem square (beach garbage, sewage).

5 The game is over when a player *throws the exact number* to land back on the START square.

Water Quest Questions

A What are large floating pieces of ice in the ocean called?

B What are clouds made of?

C Off the shores of what province or territory would you likely see the greatest number of icebergs?

D What depth of water would a depth of 20 cm of snow produce?

E In what type of water would a swimmer float more easily: salt water or fresh water?

F What are moving masses of ice called?

G Which area in Canada has the greatest annual precipitation?

H Which lake is the world's largest freshwater lake? Where is it located?

I Where would you find the world's highest tides?

J What are the deepest parts of the ocean called?

K Which is the largest ocean?

L How are waves formed?

M What ocean current most influences the weather in eastern North America?

N What region in the world has the greatest number of foggy days?

O What percentage of the world's fresh water is found in Canada?

P What is the most abundant substance dissolved in ocean water?

Q What river in the world carries the greatest flow of water?

R What is the most common substance found on earth?

S What is Canada's longest river?

T What liquid freezes at 0° C and boils at 100° C?

U What is the longest river in the world?

V What is water found underground called?

W What is the name of the giant waterfall located between Lake Ontario and Lake Erie?

X Where would you find the world's largest concentration of frozen water?

Y What is the large river that flows through the Amazon rain forest?

Z What is the only substance on earth to occur in all three states?

If you played Water Quest, you may have found out that you know a lot about water, probably more than you thought. After all, you've studied about water in school. You've used it, drunk it, washed in it, played in it, walked or skated on it. Because you live in Canada, you see water in the environment all the time—in lakes, rivers, streams, and falling from the sky. Canada is a water-rich country. Most countries in the world have much less fresh water than we do. In fact, in some areas of the world, it hasn't rained in years!

How much water is there on earth, and what kind of water is it? Think about a map of the world and what you know about water already. Draw a rough circle. The whole circle represents the *total amount* of water on earth. If the circle was a pie, how big a piece of this pie do you think would represent all the *drinking* water in the whole world? Draw this piece on your circle graph. Keep your prediction handy so you can refer to it later in this section.

PROBLEM SOLVER

WATER, WATER EVERYWHERE

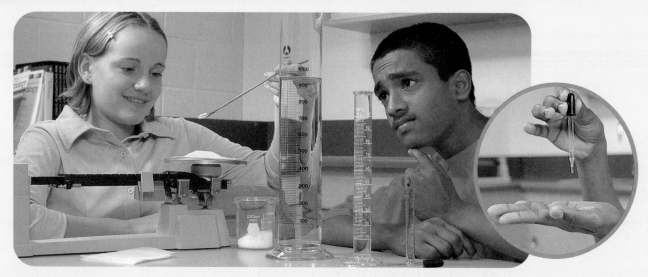

So, how much drinking water is available on earth? Here's one way to represent the amount.

- Fill a 1000-mL graduated cylinder with water. This represents *all* the water on earth.
- Take 30 mL of this, and place it in a 100-mL graduated cylinder. This is the total amount of fresh water.
- Dissolve 29 g of salt in the 970 mL of water remaining in the larger graduated cylinder. This is the amount of water in all the oceans. It is so salty that it is not drinkable. Put it aside.

- Now take 7 mL of the 30 mL of fresh water put aside, and place it in a 10-mL graduated cylinder. Keep this cylinder in front of you.
- Take the other graduated cylinder that now contains 23 mL of water, and put it in the freezer. This is the fresh water that is frozen in glaciers and ice caps.
- Use an eyedropper to remove a single drop of water from the remaining 7 mL and let it drop into your palm. This represents all the fresh water on earth that is available for people to drink at any given moment. It is about 0.003% of the total amount of water on earth!

continued on next page ⋯⋯▶

Now, fill in the missing amounts in the Water Facts box below.

> ## Water Facts
>
> **1** About 74% of the earth is covered with water.
> **2** Of all the water on earth, ?% is salt water in the oceans, and ?% is fresh water.
> **3** Of the fresh water, ?% is ice. The remainder is about 22% groundwater, about 1% in lakes, rivers, and wetlands, and about 0.035% in the atmosphere.

Another way to represent the earth's water reserves is to graph their amounts. By hand or using graphing software, draw three separate circle graphs, one for each of the statements about water.

- Remember to be accurate when graphing. If you are doing it by hand, make sure to convert the percentages to degrees and use a protractor to measure the angles accurately.
- Colour your graphs, and give each one a title and a legend.
- Go back to the circle graph that you drew to predict the amount of drinking water compared with the total amount of water on earth. How big a piece of pie would 0.003% represent? Was your prediction close? Why or why not?
- Does what you have learned change the way you think about water use?

In what ways do you use this precious water? With a partner, brainstorm all of the ways you can think of that you use water. Look over the items on your list, and identify the ones where you might be wasting water. One example might be leaving the tap running while you brush your teeth. For each of these items, suggest a way that you could reduce your water use. Add your ideas on how to reduce water consumption at home to a class suggestion board.

The uses you just identified are only the direct ways that you use water. All day long, you're also using water indirectly. Every food you eat, every item of clothing you wear, every vehicle that you travel in—everything you use involves water in some part of its production.

- Water for irrigation is important in growing fruit and other crops.
- In manufacturing jeans, water is used for washing fabrics and dyeing.
- In making soft drinks, water is an ingredient, as well as part of the cleaning process for bottles.
- In mining, water is often part of the process for separating the metal from the rest of the rock. This metal is then made into metal products that you wear or use, such as buttons for your jeans.

All of these uses of water can have negative impacts on the earth's water resources. It's up to all of us to understand the earth's water system—what it is, how it works, and how we affect it—so we can keep our home planet healthy.

Irrigation can be both helpful and harmful to society. It allows crops to be grown in dry climates. If used incorrectly, irrigation causes the soil to accumulate salt deposits. Soil that is too salty kills plants and can lead to desertification.

Focus Your Thoughts

1 Take a large sheet of paper and, working with a partner, create a poster with the title "Water Flows Through the Seasons." Using words, drawings, photos, and graphics, describe how the water in your local environment changes through the seasons. As you work on your poster, think about the following questions:

a) In how many different states (liquid, solid, gas) can water be during each of the four seasons?

b) How does air humidity change with the seasons?

c) How does the amount of water in rivers, lakes, and streams change from season to season?

In your Science Journal, write any questions about water that came up while you were working on your poster. Jot down what you would like to know about these questions.

2 Earlier, you saw that most of the water on earth is in the oceans.

a) How is the water in the oceans different from the water in rivers and lakes?

b) Do you think that the organisms that live in rivers and lakes could just as easily live in the oceans? Why or why not?

3 Is the water in a wilderness lake far from human communities pure water or might it contain impurities? Why or why not?

4 Imagine that you were out in a boat in the ocean, far from shore and you threw a sealed bottle, with your name and address in it, into the ocean. Months later, you receive a letter from someone who found your bottle thousands of kilometres from where you threw it into the water.

a) Describe how your bottle might have travelled so far.

b) Do you think, on a smaller scale, the same thing could happen in a large lake? Why or why not?

5 You have already identified some of the many ways *you* use water. The chart below shows how much water each person in selected countries uses per day in three categories: domestic use, agricultural use, and industrial use.

a) Which countries are most likely to rely on irrigation to grow their crops? Which countries are least likely?

b) In which countries is agriculture probably the main source of commercial income?

c) What type of domestic or personal water systems are countries like Cambodia and Gambia likely to have?

d) What climate do you think Turkmenistan has during the growing season?

e) Which countries probably receive the most rain during the growing season?

f) Why do you think there are differences in water use among these countries?

Drilling for water in Niger

Freshwater Use or Withdrawal (litres per person per day)			
Country	Domestic Use	Agricultural Use	Industrial Use
Cambodia	6	118	1
Canada	431	313	3136
Egypt	132	1906	177
Gambia	3	39	1
Mexico	129	1849	172
Swaziland	36	1754	36
Turkmenistan	145	14 254	145
United Kingdom	110	16	424
U.S.A.	554	1942	2127
Uruguay	32	496	16

Projected use for the year 2000

Source: *The World's Water 1998–1999: The Biennial Report on Freshwater Resources,* by Peter H. Gleick, published by Island Press, Washington, DC.

Water exists naturally in all three states on the earth's surface.

If you were standing on the moon, the earth would look mostly blue to you, with a little bit of white. That blue colour is the colour of the water in our huge oceans. The white is the colour of the water that forms clouds in the sky and the polar ice caps. Earth is unique among all the planets in our solar system. While Mars and the moon have frozen water, earth is the only planet with lots of liquid water. It also has water in all its three states, as a **solid**, **liquid**, and **gas**. Because of this abundance of water, plants, animals, and other organisms live everywhere on the planet.

1.1 THE STATES OF WATER ON EARTH

Explore

In the Invitation to Explore, you discovered that most of the water on earth is liquid. Only a small percentage of water occurs as a solid and as a gas. Where would you look for water in all three states: solid, liquid, and gas?

PROBLEM SOLVER

WHAT'S THE STATE OF THE WATER?

Brainstorm with a partner all the places where the different states of water can be found on earth. For example, you'll find liquid water in a lake, but you'll also find it in rain.

- What states of water will you find underground?
- Where would you look for solid water?
- Where is water a gas?
- Share your ideas with your class. As you listen to your classmates' ideas, add any places you missed to your list.

- Now use the information you've just collected to write a water information outline that you could present in the form of a story, dramatic video, comic strip, etc. Create a story about a student like yourself who must bring back samples of water in all three states: one set of samples from each of the northern and southern hemispheres. The samples contain the key to solving an important scientific mystery. Make your story a combination of words and pictures.

Water as a Liquid, Solid, and Gas

The Three States of Water

■ Nearly all the water on earth is liquid most of the time. The water in the oceans is home to many animals and plants, but it is too salty for humans and other land animals to drink. We rely on water in lakes, rivers, and streams, as well as water in the ground for our use.

■ Most of the *fresh* water on earth is in a solid state, and most of that is in Antarctica, where the ice is up to 4.8 km thick. Greenland has another huge ice cap. Ice and snow exist all year round in these ice caps and on the tops of high mountains as glaciers—even at the equator. Ice also exists year round in the Arctic Ocean near the North Pole. In many other places on earth, water is solid only at certain times of the year.

■ Only a tiny amount of all the water in the world is in the atmosphere as a gas, called **water vapour**. You may not be able to see it, but sometimes you can feel water vapour. During the summer especially, the air may contain so much water that it can make your skin feel damp. Water in the air is called **humidity**. On hot days with lots of water vapour in the air (high humidity), the temperature may feel higher than it really is (called the "humidex reading"). The water in the air increases our feeling of uncomfortable heat. Clouds form when water vapour condenses to form tiny water droplets or ice crystals. White clouds, like these, just drift by, maybe blocking out the sun for a few minutes. Darker, heavier clouds may contain rain, snow, hail, sleet, or freezing rain.

1 The oceans are liquid most of the time. This picture was taken near St. John's, Newfoundland, in the early summer. Where do you think the iceberg came from? Explain how it might have formed.

2 a) In the middle of summer, would you be able to find water outside in all three states of matter? Why or why not?

   b) In the middle of winter, would you be able to find water outside in all three states of matter? Why or why not?

3 Create a concept map with the phrase "water as a solid, liquid, or gas" in the centre. Use the information from this section to start your diagram. Continue to build your concept map as you learn more about the water cycle and groundwater.

1.2 THE WATER CYCLE

Every winter, it snows in northern climates, but in the spring, the snow disappears. Rivers and streams flood in the spring, but by late summer, they are flowing quietly in their banks. Sometimes, they dry up completely. Rain, especially in the spring and fall, keeps plants green and growing. But in the northern winter, the plants are covered with snow. What is the connection between the snow of winter and the floods of spring? Where do the flood waters go? Where does the water come from that becomes rain or snow?

Ever Changing Water

infoBIT

The tiny percentage of water in the atmosphere (about 0.0009% of all the earth's water) does not stay very long in the gaseous state. The average length of time water particles stay in the atmosphere is only about 12 days. Compare this with some water particles that have been locked in Antarctic ice for millions of years.

Water is constantly changing state all over the world. It *evaporates* from lakes and oceans into the air. In the air, it *condenses* to form clouds and falls as rain or snow. Plants take up water from the ground and release some of it into the air through *transpiration*. This movement of water through different states is called the **water cycle**. A cycle is a repeated movement from one event to another.

Other examples of cycles are the seasons and your school year. Take a look at the diagram of the water cycle. What examples of the water cycle are happening now outside your classroom window?

All three states of matter can be seen in this picture.

The Water Cycle

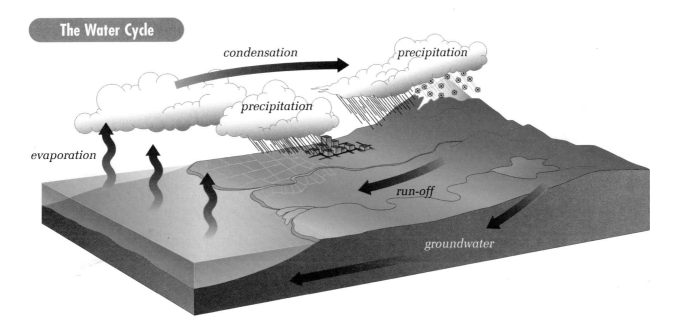

condensation

precipitation

precipitation

evaporation

run-off

groundwater

PROBLEM SOLVER

THE WATER CYCLE IN ACTION

A group of students built the model of the water cycle shown here. Explain how water moves through this device to simulate the water cycle.

- Are any parts of the water cycle missing from this model? If so, what do you think they are?
- Working with other students, design and build your own model of the water cycle. Start by drawing a diagram of what you plan to build. Show it to your teacher and explain how it will work.
- Write up your explanation, describing how your model of the water cycle is the same or different from the one shown.

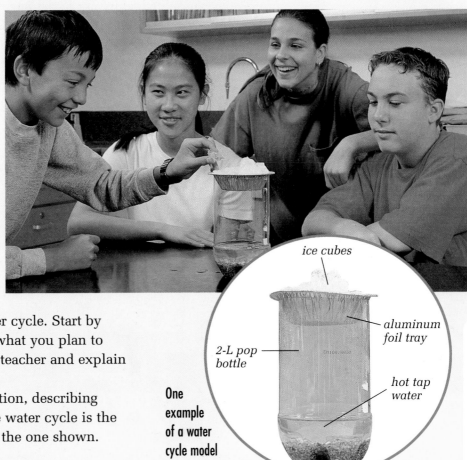

ice cubes

aluminum foil tray

2-L pop bottle

hot tap water

One example of a water cycle model

1 Work with a partner to create a diagram that shows how water moves from a snowbank to a stream to a lake to the air and back down again. Use the following terms as labels in your diagram. You have learned these terms in other chapters and other grades.

- **evaporation:** the change of state from a liquid to a gas
- **condensation:** the change of state from a gas to a liquid
- **melting:** the change of state from a solid to a liquid
- **freezing:** the change of state from a liquid to a solid
- **precipitation:** solid or liquid water that falls from clouds

2 Suppose that one part of your water cycle model was contaminated by pollution. How would this affect all the other parts of the model? Be sure to refer to all parts of the cycle.

3 Add information about the water cycle to your concept map that you began earlier in this section.

1.3 THE WATER TABLE

Explore

If you live in the country, or if you have ever visited someone in the country, you have probably used water from a well. A **well** is a hole in the ground into which water from the soil drains. A well can be just below the surface or it can be dozens of metres deep. A device that lifts the water, called a pump, brings the water to the surface where it can be used.

Drilling rigs like this are used to tap into the water table, below the earth's surface.

But where does the water in the soil come from? Think about the water cycle. Water in the atmosphere condenses and falls as rain or snow. Some of this water falls into the oceans, but much of it falls on land. Some of the water that falls on the land collects in rivers, streams, lakes, and ponds, but much of the water soaks into the ground. There, it collects in the spaces between grains of soil and in cracks in underground rocks. That's why it's called **groundwater.**

When you studied soil in earlier grades, you probably looked at soil samples with a magnifying glass or a microscope. The spaces in the soil are so small that you can't see them without the help of a magnifier of some kind. Although the spaces are tiny, there are so many of them that they can store a huge amount of water. In fact, 95% of the fresh water in the world, not frozen in glaciers or ice caps, is found underground!

After the rain stops or the snow melts, the water soaks into the ground until it is stopped by rock. Look at the diagram below. You can see that the soil just below the surface has a mixture of air and water in its spaces. But below that, all the spaces in the soil are full of water. The top of this level is called the **water table.** If you want to drill a well, you have to drill down below the level of the water table to make sure you have enough water all the time.

What do you think will happen to the water table if the weather stays dry for a very long time? Will it stay the same, move closer to the surface, or move deeper?

- Discuss with a partner how weather and climate might affect the water table.
- Share your ideas with your classmates.
- Describe any experiences you may have had or heard about with wells going dry.

reSEARCH

Where Did All the Water Come From?

According to the most accepted theory today, the earth formed several billions of years ago from a cloud of hot gases and dust. Two of the gases, oxygen and hydrogen, combined in this ancient atmosphere to form water vapour. As the earth cooled, the water vapour condensed into storm clouds. The clouds produced rain which slowly collected in hollow depressions on the earth's surface to form puddles, ponds, lakes, seas, and finally huge oceans.

- What were the lakes and rivers like in your area at the end of the last ice age (about 8000–10 000 years ago)?

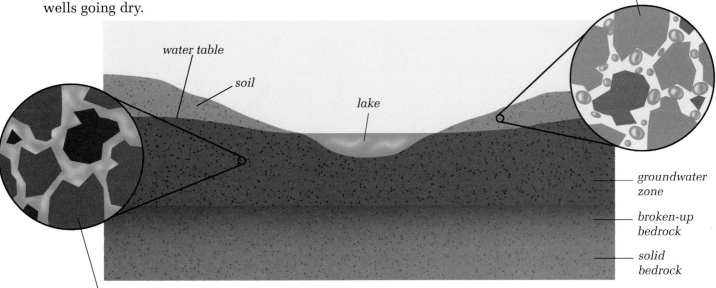

Soil above groundwater zone has air spaces.

water table

soil

lake

groundwater zone

broken-up bedrock

solid bedrock

Soil in groundwater zone has all the spaces filled with water.

Develop
The Water Table and the Water Cycle

The water table is the top level of groundwater, but it shows up at the surface as well. Lakes and ponds can show you where the level of the water table is. In this next Investigator activity, you will discover the connection between water on the surface and groundwater.

INVESTIGATOR

WATER ABOVE AND BELOW

The Question

How does precipitation collect as surface water and groundwater?

Materials & Equipment

- *dry, coarse sand*
- *large, glass baking dish or other clear, plastic container*
- *2 500-mL pop bottles with their tops and bottoms cut off*
- *water supply*
- *beaker or paper cup*

Procedure

1. Stand the two bottles, with their bottoms and tops cut off, on the bottom of the container.
2. Add sand to the container to a depth of about 5 cm, being sure not to disturb the bottles or get sand inside them.
3. Clear out the sand, all the way to the bottom, in one small area of the container to form a lake.

Shallow and deep wells

Slowly pour water into the sand (step 6).

continued on next page ······➤

1.0 Water Exists Naturally in All Three States on the Earth's Surface

4 Remove enough sand in another area to create a shallow depression. This is a pond. There should still be sand under the pond.

5 Raise one of the bottles so that its bottom edge is about 2 cm from the surface of the sand. Fill it with sand inside to the same level as the sand surrounding it. This is your shallow well. The other cylinder, which should still be resting on the container bottom and free of sand, is the deep well.

6 Put water in the beaker, and pour some very slowly onto the sand in the "land" part of the container. Observe what happens to the water.

7 Continue pouring gently until water appears in one of the holes (pop bottles, lake, or pond) in the container. Where does the water appear first?

8 Continue pouring. Note when the water appears in the other holes, on the surface, and on the sides of the containers.

Keeping Records

9 Record your observations of when and where the water appeared.

Analyzing and Interpreting

10 Where did the water go when you first started pouring it into the sand?

11 In which hole did the water first appear? Where did the water appear next?

12 Where did the water appear first on the sand's surface?

13 Where was the water table in your model? Draw a diagram of your activity set-up to show it.

Forming Conclusions

14 What do you think would happen to the water table if there was no precipitation for a long time? Why?

15 What do you think would happen to the water table if an area had much more rainfall than usual? Why?

Communicate

1 When Jani went to visit her uncle's cottage in the spring, the pond had been full of water with tadpoles swimming in it. When she came back in August, the pond had dried up completely. Her uncle said that the old well was dry, too. He was glad they had drilled a deeper well last year because it still had lots of water in it. On the following page, look at the drawing of the cottage area and the diagram showing the location of the wells, the pond, and the water table in the spring.

a) Copy the diagram on the next page and show where you think the water table would be in August. Explain why you put it there.

b) Would the level of the water in the stream or the lake be different in August? Why or why not?

c) Think about the diagram of the water cycle that you studied earlier. How does it change during the year?

d) Explain how the changes in the water table and in the pond are related to changes in the water cycle during the year.

1.4 CHECK YOUR PROGRESS

1 Complete the concept map for water as a solid, liquid, and gas that you started in section 1.1. Describe two new things you learned in this Big Idea that you didn't know before.

2 Look at the newspaper clipping below.
   a) How would the chemical get from the factory to the wells?
   b) Is it possible that the wells might not be polluted? Explain your answer.

No drinking water for residents

Ministry of Environment officials have warned residents of the Cardassa area not to drink the water from their wells until the water can be tested. A recent accident at a local factory resulted in thousands of litres of a poisonous chemical soaking into the ground. Officials fear that nearby wells may be polluted. Residents are requested to contact ministry offices for testing.

3 Draw a diagram to show the water cycle in your area in the winter. Would this diagram look different in the summer?

4 What do you think could happen if it rained so much that the water table reached the surface of the ground? Why?

BIG IDEA 2.0 The different characteristics of salt and fresh water support a diversity of living things.

Think back to the view of earth at the beginning of Big Idea 1.0. What did it tell you about the earth's most common surface feature? Most of the earth is covered in a salty water solution we call the oceans. This water is home to a wide range of living things, from microscopic organisms to the largest animals on earth, blue whales. Some of the same organisms that live in salt water can also live in fresh water, although not all of them can. In fact, salt water and fresh water are really very different in several important ways.

2.1 COMPARING SALT WATER AND FRESH WATER

Floating *on* the Dead Sea

Explore

Have you ever tried to float in a lake, a river, or a swimming pool? How easy was it? It probably wasn't as easy as it is for the person in this photo. This person is floating in the Dead Sea in Israel. The Dead Sea is one of the saltiest bodies of water on earth. Why do you think it might be easier to float in salt water than in fresh water?

- Working with a partner, make a Venn diagram to compare what you know about salt and fresh water. (See the example below.)

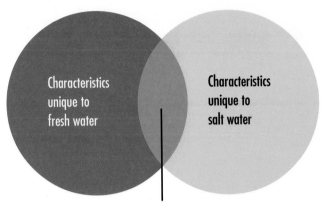

Characteristics unique to fresh water

Characteristics unique to salt water

Characteristics shared by both fresh and salt water

Develop Salt Makes the Difference

When you studied fluids earlier in this grade, you learned about density and buoyant force. You found that density depended on the ratio between mass and volume. What do you think would happen if you added salt to water? Would it affect its mass or volume? Would that affect its density? How would the buoyant force in salt water compare with the buoyant force in fresh water? (Think back to the picture of the person floating in the Dead Sea.) In the next Investigator activity, you will explore how salt and fresh water differ in density and buoyant force.

INVESTIGATOR

COMPARING SALT AND FRESH WATER

Before You Start...

Predict what will happen when you mix fresh water with salt water. Which is more dense, salt water or fresh water? Which type of water will have the greater buoyancy?

The Question

How does salt affect the density and buoyant force of water?

Materials & Equipment

- *water*
- *2 250-mL beakers*
- *15-mL measuring spoon*
- *table salt*
- *food colouring*
- *2-L clear glass bowl or large, clear glass baking dish*
- *100-mL graduated cylinder*
- *pencil and 1 thumbtack*

continued on next page ·······➤

Procedure

1. Put 200 mL of water in the beaker. Use the measuring spoon to add 60 mL of salt to the water, and stir well until most of the salt dissolves.

2. Add drops of food colouring to the beaker until the water is a very deep colour.

3. Put 200 mL of clear water into the bowl or baking dish. *Very slowly,* pour the coloured, salty water down the side of the bowl or baking dish and observe what happens. Then empty the bowl.

4. Mix another solution of 200 mL of water and 60 mL of salt in a beaker. Colour it with food colouring. Pour the solution into the bowl. *Very slowly,* add clear water to this coloured, salty solution. Observe what happens.

Keeping Records

5. Draw a labelled diagram to show what happened in steps 3 and 4.

Analyzing and Interpreting

6. What happened to the coloured water when you poured it into the clear water?

7. What happened to the clear water when you poured it into the coloured water? Were your predictions correct?

8. Design and build a simple hydrometer like the one shown below. Use it to test the freshwater and saltwater solutions. What do your results tell you about their densities?

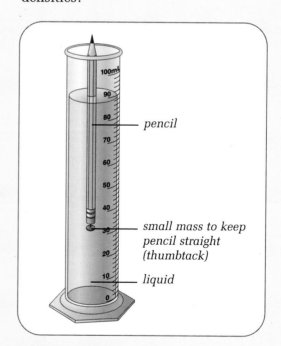

pencil

small mass to keep pencil straight (thumbtack)

liquid

Forming Conclusions

9. Explain your observations about salt water and fresh water using the terms *density* and *buoyant force.*

10. What "real-world" applications can you suggest for what you have learned about salt water and fresh water?

Other Differences Between Salt and Fresh Water

Many substances are dissolved in both fresh and salt water. (Remember, they are both solutions.) However, it's the amount of sodium chloride that determines if water is salt or fresh. Sodium chloride is the same mineral that we use as table salt. The amount of salt in water is called its **salinity**. Seawater (that is, water in the oceans) has a much higher salinity than fresh water. The average salt content of seawater is 3.5%. Seawater also contains many other substances in much smaller amounts. It even contains gold and silver! But you would have to process an enormous amount of seawater to obtain even a small amount of gold.

At the point where a river flows into the ocean, fresh water mixes with salt water. The salinity here is higher than in fresh water, but lower than in the open ocean. This water is called **brackish water**. Some species of plants and animals can exist *only* in brackish water. Pictured here is the Gualala River in California, flowing into the Pacific Ocean.

Variations in the amount of substances in fresh water are caused by the rocks and soil that the water passes through.

- Even though fresh water contains much less salt than seawater does, in some places the salinity of the fresh water is still high enough that you can taste it. In Canada, salty fresh water can be a problem in places on the Prairies.
- In parts of Ontario, water contains so much iron that it affects the taste.
- Too much calcium and magnesium make water "hard" so that it is difficult to use soap in it.

Recall from your study of mixtures that water is the "universal solvent." It dissolves minerals and other substances in rocks and soil. It will also dissolve harmful substances such as pesticides and herbicides. This is why we have to be careful when we dispose of dangerous substances.

In the Investigator activity you did earlier in this section, you discovered that salinity affected density and buoyant force. The coloured, salty water had a higher density. It sank when poured into clear water. Salinity also affects water's freezing point. The more salt that is dissolved in water, the lower the freezing point of that water. Salt is used on the roads in the winter because of this property. It lowers the freezing point of the salt and ice mixture, keeping it from freezing.

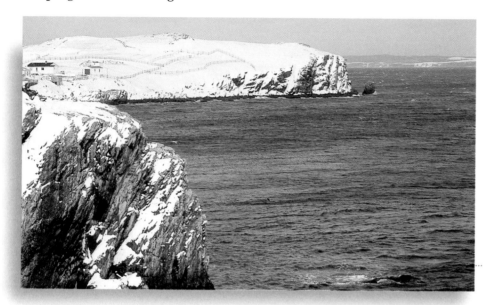

The salt content of seawater is one of the reasons that the oceans don't freeze as quickly as lakes. Another reason is the amount of water in the oceans and the heat stored in them. You'll learn more about this later in this chapter. Only in the Arctic and Antarctic do temperatures stay low enough for long enough periods of time to allow large amounts of seawater to freeze.

Why We Can't Drink Salt Water

You know that eating salty potato chips or other salty foods will make you thirsty. So will drinking salt water. But the effect of drinking salt water is much more serious than just making you thirsty. A person who drinks only seawater will soon die! The salt in the water actually draws water out of the body's cells. The body becomes dehydrated, and the person's organs can no longer function. The same thing happens if a person goes without any water for more than about three days.

Some land animals can drink salt water and others can't. Some sea birds have special glands above their eyes that help them get rid of extra salt in their bodies, so they can drink seawater. Horses can't drink even brackish water. Their bodies absorb the salt from the water too easily, and it harms their organs.

Sea gulls are one type of sea bird that can drink seawater.

CHANGING SALT WATER TO FRESH WATER

Many places in the world don't have very much fresh water, but they may be close to the ocean. How can salty seawater be turned into drinkable fresh water? One way is to use the sun. After all, it's the sun that converts the salt water of the oceans into the fresh water of the rain. To see how this works, all you need is a clean, clear plastic bag, a twist tie to close the bag, some table salt, and a shallow, metal bowl of water.

Procedure

1 Dissolve a tablespoon of salt in about 3 cm of water in the bowl. Taste the water by touching it and tasting it off your fingertip. It should taste very salty.

2 Place the bowl inside the plastic bag and close the top of the bag tightly with the twist tie.

3 Set the bag and bowl next to a sunny window, and leave it there for 24 h.

If it's a cloudy day, put your freshwater converter under a 100-W bulb for 3 or 4 hours.

4 After 24 h, open the bag, and touch the liquid collected on the inside of the bag. Taste it.

Communicate

1 Look again at the Venn diagram that you and your partner did at the beginning of this section.
   a) Add any differences that you did not include in your original diagram.
   b) Did you list any other differences that were not described in this section? With your partner, do research to find out more about those differences.

2 If you wanted to set up a saltwater aquarium, you would have to buy a special mixture from the pet store or aquarium store to use in the water. You could not just dissolve table salt in the water to make the right concentration. Saltwater animals and plants can't live in a simple solution of table salt and water. Discuss with a partner why you think this is so. Share your ideas with your classmates.

3 Do you think the freezing point of all seawater is the same, whether it's near the shore or far from shore? Explain your answer.

4 A ship leaves a saltwater port, heavily loaded with cargo. It sails across the ocean, but when it arrives at its destination, it has to dock at a port located in the mouth of a river. As it approaches this port, it starts to sink lower in the water. The cargo has not shifted or changed in any way. Why is the ship floating lower in the water?

reSEARCH

Visit a local pet store and find out more about freshwater and saltwater fish.
- What different foods do they eat?
- How are aquariums set up for both types of fish?
- Why are some species of fish difficult to breed in aquariums?

2.2 THE DIVERSITY OF LIVING THINGS IN SALT AND FRESH WATER

Explore

In earlier grades, you learned that an *ecosystem* is any place on earth where living things interact with other living and non-living things.

Imagine snorkelling in a warm ocean with colourful fish darting by like the ones in this photo of a coral reef. Coral reefs in tropical areas are among the most diverse ecosystems in the world. Many different kinds of fish, shellfish, and other animals live in and around them. The coral itself is a living thing. It's a tiny animal that lives in large colonies. The hard substance that we usually call coral is only the outer shell of these colonies. A coral reef is just one example of the many marine ecosystems all over the world. (**Marine** is used to describe anything related to the ocean.)

Coral needs water temperatures above 20°C to live.
- Where would you expect to find coral reefs?
- How might your observations snorkelling in a coral reef be different from diving in a local lake?

Develop

Living Things in Saltwater and Freshwater Ecosystems

A coral reef is a good example of the wide diversity of living things in the earth's oceans. Many different kinds of organisms live in freshwater lakes and rivers. However, even more different kinds of organisms live in salt water because the oceans have a greater variety of environments. Two-thirds of all the world's major types of organisms live all or part of their lives in salt water. The following pictures will help you compare the diversity of saltwater and freshwater ecosystems. Create a chart that lists the differences between salt and fresh water.

Ocean Diversity

The ocean is similar to a huge lake because it has a shoreline, shallow areas, and deep areas. But in the oceans, there are greater differences in water motion, salinity, and depth than in a lake. The deepest part of the ocean is about 11 000 m. The deepest lake in the world is Lake Baikal in Russia, with a depth of about 1700 m. Areas that have similar ecosystems are called **zones**.

Intertidal Zone

Animals and plants that live along the shoreline of the ocean have to be able to withstand the pounding of the waves. They also have to be able to live out of the water for some time every day at low tide. This shoreline area they live in is called the **intertidal zone**.

- Animals have developed special adaptations to live in this zone.
- Different ecosystems form in intertidal zones, depending on whether the shore is rocky, sandy, or muddy.

Estuary

mix of salt and fresh water

One of the most diverse and richest ecosystems is an **estuary**. This is where fresh water from rivers and streams mixes with the salt water of the ocean.

- Marshes often grow in or around estuaries.
- Many different kinds of plants, animals, and insects that can tolerate the brackish water live here.
- Estuaries are rich in bird life, because of all the food and shelter available.

Continental Shelf

The **continental shelf** is a shelf of land that extends out from the edge of a continent below the ocean's surface.

- Canada's largest continental shelf is on the east coast. The water here is warmer than in the open ocean, and light penetrates almost all the way to the bottom. The combination of warm water, light, and nutrients make this a very rich area for both plants and animals.

- Large numbers of a small fish, called a _capelin_, feed off tonnes of microscopic plants. Larger fish, such as cod, feed off the capelin. Other fish and sea creatures that thrive here include herring, haddock, halibut, mackerel, tuna, humpback whales, and seals.

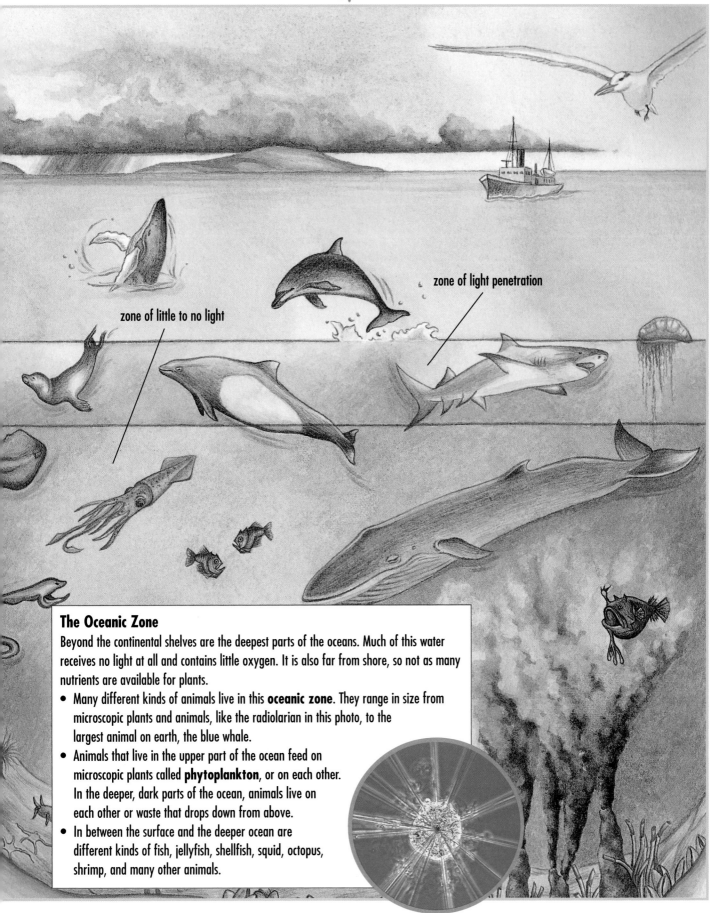

zone of light penetration

zone of little to no light

The Oceanic Zone

Beyond the continental shelves are the deepest parts of the oceans. Much of this water receives no light at all and contains little oxygen. It is also far from shore, so not as many nutrients are available for plants.

- Many different kinds of animals live in this **oceanic zone**. They range in size from microscopic plants and animals, like the radiolarian in this photo, to the largest animal on earth, the blue whale.

- Animals that live in the upper part of the ocean feed on microscopic plants called **phytoplankton**, or on each other. In the deeper, dark parts of the ocean, animals live on each other or waste that drops down from above.

- In between the surface and the deeper ocean are different kinds of fish, jellyfish, shellfish, squid, octopus, shrimp, and many other animals.

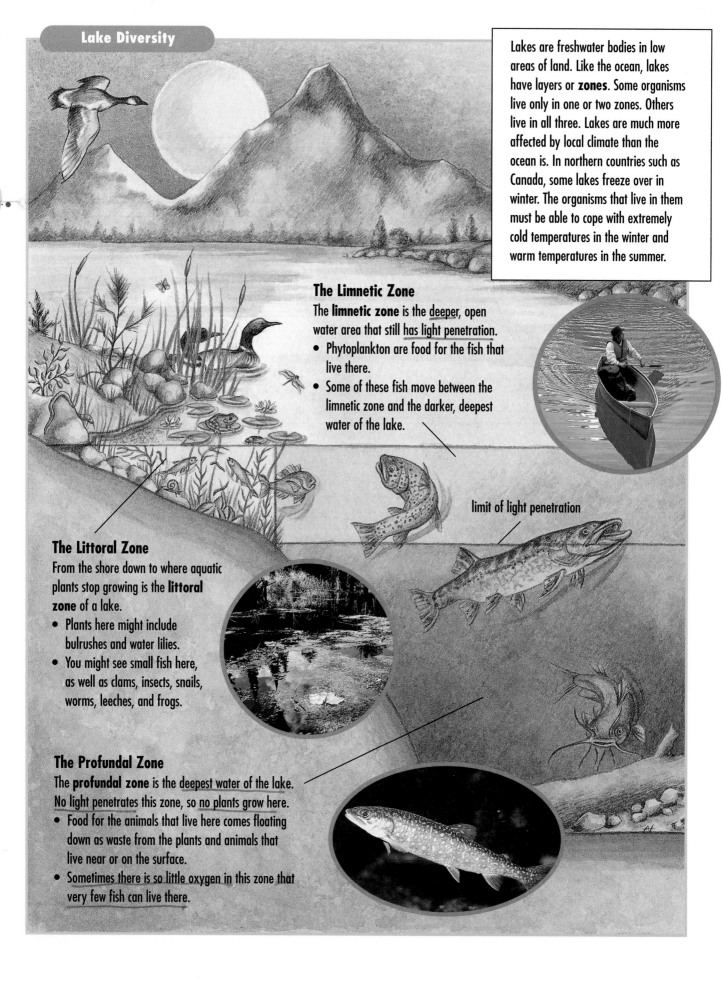

Lakes are freshwater bodies in low areas of land. Like the ocean, lakes have layers or **zones**. Some organisms live only in one or two zones. Others live in all three. Lakes are much more affected by local climate than the ocean is. In northern countries such as Canada, some lakes freeze over in winter. The organisms that live in them must be able to cope with extremely cold temperatures in the winter and warm temperatures in the summer.

The Limnetic Zone

The **limnetic zone** is the deeper, open water area that still has light penetration.

- Phytoplankton are food for the fish that live there.
- Some of these fish move between the limnetic zone and the darker, deepest water of the lake.

limit of light penetration

The Littoral Zone

From the shore down to where aquatic plants stop growing is the **littoral zone** of a lake.

- Plants here might include bulrushes and water lilies.
- You might see small fish here, as well as clams, insects, snails, worms, leeches, and frogs.

The Profundal Zone

The **profundal zone** is the deepest water of the lake. No light penetrates this zone, so no plants grow here.

- Food for the animals that live here comes floating down as waste from the plants and animals that live near or on the surface.
- Sometimes there is so little oxygen in this zone that very few fish can live there.

A Threatened Diversity

The trawler in the picture below is fishing off the coast of Newfoundland in an area called the **Grand Banks**. For at least 1000 years, people have been coming here to fish its vast stocks of fish, especially cod. This results from two natural conditions: the continental shelf makes the area much shallower than the deep ocean and a current from the Caribbean (the Gulf Current) warms the waters. A third condition, however, has influenced this marine ecosystem: human interference.

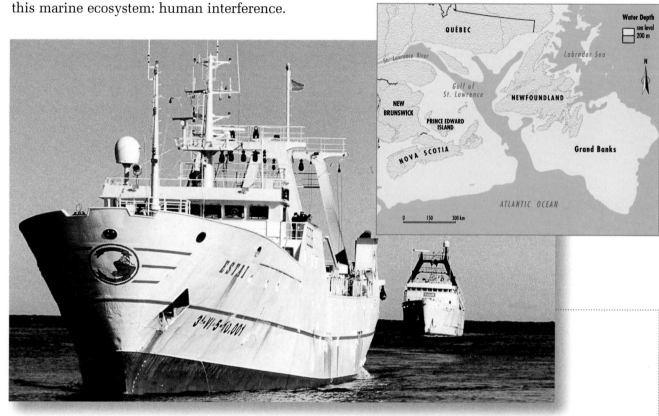

Factory trawlers can catch and process huge amounts of fish. This Spanish trawler has been caught fishing illegally in the Grand Banks by a Canadian fisheries patrol boat.

Serious fishing in the Grand Banks started in 1501 when the "Company of Adventurers to the New Found Land" began making summer voyages from England. For nearly 500 years, people fished these waters without depleting its marine resources. Then in the 1950s, factory trawlers were introduced to the Grand Banks. Using the latest technology, they were able to catch all the fish in an area, hauling in as much as 100 tonnes of fish (mostly cod) in just two hours. As many as 50 ships might fish an area, working non-stop until there was nearly nothing left in the sea.

Of course, this kind of fishing couldn't last forever. By 1992, cod had become an endangered species in the Grand Banks, and Canada had closed down its cod fisheries. No one knows whether the cod will ever come back to their traditional numbers. No one can say for sure if other species might also become endangered. What had existed for thousands of years had all but disappeared in forty!

1 a) Why is the diversity of living things in salt water greater than in fresh water? List as many reasons as you can.

*Bigger body of water.
Plankton fis...*

b) What do you think are the threats to the oceans' diversity? *Pollution fi...*

2 George and his family went on a car trip in the summer. They visited their friends' cottage by a large lake, and later they drove to the seashore. George took pictures of the shorelines of both the lake and the ocean. Look at the photos below. Which one was taken at the seashore? Which one was at the lake? How do you know?

reSEARCH

Water Facts

Canada has tremendous resources of fresh water, not to mention its 243 791 km of ocean shoreline. That's the longest shoreline in the world.

- Find out what province has the greatest number of lakes. How many lakes are there?
- What's the deepest lake in Canada? What's the biggest?
- What percent of electricity in Canada is generated by hydro-electric plants?

*seashore
..t haves waves*

*lak
doesn't have waves*

3 Explain what an estuary is. Do many different kinds of organisms live in an estuary? Why or why not?

2.3 FACTORS AFFECTING LIVING THINGS IN FRESH AND SALT WATER

Do you get hay fever? Most of the time you probably don't notice what's in the air that you breathe. But if you get hay fever, you know exactly when the season for it starts. You begin to sneeze because of the pollen in the air. Just as we can be affected by the air around us, aquatic animals and plants can be affected by the water around them. The following article describes one event that affected some of the organisms in a lake. After you read the article, discuss with a partner possible answers to the questions on the following page.

Company in Hot Water for Spilling It

Alderon Manufacturing Limited has been fined $10 000 for releasing warm water into Frank Lake last June. The Ministry of Environment levied the maximum fine because the company had failed to report the accidental spill immediately. The spill was first detected when local residents complained to ministry officials about dead fish washing up on the lakeshore. Ministry investigators determined that no toxic chemicals had been involved in the spill. However, the temperature of the water was high enough to kill some types of small fish.

- Why did the fish die?
- Why didn't all the fish, frogs, plants, and other organisms in the lake die?
- What do you think might happen now to the large fish that would usually eat the fish that were killed?
- What might happen now to the size of the population of tiny animals that the dead fish would usually have eaten?

Develop

Problems in the Aquatic Environment

The newspaper article describes a type of pollution called **thermal pollution** ("thermal" means "heat"). This is just one of the factors that can affect organisms that live in water. Not all these factors are caused by pollution. For example, natural changes in water temperature caused by an unusually hot, dry summer can affect a great many animals and plants in small lakes. When they die, they fall to the bottom and decompose. With so many dead organisms, the number of decomposer bacteria increases. They use up more and more of the oxygen in the water. Soon, no fish can live in the lake because there isn't enough oxygen.

Another example is a natural change in salinity in an estuary, which might be caused by a stream drying up or changing its course. With no or much less fresh water mixing with the salt water, organisms that can't tolerate higher levels of salt will die.

While natural factors may be important in some areas, human activities do most to harm aquatic organisms. Some of these activities are illustrated on the next page. What examples can you find in your community?

Rivers and lakes are affected by many human activities. Some of these activities can affect the ocean as well.

Factories might add dangerous chemicals to the water or practise thermal pollution, killing aquatic plants or animals. Some of these chemicals can cause tumours, birth defects, or make organisms unable to breed.

Run-off from farmland may contain fertilizers that can cause excessive plant growth, changing the ecosystem. It may also contain herbicides or pesticides that can harm animals and plants.

Power stations sometimes discharge warm water into lakes or rivers that can kill some animals and encourage excessive plant growth.

Run-off from city streets contains large amounts of oil and other chemicals, including salt. These substances affect plants and animals.

Sewage contains large amounts of nitrogen, which causes the number of micro-organisms to increase. If these micro-organisms use up the oxygen, fish will suffocate. Phosphorous in sewage promotes plant growth that can also change the whole ecosystem.

Habitat destruction takes away the places that animals can live and plants can grow.

Oil spills from ships can harm animals in, on, and near the water.

Communicate

1 Describe two effects that chemical pollution could have on aquatic animals.

2 A new ocean-side resort brings in tonnes of fine, clean sand to create a beach along a rocky shoreline. In what ways could this change to the rocky shore affect the animals that live there?

3 Salmon are fish that live in the open ocean, but they must return to freshwater streams and rivers to lay eggs (to spawn). They travel upstream, against the current, to reach the place where they were born. Here, they spawn.
   a) What do you think would happen if a dam were built across a river or stream that salmon use?
   b) What effect would this have on aquatic animals above the dam that normally eat salmon hatchlings (called *fry*)?
   c) One of the effects of the dam is reduced flow in the river below it. How would this affect the salmon?
   d) What do you think dam builders can do to reduce the effects of the dam on the salmon and other animals?

Salmon jumping—Brooks Falls, Alaska

2.4 CHECK YOUR PROGRESS

1 You are given two large pails of water. You have to determine which water sample is from the ocean and which one is from a lake. But you are *not* allowed to taste them. How would you test them to determine their sources?

2 The lake in this photo is in northern Saskatchewan. What effect could the following factors have on the animals in the lake during the year?
   a) a very hot, dry summer
   b) a very cold winter

Zebra Mussels

Another factor that can affect aquatic organisms is the introduction of species that aren't normally part of that ecosystem. The Great Lakes have been seriously affected by animals that have arrived by ship from other parts of the world. One of the most successful of these alien species is the zebra mussel from Europe. Six years after its arrival, almost all the native freshwater clams in the Lake St. Clair–western Lake Erie area had disappeared. The ecosystem had changed from a community that included a variety of clams to one that supported only one kind of shellfish: the zebra mussel.

3 Agree or disagree with this statement: *Saltwater and freshwater bodies contain exactly the same amounts and types of organisms.* Provide evidence to support your answer.

4 Ten years ago, there was only one house beside the lake shown in the illustration. Today, there is a small community, including a marina and a campground. Ten years ago, the fishing was good here, but now very few fish are caught.

  a) What factors do you think might have affected the fish population? (Hint: Think about factors other than overfishing.)

  b) What effect do you think the change in the fish population might have had on the other animals and plants in the lake?

5 Pollution can affect both plants and animals in a water ecosystem. What do you think might happen to a water ecosystem for each of these situations?

  a) Warm water is discharged into an ocean harbour.

  b) Road run-off enters a river system.

INVESTIGATING THE OCEAN

Christine Erbe is an oceanographer in British Columbia. She studies the noise boats make in the ocean in order to find out if it bothers marine mammals such as whales and sea lions. Artificially produced noise can have a serious effect on the way marine animals communicate, navigate, find prey, and detect predators. It can even damage their ears and other organs!

Christine Erbe: "Oceanography is an exciting job and every day presents a challenge. You try to figure out how nature works. You learn new things all the time, but in a fun and enjoyable way."

Whale watching can be a serious problem. Christine studies whether the noise motorboats make can harm whales.

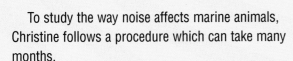

Christine is recording underwater noise from whale-watching boats.

To study the way noise affects marine animals, Christine follows a procedure which can take many months.
- First, she studies what has already been written about marine mammals, their hearing, and their habitat. Christine designs her own research on what she finds out.
- Next, Christine works with whales and sea lions in aquariums. Marine animals hear differently than humans do. Christine has to find out what sounds they can hear and what noises, such as boat noise, bother them.

- Finally, she takes all the data she has gathered to her lab and uses it to develop a computer program comparing the sounds whales and sea lions can hear to the noise made by boats. This program can be used to predict whether the noise made by a boat will bother marine animals or not.

"The particular fun of oceanography is that it is a broad field combining many different branches of science," says Christine. "You work together with biologists, chemists, physicists, geologists, and engineers. Teamwork is very common, which is really great, because you learn from each other."

BIG IDEA

3.0

Bodies of fresh and salt water are created by geological processes.

The Mackenzie River

Northern lakes in the Canadian Shield

Islands in the sea, like the Hawaiian Islands, are really ocean mountains.

Some people have suggested that earth should really be called "oceanus" because so much of its surface is covered with water. But beneath all that water are features just as varied as those we see on dry land: mountains and valleys, flat plains, and rolling hills. These features are formed by the same processes that formed the mountains, valleys, plains, and hills on the continents. And the continents are also marked by water—carved by rivers and dotted with lakes, especially in Canada. We have about 3 million lakes and some of the largest river systems in the world: the Mackenzie-Peace, the Yukon, the Nelson, and the St. Lawrence. Our rivers drain into three different oceans: the Atlantic, the Pacific, and the Arctic. In this Big Idea, you'll learn about the pattern that fresh water makes when it runs to the oceans and how bodies of water form.

3.1 WHERE THE WATER FLOWS

Explore

The next time it rains, watch the water flowing through your neighbourhood. With a partner, discuss where the rainwater goes after it lands in the following places:

- the roof of a building
- a lawn
- the street

Draw a diagram that includes a building, a lawn, a street, a gutter, a storm drain, and rain falling. There is an example shown on the next page. Indicate the path of the rainwater from each of the points listed above to the farthest point you can show. Think about these questions as you discuss the water's path and mark your diagram.

- Does all the water flow away or does some of it collect in places?
- Where does the water flow to?
- Where does it collect?
- If the water runs down a drain, where does it go then?
- Is there a pattern to any of this flow?

Rain

Rain flows
off roof

Gutter

Lawn

Storm Drain

Develop

What Makes a Watershed?

Your neighbourhood is part of a watershed. A **watershed** is all the area of land that drains into one main lake or river. It can contain many smaller rivers and lakes, which all eventually drain into a larger one. In the following activity, you can see how a watershed works.

INVESTIGATOR

BUILDING A WATERSHED

The Question

How does water flow through a watershed?

Materials & Equipment

- *a metal baking pan*
  (22 cm wide × 33 cm long × 6 cm deep)
- *2 sheets of newspaper*
- *1 sheet of thin, opaque plastic at least 30 cm larger in all dimensions than the baking pan*
- *waterproof marker*
- *spray bottle full of coloured water*
- *book*

Procedure

1 Crumple the sheets of newspaper and place them at one end of the pan.

continued on next page ·······➤

2 Drape the plastic sheet over the crumpled newspaper. Press the plastic sheet down into the bottom of the container to prevent water from overflowing the sides, as shown in the illustration.

3 Put a book under one end of the container to raise it slightly.

4 Use the marker to draw on the plastic where you think the main rivers will flow in your model. Draw a sketch to record your prediction.

5 Spray the newspaper mounds with the coloured water until the water flows. Watch where it flows and collects. Record your observations.

Keeping Records

6 a) *Before* spraying the model, sketch the model's surface. Mark your sketch to show where you think the water will flow and where it will collect.

  b) *After* spraying the model, use a different colour pen or pencil to mark on your sketch where the water actually flowed and collected.

Analyzing and Interpreting

7 a) Why do rivers flow where they do?

  b) What makes them flow?

8 How many watersheds are above the lake that forms at the bottom of the model?

Forming Conclusions

9 Design a simple model to represent the concept of a watershed. You can use your hands or a piece of paper or anything else you can think of. Use your model to explain to a partner what a watershed is.

The Formation of Rivers and Lakes

In your model watershed, you created high and low places. The way these connected together determined which way the water flowed and where it collected. Real watersheds work the same way. The *source* or beginning point of a river may be in a glacier or a lake. Because of gravity, rivers flow down from these higher places to lower ones.

A river usually starts small and gradually grows larger as streams flow into it on its downward journey. It may flow over rocks or through soil. Wherever it flows, the process of erosion means it slowly cuts deeper and deeper into its bed. In your earlier studies, you learned how powerful moving water can be in wearing down and carrying away rocks, rock fragments, and soil. Over thousands and millions of years, river beds can grow deeper and deeper or even change course.

Some rivers flow for thousands of kilometres from their source into the ocean. Others drain into lakes out of which other streams and rivers flow. Lakes form at low places in a watershed. Most lakes in Canada were formed by glacial action. **Glaciers** are large moving bodies of ice that form part of the water cycle. Today glaciers are small, existing mainly near the tops of the highest mountains. But between 1 million and 10 000 years ago, huge glaciers advanced and retreated across the northern part of the world.

As glaciers moved slowly down from the north, they picked up rocks and rock fragments. This moving ice and rock acted like giant sandpaper to gouge out holes in the earth's surface and round off the tops of mountain peaks. Most of Canada's lakes lie in areas eroded by glaciers.

These lakes, like most other Canadian lakes, were formed by glacial action.

*re*SEARCH

Great Lakes Watershed

Nearly 20% of the world's fresh water flows out of Canada's watersheds. Much of that water comes from the Great Lakes basin. Here is a map of the Niagara Peninsula watershed.

- Into what famous waterfall does most of this water drain?
- Investigate a watershed in your province or region. Draw a map of its principal streams and rivers.

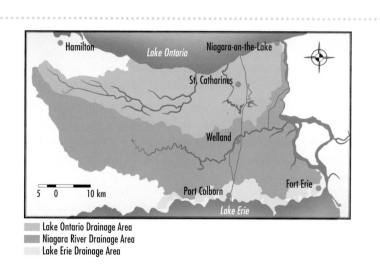

Lake Ontario Drainage Area
Niagara River Drainage Area
Lake Erie Drainage Area

The Continental Divide

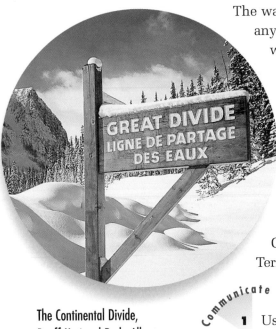

The Continental Divide,
Banff National Park, Alberta

The watershed you built in your Investigator activity couldn't drain any farther than the lake at the bottom of the pan because there was no outlet. Most real watersheds drain into lakes and rivers that drain into other lakes and rivers, which finally drain into an ocean. The ocean that a watershed drains into depends on where it is relative to the highest point of land on the continent. This point is called the **Continental Divide**. In North America, rivers to the west of the Continental Divide flow into the Pacific Ocean. To the east of the Continental Divide, rivers flow either into the Arctic Ocean or the Atlantic Ocean. This divide is along the Rocky Mountains. The borders between British Columbia and Alberta, and the Yukon and the Northwest Territories follow the Continental Divide.

Communicate

1 Using maps and references, create your own map showing which streams, rivers, and lakes are part of the watershed you live in.

a) Find out how your watershed is related to the Continental Divide.

b) Mark, on your map, the direction to the Continental Divide from your community and the direction to the ocean that your watershed finally drains into.

c) Into what lakes, if any, does your watershed drain?

3.2 THE FORMATION OF FEATURES ON THE OCEAN FLOORS

Explore

If all the water drained out of the oceans, we'd see a land surface even more rugged than that on the continents. We'd see towering mountain ranges higher than any on dry land, and deep valleys, called **trenches**. We'd see underwater volcanoes and steaming cracks releasing heat from deep within the earth. The deepest place on earth is the Marianas Trench on the west side of the Pacific Ocean. It's 11 034 m below sea level. This is so deep that no human has yet been able to travel down to the bottom of it. Of course, it isn't possible to drain all the water out of the oceans, yet we do know what features are below the oceans' surface. Scientists use different kinds of technology to "see" into a world that they cannot visit directly.

Plate Movements Formed the Oceans

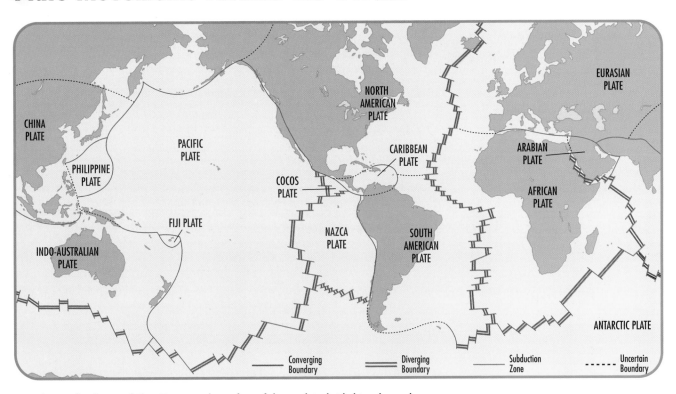

CHINA PLATE

PHILIPPINE PLATE

PACIFIC PLATE

FIJI PLATE

INDO-AUSTRALIAN PLATE

COCOS PLATE

NAZCA PLATE

NORTH AMERICAN PLATE

CARIBBEAN PLATE

SOUTH AMERICAN PLATE

EURASIAN PLATE

ARABIAN PLATE

AFRICAN PLATE

ANTARCTIC PLATE

Converging Boundary   Diverging Boundary   Subduction Zone   Uncertain Boundary

According to the Theory of Plate Tectonics, the surface of the earth is divided into huge plates.

In earlier grades, you learned that the hard outer layer of the earth is called the **lithosphere**. The lithosphere is made of solid rock that is broken into huge plates. The map on this page shows the shape and position of these plates today, but these plates are not fixed in these positions. They are moving very slowly over the earth's surface because of convection currents in the interior of the earth. Some plates are moving toward each other. Others are moving apart. And some are moving alongside each other in opposite directions. These movements have shaped the geological features on the ocean floors. The illustration on the next page shows the major features on the ocean floors, and some of the technologies used to learn about them.

The pressure in the oceans is so great that no human being could stand it unprotected. Only by travelling in submersibles built with thick walls and windows, and bright lights can scientists see into the dense darkness of the deep ocean. Robot submersibles make travel to even deeper regions possible. They provide a video feed of what they see directly to the surface. Here, a dolphin swims near a submersible in the Caribbean Sea.

The geological features on the ocean floor are the result of **plate tectonics**. Where plates move toward each other, trenches form. Where they move apart, ridges and faults form. Ridges are a sign that new crust is forming. This is where some of the youngest rocks on earth are found.

[1] **Sonar** *stands for* **so***und* **na***vigation and* **r***anging and uses sound waves for mapping the ocean floor.*

[2] **Submersibles** *allow scientists to travel much deeper than divers can go.*

[3] **Drill ships** *allow scientists to drill deep into the earth's crust to find out more about the rock that forms the crust beneath the oceans.*

[4] **Satellites** *allow scientists to track the movement of the tectonic plates and to map the ocean floor.*

[5] *The* **continental shelves** *are shallow areas around the edges of the continents.*

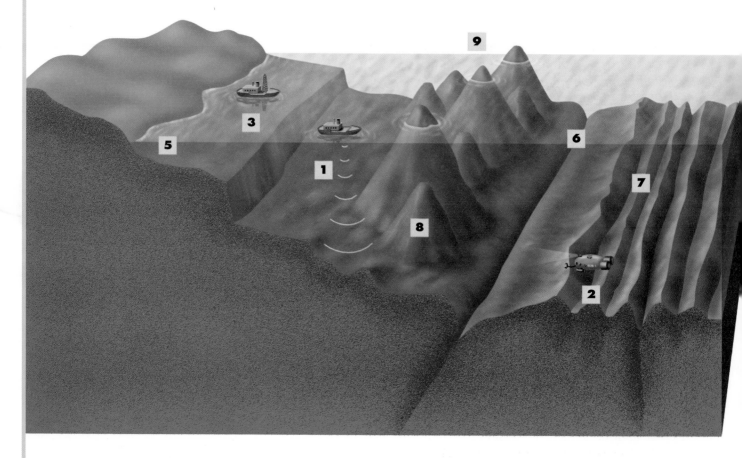

[6] **Trenches** *form where two plates are moving toward each other. The thinner oceanic plate is pushed down below the thicker continental plate.*

[7] **Mid-ocean ridges** *form where molten rock pushes up from the interior of the earth.*

[8] **Seamounts** *are underwater volcanoes that do not come all the way to the ocean's surface.*

[9] **Volcanic islands** *are formed by volcanoes that grow up all the way from the ocean's floor.*

5 WATER SYSTEMS

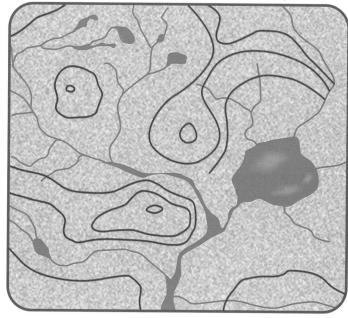

1 A frontier is an area that hasn't yet been fully explored or developed. You may have heard outer space being referred to as "the final frontier." But we have a huge frontier right here on earth. Working with a partner, discuss why the oceans can be called a frontier. As you discuss the ocean frontier, answer the following questions, and then share your ideas with your classmates.

a) Why do we still have so much to learn about the oceans?

b) How has technology helped us explore the oceans?

c) In what ways is oceanic exploration similar to space exploration?

3.3 CHECK YOUR PROGRESS

1 a) How were most of the lakes in Canada formed?

b) Is this method the same or different from the way in which the features on the ocean floor formed? Explain your answer.

2 Copy the diagram shown here of the drainage pattern of a watershed that drains into the Atlantic Ocean. Label the following features on your diagram:

a) lakes, streams, and rivers

b) sources of streams and rivers

c) direction of the flow of water in the watershed

d) the point where the watershed enters the ocean

e) the highest points of land (Hint: Water flows from a high elevation to a low elevation.)

3 Describe two types of technology that are used to explore the ocean floor.

4 Write a poem or a journal entry about the feelings of a young scientist who sees an underwater volcano for the first time.

BIG IDEA

4.0

Waves, tides, and currents are powerful forces that interact with the environment.

5

WATER SYSTEMS

What forces do you think are acting on this boat?

In the springtime, streams and rivers roar along, full of water tumbling over rocks, sometimes even overflowing their banks. You have probably seen water moving this way, as well as flowing gently between its banks. But water can also move in other ways. Waves, tides, and currents are all different ways that water can move.

4.1 WAVES

Explore

Think about the different kinds of waves that you have heard of—microwaves, sound waves, radio waves, and water waves. Are they all the same? With your classmates, try making a human wave like the ones you've seen in stadiums. How do you think this human wave is similar to a water wave? How is it different?

Develop

What's a Wave?

PROBLEM SOLVER

MAKING WAVES

Here's how you can create the action of waves.

- Fill a deep, flat baking pan with water. Wait until the surface of the water is calm. Then blow across the water to produce waves. Look at the pan from the side, and draw a picture of the waves you made. Take turns trying to produce different kinds of waves. How can you change the height of the waves?
- Now place a cork on the water, and wait until the water is calm. Blow on the water, but do *not* blow directly on the

cork. By creating waves, can you move the cork across the pan? Explain why or why not.

What causes waves?

Water Waves

Waves are patterns that move along the water's surface. The water itself does not move very far. It just moves up and down. Waves, however, can travel thousands of kilometres across the surface of the ocean. Think about using a rope as a model of wave motion. In the picture on this page, a student is shaking a rope to create waves. The waves move down the rope, but the rope itself doesn't go anywhere. When your class made a human wave, you saw the wave moving along the line of people, but no one actually moved out of place.

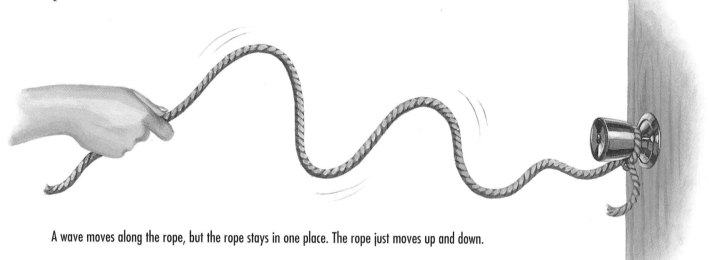

A wave moves along the rope, but the rope stays in one place. The rope just moves up and down.

In the Problem Solver activity, you tried to move the cork by making waves. But the water that the cork was floating in did not move forward, only the wave did. You may have observed the cork bobbing up and down. Within the wave, the water particles move up and down in a circular motion. But the water particles themselves do not move long distances.

Most waves are caused by the wind. The stronger the wind, the bigger the waves. Out in open water, waves appear as **swells**. If you were in a boat, you would feel up-and-down movement as the waves passed under your boat. Near the shore, the water becomes shallower, and the lower part of the waves drags on the bottom of the ocean or lake. This slows the waves down while the tops of the waves continue to move forward and eventually break, crashing onto the shore. This is where waves do the most damage.

The force of waves crashing against a shoreline can change the shape of the shore, whether it's hard rock or soft sand. Large waves erode away the shore. But small waves move gently onto the shore, where they can deposit sand or other materials. The following photos show some examples of the effects of waves on coastlines.

Percé Rock is the most famous landmark on the Gaspé Peninsula. Wave erosion has pierced a hole through it and is gradually eroding away the whole rock.

Waves are constantly eroding and depositing gravel along the shores of Lake Erie in Ontario.

Communicate

1 It's important for boaters to understand waves, so they can steer their boats safely. Look at the diagrams below. If you were canoeing on a lake with large waves, how would you steer your canoe? Would you try to travel sideways to the wave crests, as shown in diagram A? Or, would you try to point your canoe perpendicular to the wave crests, as shown in diagram B? Explain your answer.

Canoe moving sideways to wave crests

Canoe pointing into wave crests

4.2 TIDES

Explore

The two photos below were taken at the same spot about 12 hours apart on the New Brunswick coast. What happened to the water in the bay? Where did it go? If you waited another 12 hours, what do you think the picture would look like?

How can this boat be moved out to sea?

What Causes Tides?

Because New Brunswick is on the shore of the ocean, the water level along its coast changes regularly every day. This change in water level is called the **tide**. People who live beside the ocean are used to seeing and working around high and low tides. **High tide** is the highest water level at the coast, and **low tide** is the lowest water level. In most places, there are two high tides and two low tides a day.

The main cause of tides is the gravitational force of the moon. This is a pulling force that the moon exerts on the earth. The diagram on the next page shows how tides occur. The side of the earth that is closest to the moon feels the strongest pull from the moon's gravity. This is where the bulge of water is the largest. But other forces, resulting from the earth's and moon's gravitational forces, are also at work. These forces cause another, slightly smaller bulge on the opposite side of the earth at the same time. These bulges are the high tides.

*info*BIT

Earth Tides

Tides occur in other places besides the oceans. The Great Lakes have a small tide with a range of about 5 cm. But there are also "earth tides." Scientists have been able to measure the pull of the moon's gravitational force on the solid surface of the continents as well! These movements are so tiny that they can be detected only with special instruments.

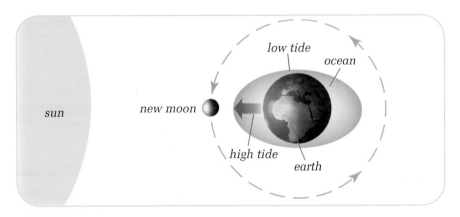

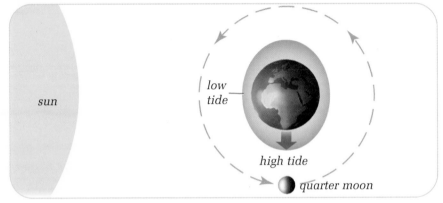

The moon is the main reason for ocean tides on earth.

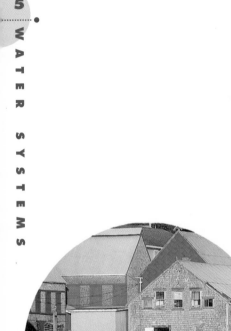

How would you determine the tidal range on this coastline?

Port	High Tide (m)	Low Tide (m)
Saint John, NB	7.7	1.0
St. John's, NF	1.2	0.3
Iqaluit, Nunavut	9.7	1.9
Tuktoyaktuk, NWT	0.5	0.2
Prince Rupert, BC	6.1	1.2
Victoria, BC	2.5	0.7

As the moon orbits around the earth, it pulls the large bulge of water along. At the same time, the earth is spinning in its rotation, *and* orbiting around the sun. All of these movements combine to create two low tides and two high tides every 24 hours and 50 minutes. Because every day is only 24 hours, this means that low tide or high tide is 50 minutes later each day. People who live along the ocean use guides, called tide tables, to tell them when the tides are that day and how high or low they will be.

The Height of Tides

Tides occur at different times around the world. They also occur at different heights at different places. The chart at left shows typical high and low tides around Canada's coastlines. The difference between high and low tide is called the **tidal range**.

Canada has the longest coastline of any country in the world, and the geography varies greatly from place to place. So it's not surprising that there are differences in the tidal ranges at different ports. What causes these differences? One of the main factors that affects the tidal range is the shape of the tidal basin. A **tidal basin** is a major indentation, such as a bay, in the coastline. It can also have smaller bays or coves within it. In the next activity, you can take a close look at one of Canada's most famous tidal basins.

FUNDY TIDES

The highest tides in the world occur in Canada's Bay of Fundy on the east coast. The tidal range there is about 15 m! That means the difference between the high tide and the low tide levels is equal to about the height of a three-storey building. Look at the map showing the location and direction that the Bay of Fundy faces. Now look at the photograph of the bay. Work with a partner to answer the following questions:

• How might the shape of the Bay of Fundy affect its tidal range?
• Which direction does the flow of ocean water come from?
• Do you think the direction that the entrance to the Bay of Fundy faces might affect its tidal range? Why or why not?
• Where do you think the tidal range would be highest in the bay?

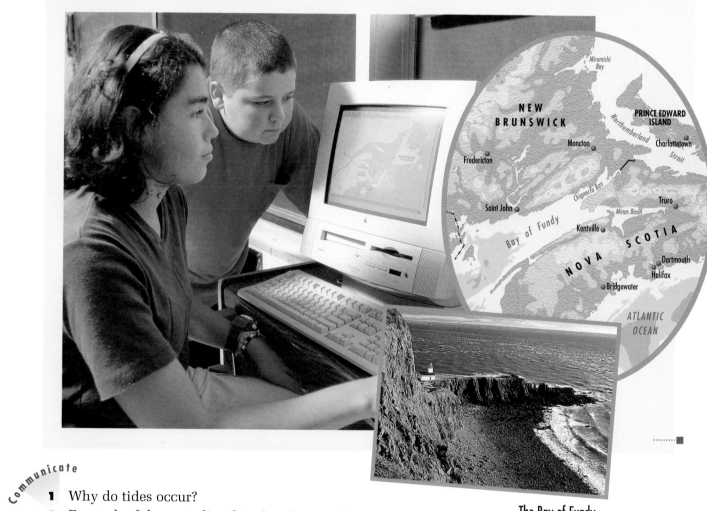

The Bay of Fundy

Communicate

1 Why do tides occur?
2 For each of the ports listed in the chart on the previous page, determine its tidal range. Using a map of Canada, find the locations of these ports. For each one, suggest a reason or reasons why its tidal range is higher or lower than those of the others.

WATER SYSTEMS 5

Before You Start...

The tidal range along Canada's coastline varies greatly from port to port. One of the important factors that affects tidal range is the shape of the tidal basin. Some ports are at the end of long, narrow bays that have high banks on either side. These bays are called **fiords**. Others are in more open, more rounded bays. In this activity, you will design a simulation to show how the shape of a tidal basin can affect the tidal range in that area. Since you want to show differences, you will have to create more than one model.

The Question

What effect does the shape of a tidal basin have on tidal range?

Your Task

1 Define your question, taking care that you test only *one* variable.
2 Make a hypothesis. (A hypothesis is a possible answer to a question or a possible explanation about a situation.)
3 Design your models, and decide what materials and equipment you'll need to test your hypothesis. Think about the answers to these questions:

Halifax Harbour is on a long, narrow bay.

a) What will you use to create the models of the tidal basins?
b) What kind of container will you use to hold the tidal basin models?
c) How will you show the movement of the tide in your simulation?
4 Plan the procedure for your simulation. Think about the answers to these questions:
a) What evidence are you looking for to support your hypothesis?
b) How will you collect data?
c) Is the test you are designing fair? How do you know?
d) How will you record your results?
5 Draw your design and write up your procedure. Show them to your teacher.
6 Build your models and carry out your simulation.
7 Compare your results with your hypothesis. Were you able to support your hypothesis? If not, what possible reasons might there be?
8 Share and compare your experimental design with your classmates. How do your results compare with theirs?

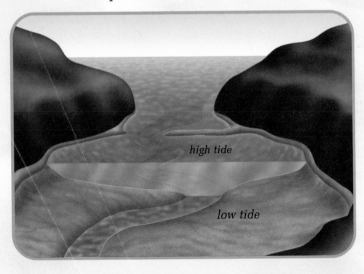

high tide

low tide

4.3 OCEAN CURRENTS

Explore

Jane spent her summer vacation by the ocean, surfing in the waves, building sand castles on the beach, and watching the different sea birds and animals. The day before she left, she went whale watching. While the boat was far out in the open water, she dropped a bottle into the water with a message in it. Back at school, Jane forgot about her bottle, until one day, a note arrived in the mail from someone who had found it—thousands of kilometres from where she had dropped it in!

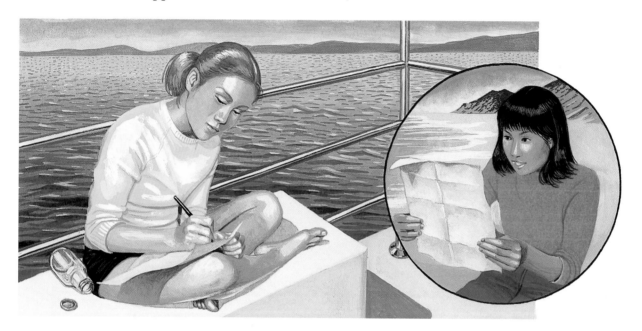

How do you think the bottle travelled so far from where she had dropped it? Do you think it would have travelled so far if she had thrown it in from the shore? Why or why not? What message would you write to put in a bottle?

Develop

Water on the Move

Water in the ocean moves constantly. Waves crash on shorelines. Tides ebb and flow. And currents flow ceaselessly over long distances. **Currents** are streams of water that move within a larger body of water. They may be caused by any of the following:

- wind
- temperature differences
- salinity differences
- the earth's rotation

Currents are different from waves because the water in currents actually *moves* from place to place. That's how Jane's bottle ended up so far from where she threw it into the water. She threw it into a current that carried it away.

Surface currents are mainly caused by steady winds that blow around the world. Called **prevailing winds**, these strong winds always blow in the same direction. Even though winds may occasionally come from other directions, the prevailing winds in the northern hemisphere of the world come from the west. The steady wind on the water drives the water along, which creates a constant flow. Differences in ocean temperatures and salinity are the usual causes of currents deep in the ocean.

The prevailing winds are from the west in North America.

try this at HOME

WIND ON THE WATER

Procedure

1. Fill a large rectangular baking dish with water. Sprinkle some pepper on the water.
2. Place an electric fan so it will blow across the baking dish. Set it on low speed and observe what happens to the water.
3. Draw a diagram to record your observations.

Things to Think About

- What happened to the water?
- Why was pepper used in this model?
- Do you think this is a good model of how wind causes surface currents? Explain your answer.

Caution!
Be careful when using an electric fan near water.

Types of Surface Currents

There are two main types of surface currents: warm and cold. **Warm surface currents** flow from tropical areas to cooler or temperate areas. The **Gulf Stream** is a good example of this type of current. Warm Atlantic water from around the equator flows into the Gulf of Mexico. As it piles up, the earth's rotation whirls it up the coast of North America. It's a very fast current that moves faster than some small boats! Look at the map below that shows the currents.

- Where does the Gulf Stream begin? Where does it end up?
- What kind of effect do you think this warm current of water might have on the places in the north that it passes near?

Cold surface currents move from polar or temperate areas to tropical areas. The cold water current that affects Canada the most is the **Labrador Current**. These are cold, arctic waters that flow southward between Greenland and Baffin Island and Labrador. At about 0°C, it's much colder than the ocean water around it. It carries icebergs from the north down past Newfoundland. When it meets the warmer, Atlantic current, it helps to make the Grand Banks both a rich fishing area and one of the foggiest places on earth.

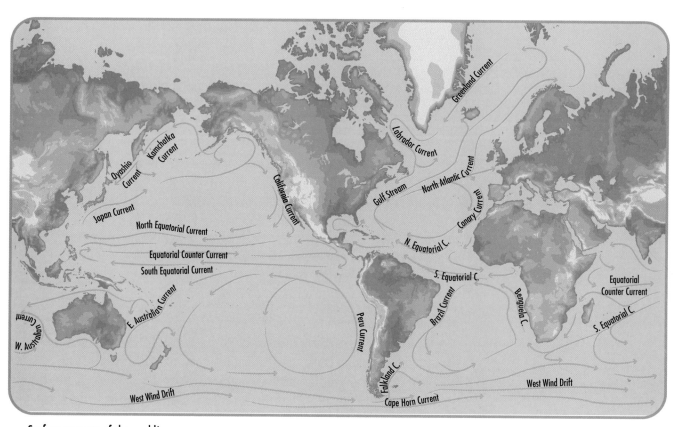

Surface currents of the world's oceans

5
WATER SYSTEMS

BENDING CURRENTS

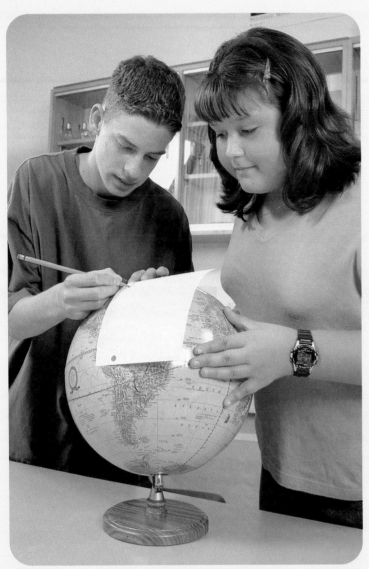

On the map of surface currents, you can see how the currents bend as they move away from the equator. This bending in their path is caused by the rotation of the earth. Although the winds that drive the current are moving in a straight line, the earth is rotating underneath them. This causes the currents to curve as they travel away from the equator. This turning is called the Coriolis [kori olis] effect, named after the French scientist who discovered it. You and a friend can test this effect yourselves.

- Place a piece of paper on a globe with the bottom of the paper at the equator and the top near Hudson's Bay. Tape can be used to keep the paper in place.
- Try drawing a straight line from Hudson's Bay toward the equator (while looking down from the North Pole). Now try it again as your partner turns the globe very slowly counter-clockwise .
- What happens to your straight line? Why?

Convection Currents

Recall from your earlier studies that temperature differences in a fluid such as air or water can cause movement within that fluid. These currents are called **convection currents**. In the oceans, huge convection currents circulate in deep waters all over the world. In the next Investigator activity, you'll explore how convection currents work.

TEMPERATURE AND CONVECTION CURRENTS

The Question

How do temperature differences cause currents?

Materials & Equipment

- *2-L or larger clear beaker or glass jar*
- *250-mL or 500-mL beaker*
- *enough warm water from the tap to fill the beaker two-thirds full*
- *2 identical thermometers*
- *ice cubes*
- *eyedropper*
- *water coloured with food colouring*
- *hot plate*
- *electrical tape*
- *ruler or tape measure*
- *stopwatch or timer*
- *marker*

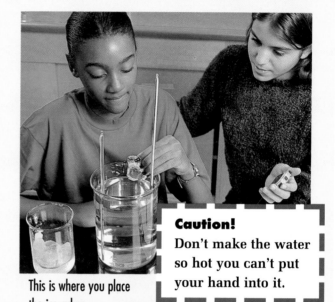

This is where you place the ice cubes.

Caution!
Don't make the water so hot you can't put your hand into it.

Step 2

Procedure

Part 1

1 Position one thermometer in the beaker so that its bulb is just above the bottom of the beaker. Make sure you can read the scale. Then tape it securely in place.

2 Mark a point on the lip of the beaker 10 cm away from the first thermometer. Now measure and mark off a point 5 cm down into the beaker. Position the second thermometer so that its bulb is at this point. Tape it securely in place, again making sure you can read the scale.

3 Using another beaker, add enough warm water from the tap so that the bulbs of both thermometers are covered.

4 Read and record the temperature of the water at the surface and at the bottom of the beaker using the two thermometers.

5 You are going to place ice cubes close to the thermometer whose bulb is near the surface of the water. Predict what you think will happen to the temperature of the water at the location of each thermometer.

6 After you have made your prediction, place a row of ice cubes against the side of the beaker close to the thermometer whose bulb is near the surface of the water. The ice cubes should be at least 2 cm from the thermometer.

continued on next page ⋯⋯▶

7 Use the eyedropper to place one drop of coloured water just below the ice cubes. Observe and record what happens.

8 Observe and record the temperature reading on each thermometer at 30-s intervals for 3 min.

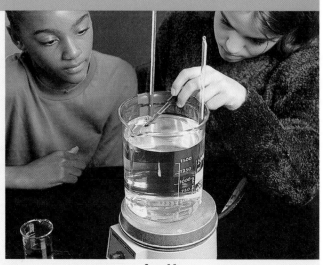

Step 11

Part 2

9 Carefully place the beaker with the attached thermometers on the hot plate. You are about to heat the water while it has ice cubes in it. Predict what you think will happen to the temperature of the water at the location of each thermometer.

10 After you have made your prediction, place a row of ice cubes against the side of the beaker close to the thermometer whose bulb is near the surface of the water. Place the ice cubes exactly as you did in step 6. Now turn on the hot plate.

11 Use the eyedropper to place one drop of coloured water just below the ice cubes. Observe and record what happens.

12 Observe and record the temperature reading on each thermometer at 30-s intervals for 3 min.

Keeping Records

13 Record your temperature readings in your data charts.

Part 1

Thermometer Near Ice Cubes		Thermometer Near Heat Source	
Time (s)	Temperature (°C)	Time (s)	Temperature (°C)
30		30	
60		60	
etc.		etc.	

Part 2

Thermometer Near Ice Cubes		Thermometer Away from Ice Cubes	
Time (s)	Temperature (°C)	Time (s)	Temperature (°C)
30		30	
60		60	
etc.		etc.	

14 Draw what happens each time you add coloured water to the container.

Analyzing and Interpreting

15 What happened to the temperatures in Part 1? Why did this happen?

16 What happened to the temperatures in Part 2? Why?

17 What did the coloured water show in each part of the activity?

Forming Conclusions

18 Imagine that your set-up for this activity is a model of an ocean. The ice cubes are in Antarctica. The other end of the container is at the equator. Use the results of your investigation to answer the following questions: *In what direction would a deep convection current move through the ocean? Why? Draw a diagram to illustrate your answer.*

1 A violent storm in the north Pacific Ocean caused a cargo ship to lose a load of 40 000 running shoes in the middle of the ocean. Six months later, people on the coast of British Columbia started finding shoes washing up on shore. Over the next year, people found shoes washing up as far south as California. The most recent shoe find, shown on the map was in the open ocean.

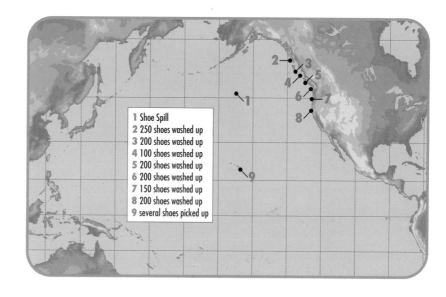

1 Shoe Spill
2 250 shoes washed up
3 200 shoes washed up
4 100 shoes washed up
5 200 shoes washed up
6 200 shoes washed up
7 150 shoes washed up
8 200 shoes washed up
9 several shoes picked up

Use your knowledge of ocean currents to answer the following questions:

a) How did the shoes get from the middle of the north Pacific Ocean to British Columbia?

b) Why haven't any shoes washed up in Alaska? Why haven't any washed up in northern Japan?

c) Where do you think the shoes will wash up next? Why?

4.4 CHECK YOUR PROGRESS

1 Are waves and surface currents the same? Why or why not?

2 Hurricanes are powerful storms that develop in the south Atlantic Ocean. When a hurricane approaches the coast of Florida, people are told to leave their homes and move inland. What do you think people are worried about? Why?

3 The picture at right shows Mont St. Michel on the coast of France. It's built on a huge rock that is an island for part of every day. The rest of the time you can walk or drive out to it.

a) Why is it an island for only part of the day?

b) What would tourists want to know if they planned to walk out to and around the island?

4 The tidal range at Chicoutimi in Québec is about 6 m. In the Bay of Fundy, it's about 15 m. Find these two places on a map. Suggest a reason why there is such a difference in their tidal ranges.

5 Do you think currents could form in large lakes? Why or why not?

6 Explain what causes convection currents.

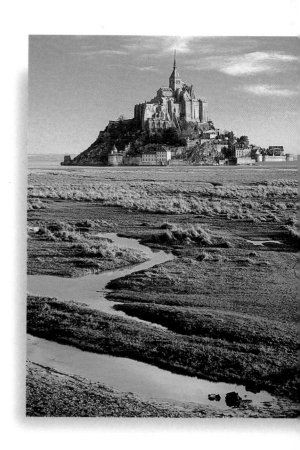

BIG IDEA
5.0
Large bodies of water and glaciers affect the environment.

Why do you think coastal areas often have thick fog?

The water that affects us most is the water in our weather. Precipitation in the form of rain, freezing rain, snow, or hail can determine what clothes we wear, what we do in a day, and where we go for holidays. Fog can stop us from going anywhere. But the amount and kind of precipitation that we receive is partly determined by whether we live close to a large body of water. Such a body of water affects the whole climate of the land that borders it.

Glaciers and ice caps also affect the environment, but in a different way. These large masses of ice grind away on the earth's surface to shape and change it. Water, in all its states, affects the environment.

5.1 LARGE BODIES OF WATER AFFECT THE CLIMATE

Explore

Sudbury, Ontario, and Victoria, British Columbia, are both located at about the same latitude, so they are both about the same distance north of the equator. But the climates in the two cities are very different. The two pictures below were both taken in early spring. If you wanted to go on a cross-country skiing holiday for March break, which city would you choose? If you wanted to go hiking, which one would you go to? Find the two cities on a map of Canada. Suggest reasons why there might be such major differences in their climates.

Sudbury's average snowfall is 267 cm in a year.

Victoria's average snowfall is 47 cm in a year.

CHOOSING A WINTER-VACATION SPOT

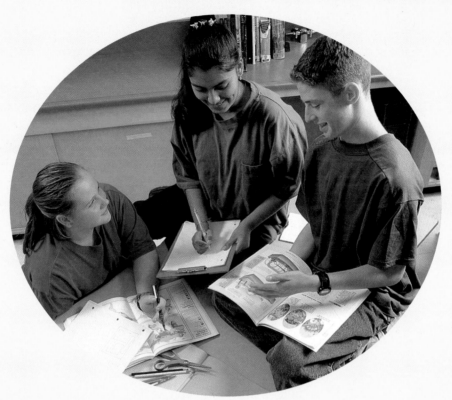

Throughout Canada and the rest of North America, there are major differences in climate from place to place. When deciding on a winter vacation, you could easily find places that would have snow for skiing. Or, you could go somewhere for a snow-free holiday. In this activity, you will investigate factors that influence climate and gather data to design promotional material for travel on a winter holiday.

Part 1: Mean Temperature and Precipitation

When you're packing for a holiday, it's important to know what kinds of temperatures and how much precipitation to expect. This activity will allow you to compare mean temperature and precipitation for several communities in Canada.

• Using a map of Canada, find the locations of the cities and towns in the information sheet that your teacher gives you.
• With a partner, and based on your own experiences, predict what a typical January day might look like in one centre in each province.
• Now, choose a latitude along which you can find at least one city or town in each province.
• Make a bar graph to compare the average summer and winter temperatures of all these cities and towns.
• Make another bar graph to compare the average rainfall and snowfall of all these cities and towns.

Part 2: Influences on Climate

Large bodies of water and landforms, such as mountains, can influence the climate of an area.

continued on next page ⋯⋯➤

- Using your bar graphs and your maps, try to explain how these two factors may have led to the differences that you see in your bar graphs.

Part 3: Travel Promotion

Now, choose one Canadian centre of interest to you and your partner.

- Design a travel brochure or a radio commercial for a winter vacation in your centre. The following topics should be included:
  a) mean annual temperature and precipitation for the area
  b) factors that contribute to local weather patterns
  c) winter recreational activities

Design Considerations

Remember, you are supposed to be "selling" your area for a winter vacation. Your brochure or commercial must grab the interest of a potential vacationer. If you choose to design a brochure, it should be illustrated and should highlight the major points that you want to get across. If you choose to produce a radio commercial, sound effects can be used to accomplish the same task.

Develop

Water, Heat Energy, and Climate

Sudbury in summer

Victoria in summer

Large bodies of water, such as the Great Lakes and the oceans, influence the weather and climate in their regions because of their heat capacity. In earlier studies, you learned that water has a higher heat capacity than most other substances. This means that it can hold a large amount of heat energy. Water takes a long time to heat up, but it holds onto heat longer than other substances do. It takes a very long time to raise the temperature of a large body of water, and a long time to lower it. Even with small lakes, it takes many hot days and warm nights in a row to raise the temperature of just the few centimetres of water near the surface.

The main effect that this has on the climate in an area is to prevent extremes in temperature. For example, Victoria is beside the ocean, so temperature differences between day and night, or between winter and summer are not as great as they are in Sudbury. Sudbury has some lakes in the area, but it is surrounded mainly by land. Land heats up and cools down quickly compared with water. It is affected much more rapidly by changes in the amount of sunlight and the air temperature.

Climate is the average weather measured over a long period of time. So, on some days in summer, Sudbury and Victoria may have the same amount of sun and the same temperatures, but over a whole year, their weather varies and has different patterns.

Other Effects of Large Bodies of Water on Weather

Anyone who lives next to a lake or the ocean knows that the wind will change direction at night after a warm sunny day. This is caused by convection currents set up by the temperature difference between the water and the land. The illustration below shows how bodies of water affect air flow.

The land absorbs heat energy from the sun more quickly than the water does. The air over the land becomes warmer as some of this absorbed heat energy is radiated back into the air. The warmed air begins to rise, and the cooler air over the water moves in to take its place. This convection current is called a **breeze**. This day-time breeze blows from the water to the land and is called a **sea breeze**.

As the sun goes down, the land cools off quickly, but the water does not. The water radiates some of its stored heat energy into the air, and this warmed air begins to rise. The cooled air over the land moves in to take the place of the rising warm air over the water. Now, the convection current is moving in the opposite direction. The night-time breeze, called a **land breeze**, blows from the land to the water.

Lake-Effect Snow

Large lakes, like the Great Lakes, can help create precipitation as well. In the winter, the large snowfalls around the Great Lakes may be caused by dry, cold arctic air passing over the warmer water of the lakes. Moisture from the lakes is absorbed into the dry, cold air. There, it condenses and forms ice crystals, which turn into snowflakes. This is called **lake-effect snow**. The diagram on this page shows how the lake-effect snow happens.

The large snowfalls that sometimes happen on and around the Great Lakes may be caused by the lakes themselves.

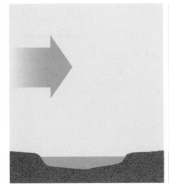

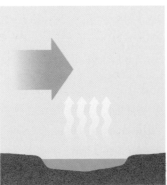

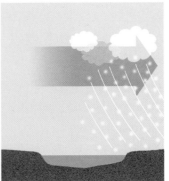

Cold arctic air moves over lake waters that are warmer than the air.

The warmer lake waters add water vapour and heat to the arctic air.

Water vapour condenses to form clouds.

Snow falls over lake and shore.

Upwelling and Downwelling

In places along ocean coastlines, wind patterns can cause upward or downward water movement. In some areas, the wind blows steadily so that it moves near-surface water away from the coast. To replace this water, deep, cold water moves up to the surface next to the coast. The meeting of cold water and warm air causes fog to form. San Francisco, California, experiences a lot of fog in summer because of **upwelling.** Areas of upwelling are important fishing areas because the cooler water is rich in nutrients that fish need. **Downwelling** occurs where the wind blows steadily toward the coast. The surface water moves toward the coast and "piles up." This extra water then sinks. Downwelling brings warm, oxygen-rich water into the deeper layers of the ocean.

Communicate

1 You are watching the Weather Channel in January, and the weather announcer is talking about cold arctic air moving in from the west over the Great Lakes.
   a) What kind of precipitation will there probably be in the forecast? Why?
   b) Draw a diagram to explain your answer.

2 Is the climate in your area affected by any large bodies of water? If so, in what ways?

3 Look at a map of North America and find a community or area at the same latitude as yours, but with a different geographical setting. For example, if you live beside one of the Great Lakes, find a place that has no large body of water near it. If you don't live near a large body of water, find a place that's beside a large lake or the ocean.

   a) Using research books and the Internet, find out what the climate is in that area, and compare it with your climate.
   b) Through the Internet, contact students in a school in that area and compare the kinds of activities that you do in summer and winter that depend on your climates.

*info*BIT

Precipitation Quiz
How many forms of precipitation do you know?
Name the following.
- Precipitation of liquid water in the form of drops
- Solid form of water that crystallizes in the atmosphere and falls to the earth
- A visible mass of water droplets, ice crystals, or a mixture of both that is suspended in the air

- A cloud that touches the earth's surface
- Precipitation of balls or pieces of ice that have a diameter greater than 5 mm
- Precipitation of balls or pieces of ice that have a diameter less than 5 mm
- Deposit of water drops formed at night by the condensation of water vapour from the air onto the surfaces of objects

5.2 OCEAN CURRENTS AFFECT THE CLIMATE

Explore

You learned in the last section that you can make some predictions about a local climate if the location is next to a large body of water or far from one. Now, consider two places at the same latitude by the same ocean that have very different climates. Look at the map below. Labrador, on Canada's east coast, and Scotland, in Great Britain, are at about the same latitude and are both beside the Atlantic Ocean. Labrador has very cold winters and short, cool summers. Scotland has a mild climate with little snow. Think about the ocean currents you studied in Big Idea 4.0. How might currents account for this difference in climate?

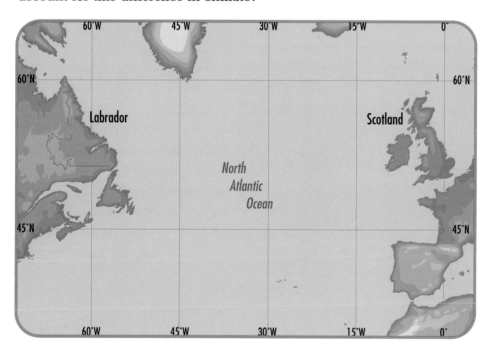

Develop

Current Events

Surface currents carry water thousands of kilometres through the oceans. If they start near the equator, they may carry warm water far into the northern hemisphere, as the Gulf Stream does. If they start closer to the poles, they may carry very cold water down into more southerly areas, as the Labrador Current does. When these currents flow close to shore, they can influence the climate of that area.

The temperatures of ocean currents affect more than just the air temperature. They also affect the amount of precipitation that a location receives. Have you ever noticed that the air is much more humid in the summer than it is in the winter? The reason is that warm air can hold more moisture than cold air can. Wind blowing over a warm ocean current and onto land will carry moisture. Wind blowing over a cold ocean current and onto land will be relatively dry. The two pictures here show the effects of this difference.

The winds that blow in from the Pacific Ocean pass over the warm North Pacific Current. They carry so much moisture that part of the coast of British Columbia is a rain forest.

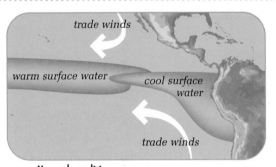

The cold Peruvian Current flows northward along the coast of Chile and Peru. The winds blowing over the current carry so little moisture onto the land that the Atacama Desert covers the entire coast. These are salt deposits. How do you think they got there?

_re_SEARCH

El Niño

A change in ocean currents is one of the key indicators of the climate event known as El Niño. In the first few months of every year, the cold current that flows north along the west coast of South America is warmed by a southward current. But every few years, the warming takes place even earlier, in December. This early warming is much stronger than usual and lasts as long as a year or two. This is El Niño, and its local effect is heavy rains and a change in the fish harvest. But scientists have discovered that El Niño affects the whole world's climate. Using the Internet and other research sources, find out:

- What causes El Niño?
- How does it affect climates around the world? the fisheries industry?
- How often does El Niño occur?
- How can scientists predict when these events will occur and how strong they will be?

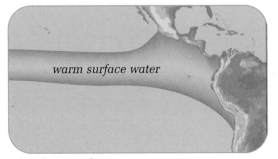

Normal conditions

El Niño conditions

1 On the map below, six cities and the ocean currents that pass near them are shown. Compare the following pairs of cities:

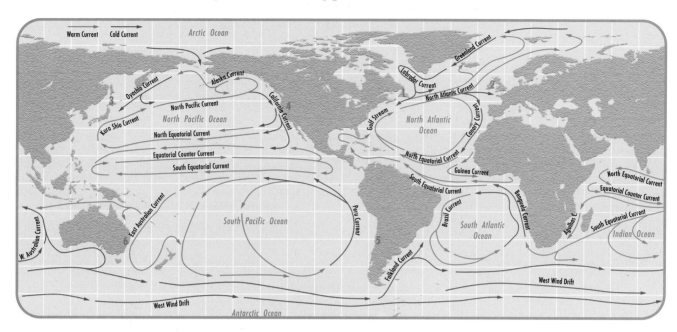

- (1) St. John's, Newfoundland, and (2) Dublin, Ireland
- (3) Sapporo, Japan, and (4) Vancouver, BC
- (5) Santiago, Chile, and (6) Sydney, Australia
a) For each pair, predict which one will have a warmer climate and which one will have more rain.
b) Explain your predictions for each one.
c) Check your predictions by using reference books and the Internet.

5.3 GLACIERS AFFECT THE EARTH'S SURFACE

Antarctica

While most of the water on earth is in the oceans as salt water, most of the fresh water is locked into the ice and snow of the polar ice caps and glaciers all over the world. The water frozen into these gleaming masses is not the fluffy snow of a New Year's snowfall. Neither is it the grainy grubbiness of a March snowbank. There may be some fluffy new-fallen snow on the surface, but it's only a thin layer on the solid, packed ice below. The weight of years, sometimes millions of years, of snowfalls has pressed the delicate snow crystals into hard, solid ice. You can make your own miniature model of glacier ice when you make a snowball. If you pack the snow in your snowball hard enough, it will turn to ice.

Shaping the Earth

Develop

As snow and ice accumulate in glaciers over the years, the masses become so great that the glaciers start to move. If you stood for a day and watched a glacier, you wouldn't notice any change. But if you put a marker in it and came back the next year, you would find that your marker had moved. It is this movement that makes ice such a powerful force in shaping the earth's surface.

Glacial Landforms

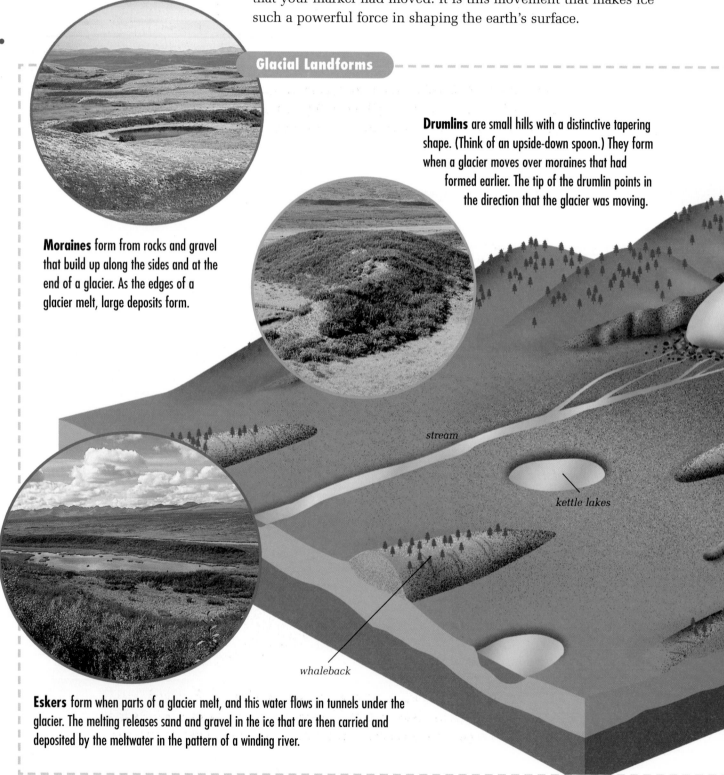

Drumlins are small hills with a distinctive tapering shape. (Think of an upside-down spoon.) They form when a glacier moves over moraines that had formed earlier. The tip of the drumlin points in the direction that the glacier was moving.

Moraines form from rocks and gravel that build up along the sides and at the end of a glacier. As the edges of a glacier melt, large deposits form.

stream

kettle lakes

whaleback

Eskers form when parts of a glacier melt, and this water flows in tunnels under the glacier. The melting releases sand and gravel in the ice that are then carried and deposited by the meltwater in the pattern of a winding river.

Glaciers are large, spreading sheets of ice. Glaciers that cover vast areas of land are called **continental glaciers**. Antarctica and Greenland are covered by continental glaciers. Elsewhere in the world, glaciers form high up in mountain ranges where the temperatures are so cold that snow and ice stay frozen all year round. These glaciers, called **valley glaciers**, spread down through the high valleys between the peaks.

When these mountains formed hundreds of millions of years ago, they had tall, sharp peaks like the Rocky Mountains. But, repeated glaciation has worn them down to the rounded hills we see today.

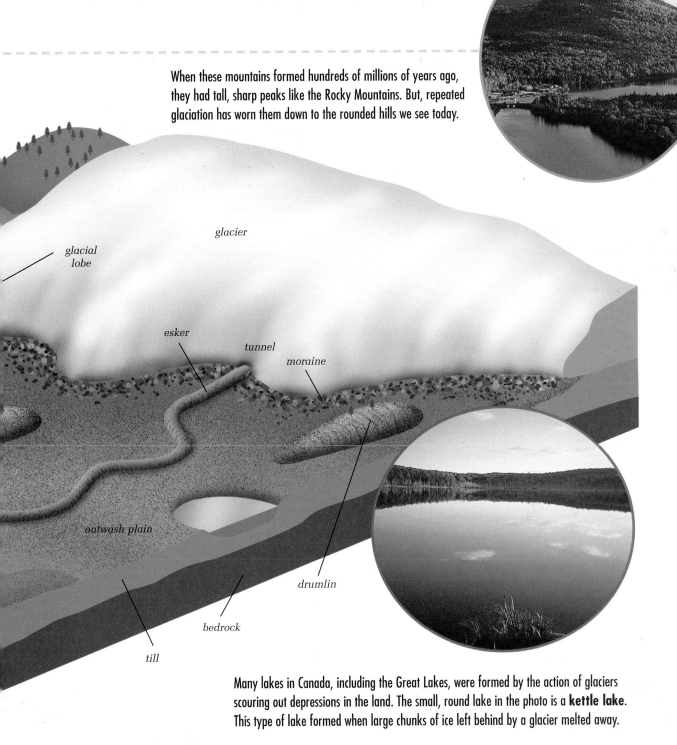

glacier

glacial
lobe

esker

tunnel

moraine

outwash plain

drumlin

bedrock

till

Many lakes in Canada, including the Great Lakes, were formed by the action of glaciers scouring out depressions in the land. The small, round lake in the photo is a **kettle lake**. This type of lake formed when large chunks of ice left behind by a glacier melted away.

As glaciers move, the weight of the ice grinds on the rock that it passes over. Pieces of rock, from tiny fragments to boulders, become embedded in the ice and are carried along. If the climate is cold enough, added snow will cause the glaciers to move forward, covering more and more land. If the climate becomes warmer, glaciers will gradually melt back or retreat, leaving behind the soil, rock, and boulders that they once contained.

Today, we have continental and valley glaciers only in specific areas, but many times over its history, large parts of the earth were covered with glaciers. These were the **Ice Ages**, and much of Canada's geography was shaped by these huge sheets of ice.

Athabasca Glacier is in the Rocky Mountains of Alberta. During the 1990s, the glacier moved an average of 9 m per year.

Can you recognize the glacial landforms in the photos on the previous pages?

- Are there any of these features in the area where you live? Have you seen any of these features in other areas you have visited?
- If wind blows across a glacier, how do you think those wind currents would affect the weather below the glacier?

Communicate

1 Find out how glaciers have formed the landscape where you live.
   a) Using reference books, maps, the Internet, and your own observations, identify glacial features in your area.
   b) Working with a partner, prepare a display showing how and when one of these features formed.

5.4 CHECK YOUR PROGRESS

1 Do you think that large bodies of water are able to influence the kinds of plants that people can grow in an area? Why or why not?

2 The Namib Desert covers the southwest coast of Africa. What kind of ocean current do you think flows along this coast? Why?

3 a) Explain how upwelling happens next to a coastline.
   b) What effect does upwelling have on the local climate?

4 Where would you likely see the following features: an esker; a drumlin; a moraine? Explain how each one forms.

5 Which of the following statements is correct? Explain why it is correct.
   a) At night, the breeze blows off the lake.
   b) During the day, the breeze blows off the lake.

*info***BIT**

Frozen in Time

Glaciers may provide evidence of global warming. Since 1900, glaciers all over the world have been retreating faster than ever before. Some glaciers have completely disappeared. In 1991, a man who died 5000 years ago was found preserved in a glacier in the Alps. His body was revealed after all that time because the glacier in which he was frozen had retreated as far back as it had been 5000 years ago. It is still retreating.

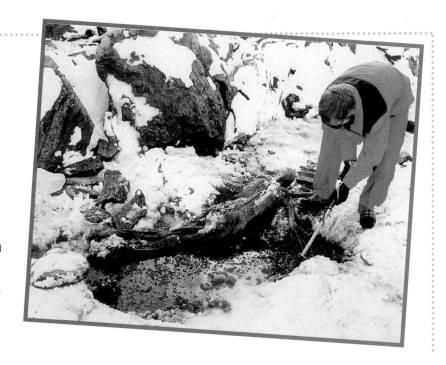

Careers and Profiles

WATER-TREATMENT PLANT OPERATOR

Water-treatment plant operators are important people in your life, even though you don't know it. Dirty and polluted water must be properly cleaned and purified before it can be pumped to your house.

Purifying Water for Drinking

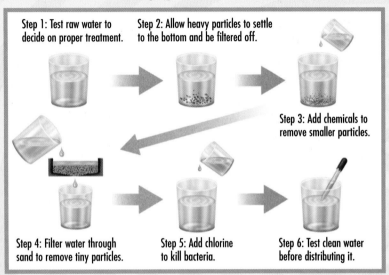

Step 1: Test raw water to decide on proper treatment.

Step 2: Allow heavy particles to settle to the bottom and be filtered off.

Step 3: Add chemicals to remove smaller particles.

Step 4: Filter water through sand to remove tiny particles.

Step 5: Add chlorine to kill bacteria.

Step 6: Test clean water before distributing it.

Plant operators must conduct tests after each step to make sure the water is being cleaned properly and to ensure the machinery in the plant is working as it should.

"Raw," dirty water is pumped into a treatment plant, where it is filtered and chemically treated to make it clean.

GLACIOLOGIST

Glaciologists are scientists who would rather spend a summer cooling their heels on ice than soaking up the sun on a southern beach. They study glaciers, investigating how glaciers move and their connection to world climate.

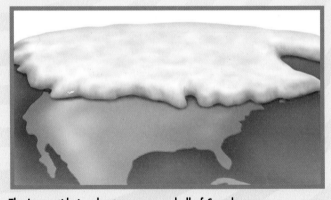

The Laurentide ice sheet once covered all of Canada.

Glaciologists use radar to find out what the ground is like under a glacier. When they have gathered enough data, they design computer programs that describe the movement of glaciers and predict how and why glaciers change.

Glaciologists exploring an ice cave

People's use of water can affect the earth's water supply and the environment.

All life on earth depends on water, but humans make the greatest use of it in the greatest number of ways. And the more people there are, the greater the amount of water that gets used. Earlier in this chapter, you saw how water cycles through the environment over and over again. This makes water a renewable resource. However, even though it's renewable on a world scale, the same amount of water isn't always available in any one place year after year. The total amount of water on earth does not change, but in some places, there may be droughts, and in others, there may be floods. And in some places, the water may be so polluted that it's not drinkable. All of these situations could be caused by natural events, or they could be caused by how people use water.

How do you use water?

6.1 HOW WE USE WATER

Explore

At the beginning of this chapter, you discovered some of the many ways that you use water, both directly and indirectly. Your direct uses are called *domestic* or *personal uses*. But your *indirect uses* reflect other uses such as those by industry and agriculture. Many of these uses have negative effects on the earth's water supply, such as depletion of groundwater supplies and pollution. So, why do we let this happen? As with many situations, there are both benefits and costs to the way we use water. Some of these are economic (for example, jobs) and some are environmental.

A "+/−" chart is one way of keeping track of benefits and costs. The "+" refers to the benefits and the "−" refers to the costs. Make your own "+/−" chart as you read through this section. After you have finished reading, work with a partner to add any other benefits or costs you have discovered that are connected with water uses.

Water Uses	
+ (benefits)	− (costs)

Develop
People Using Water

These photos show the three major types of water use worldwide.

Agriculture

Of the fresh water used by people all over the world, 73% is used in agriculture for irrigation to grow crops. Irrigation is important to the economy of many countries. It helps to provide jobs to people in agriculture, as well as producing higher crop yields.

Irrigation ditch, India

Irrigation, British Columbia

While irrigation is important in food production in many places in the world, it can also cause problems. Over-irrigation can dissolve salts in the soil and deposit them on the soil's surface. Most plants won't grow in salty soils, so this reduces the fertility of the cropland. Irrigation can also deplete groundwater supplies.

Salt deposits

Industry

The next biggest use of water worldwide, about 22%, is in industry. Industry uses water as a coolant, as a solvent, for washing, for diluting pollutants when releasing them into the environment, and for an energy source of hydro-electric power. Many of these activities can affect water in the environment. This is especially true if efforts aren't made to clean or dilute the used water before it is discharged.

Different products require different amounts of water to produce. Plastics manufacturers, for example, are huge users of water.

Pulp mill in British Columbia

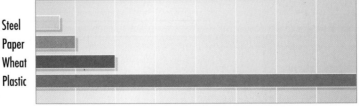

Steel	150 cu m
Paper	250 cu m
Wheat	500 cu m
Plastic	up to 2000 cu m

Amount of water used in producing 1 t (tonne) of different products

Domestic

Domestic use, or use in the home, makes up about 5% of total water use worldwide. In developed countries like Canada, water is purified and piped into homes. However, in developing countries, many people do not have clean water piped into their homes. This may be because a distribution system doesn't exist or people can't afford it.

Washing up in Canada and India

*info*BIT

Water Use in Canada

This graph shows the major ways that water is used in Canada. How do these uses compare with the ones already described in this section?

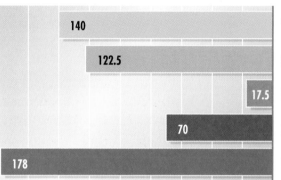

Value	Use
140	Toilet flushing (26.5%)
122.5	Showers and baths (23.2%)
17.5	Drinking and cooking (3.3%)
70	Laundry and dishes (13.3%)
178	Lawn watering/car washing (33.7%)

Litres/person/day

DECISION MAKER

WATER FOR FUN

The Question

What's the best way to protect water for recreational use?

Background Information

1 Agriculture, industry, and domestic use are the main uses of water worldwide. However, recreational use is important to many people in Canada. Swimming, boating, fishing, canoeing, white-water rafting, and skating in the winter—these are just some of the ways that Canadians use our many lakes and rivers. Working with a partner, research the recreational use of water in your area. For example:

a) In what ways do people use water for recreation in your area?

continued on next page ·······➤

b) What are the positive and negative effects on the environment of these uses of water?

c) Have there been any problems with recreational use of water in your area? If so, what caused the problem and how was it resolved? For example, if pollution was a problem, was it caused by a completely different use, such as industry, or was it caused by another recreational use, such as oil from motorboats?

d) What roles do government agencies have in protecting the water used for recreation?

2 Decide how you want to present your information. Be prepared to share your findings with the rest of the class.

In Your Opinion

3 Do you think water for recreational use needs to be protected? Why or why not?

4 Who should have the final say in determining whether water should be used for recreational purposes in an area or limited to domestic, industrial, or agricultural uses: people in the area, organizations or individuals who want to use the water, or government officials?

Communicate

1 Work with a partner or in a group to plan a one-day water festival. This festival will make other students in your school aware of the many ways that water is used in your community. Your festival could include speakers, tours of the local water-treatment plant or other facilities, posters, plays, or any other activities you can think of. Don't forget to include information about the natural environment. Think about the following questions as you plan your festival.

a) Who are the major water users in the community?

b) How does their water use affect the local water supply?

c) What kind of information should other students know about their local water supply?

d) Are there any natural wetlands in your area? Are they protected from human use?

*re*SEARCH

Ancient Plumbing Systems
Indoor plumbing and town water and sewer systems aren't modern inventions. They've existed for over 4000 years. One of the earliest known examples is found in the ancient cities along the Indus River in what is now Pakistan. This is the Indus Valley or Harappan Civilization that flourished around 2500 B.C.

• Research the Indus Valley civilizations. Learn about how these communities organized their water and sewer systems.

The ruins of the ancient city of Leh in the Indus Valley

6.2 CONTROLLING THE DESTRUCTIVE POWER OF WATER

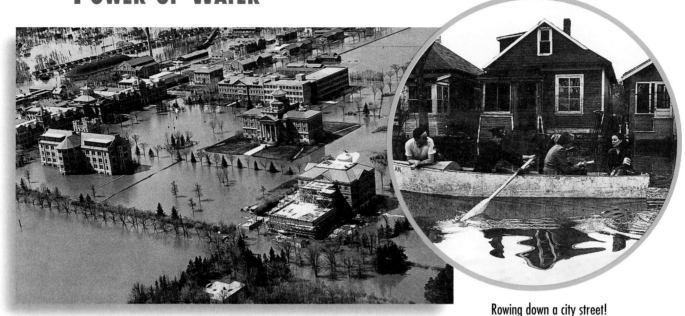

Rowing down a city street!

Explore

In 1950, the Red River in Manitoba flooded its banks. The river, which is normally about 152 m across, expanded to 64 km wide! The devastation was colossal.

- Total land flooded covered an area of 1036 km².
- Cars, buildings, and roads were swept away by the quickly rising water.
- 80 000 people had to be evacuated from the city of Winnipeg and 20 000 more from the surrounding area.
- 13 000 homes were damaged.

infoBIT

High Water!
When a river floods, it can cause a great deal of damage. Unfortunately, there's no way to predict when the next flood will come or how big it will be. However, past flooding gives some clues about what to expect. For example, the data on the right, collected on the Mississippi River over the past 100 years, shows that a water level between 13 m and 14 m can be expected about 6 times a century, whereas, a water level above 17 m can be expected only once a century. Note: the *flood stage* is the level at which a river overflows its banks.

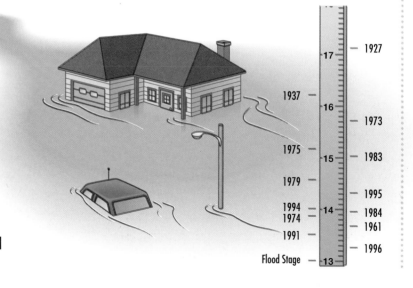

Rivers all over the world cause similar problems when they overflow their banks. When a river floods, like the Red River, most people think of it as a disaster because of the damage it causes. But is flooding really a freak disaster? Is it always harmful, or is it actually a natural and necessary part of a river's activities? Make a list of the problems caused by floods. Then, make another list of any benefits to the environment that might be caused by flooding.

Develop River Systems and Floods

Rivers are the major transportation routes for flowing water. Think of them as "water roads." They take the water that drains out of lakes and the nearby surface water run-off and move it downhill. Eventually, many large rivers end up draining into the oceans.

What Is a Flood Plain?
Each spring, heavy rainfall and melting snow and ice find their way into river systems. Most of these rivers (as well as the smaller streams and creeks) cannot contain this increased water. It spills over the river banks and floods the surrounding land. The area flooded is called a **flood plain**.

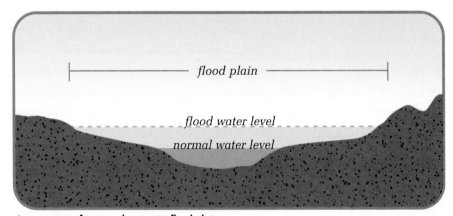

Cross-section of a river showing its flood plain

Flood plains are fairly flat areas beside rivers and are nearly at river level. Large rivers can have flood plains that cover many square kilometres. Streams may only flood a few metres on either side. Some creeks are dry all year and only flow during the spring flooding season.

So, flooding is a natural occurrence. It's part of the water cycle. Most rivers, streams, and creeks—if left alone by people—will flood a certain amount each spring. And like most elements in the natural environment, the amount of flooding varies from year to year, from river to river, and is more often a benefit than a disaster.

For example, sediment, eroded from a river's banks, washes over the flood plain and is left behind when the water subsides. Repeated flooding causes sediments to build up. The sediment acts like fertilizer, enriching the soil and making it very fertile for plants. Some of the earliest civilizations developed on the flood plains of rivers because the soil there was good for farming. The ancient Egyptians relied on the Nile River to flood each year and fertilize what would have otherwise been poor farmland. Farming the rich soils of the Nile allowed ancient Egypt to become a major civilization for thousands of years.

An aerial view of prime farmland on the flood plain of the Nile River, Egypt

The Costs of Building on a Flood Plain

Then why are people concerned about floods? Many modern towns and cities are built on the flood plains of large rivers. Settlers were originally attracted to these areas because of the fertile soil, easy access to running water, and nearness to water transportation. However, people living in these areas often had to spend millions of dollars building dams, dikes, and spillways in an effort to protect themselves from flood waters.

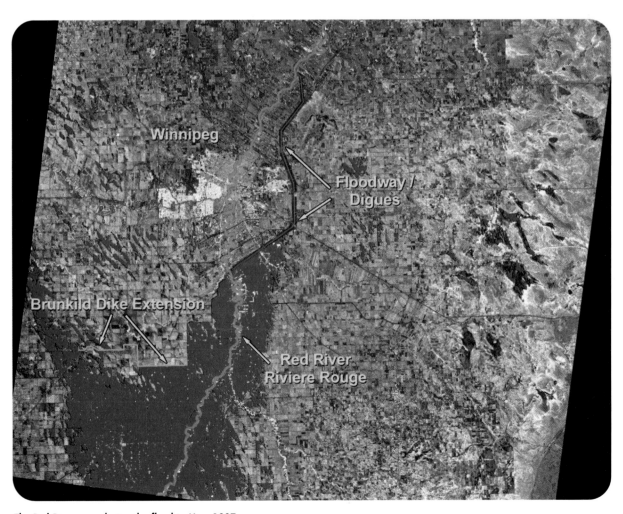

The Red River area during the flood in May, 1997

The city of Winnipeg is built on the flood plain of the Red River. After the great flood of 1950, the city wanted to prevent the same thing from ever happening again. This required several major undertakings. A massive 47-km-long ditch, called the Red River Spillway, was built to divert the Red River around the east side of the city during a flood. It was completed in 1968 and cost $350 million (in today's dollars). Also, the 40-km-long Brunkild dike was built to the south of Winnipeg to protect the city's southwest flank.

The Red River Spillway. This huge "ditch" can be seen by astronauts orbiting the earth.

All the effort paid off. In 1997, the Red River had another massive flood. Even though it was bigger than the one in 1950, it still caused much less damage because of the new spillway and dike.

Constructing large dams, dikes, and spillways is very costly, though, and can often create previously unforeseen problems. Consider the Aswan High Dam, built across the Nile River in Egypt. It was completed in 1972 at a cost of millions of dollars. It was built to produce electricity, irrigate farm fields, and stop seasonal flooding.

Because of the Aswan High Dam, flooding in the Nile River in Egypt has been greatly reduced.

When the dam was built, 98% of the sediment, which once fertilized the soils of the flood plains, was trapped behind the dam. As a result, farmers have had to buy millions of dollars worth of fertilizer, and a costly system of irrigation ditches had to be constructed. Now, the river runs the risk of becoming polluted by fertilizer run-off. The soil needs protection from the negative effects of irrigation. What was once "free" farmland around the Nile River has become very costly.

Communicate

1 a) What is a flood plain and how is it formed?
   b) What are some of the advantages of building on a flood plain?
   c) What are some of the consequences of building on a flood plain?
   d) What are some of the consequences of building dams?

2 The table shows the peak water levels for seven Red River floods. Make a graph using these numbers. What trend do you notice?

Year	Water level (m)
1826	11.12
1852	10.51
1861	9.9
1950	9.23
1974	5.36
1979	5.85
1997*	10.45

*Note: 1997 shows the estimated peak water level that would have occurred if the Red River Spillway had not been built. The actual peak water level for 1997 was 7.46 m.

6.3 PROCESSING WATER FOR HUMAN USE

Explore

Where does the water you drink come from? If it comes from your own well, it is probably pumped straight out of the earth to you—no processing is needed. However, if you live in a community that takes its water from a lake or river, the water is processed to make it safe to drink. Why would water that is natural need to be treated to make it safe? Look at the following photos. What conditions might make the water from these sources unsafe for people to drink? Remember that just because water looks clean, that does not mean that it's safe to drink.

Making Water Drinkable

Develop

The water that pours out of your taps goes through a special system to get to you. This system includes collecting the water, treating it, and distributing it. In the next Investigator activity, you will simulate some of the steps in the treatment part of the system.

TREATING WATER

The Question

What steps are used in treating water for human use?

Materials & Equipment

- *3 2-L plastic bottles*
- *500-mL beaker*
- *scissors*
- *2 L dirty water*
- *measuring spoon*
- *30 mL potassium aluminum sulphate (alum powder)*
- *cotton batting*
- *500 mL medium coarse, clean sand*
- *500 mL clean aquarium gravel*
- *500 mL activated charcoal*
- *30 mL bleach*
- *glass of tap water*

Procedure

1. Use the scissors to cut the tops off two of the plastic bottles. Make the cut about 3 cm above the point where the sides are straight. Cut the bottom off the third bottle.

2. Observe and smell the dirty water. Record your observations. Pour about 1.5 L of dirty water into one of the bottles with the top cut off. Use the measuring spoon to add the potassium aluminum sulphate (alum powder) to the water. Clean the measuring spoon after using it.

3. Stir the mixture slowly for 3 min, and then let the water stand undisturbed for 15 min. Observe the water every 5 min and record your observations.

4. While you are monitoring the water, assemble the filter. Remove the cap off the bottle with the bottom cut off. This is the filter holder. Plug the neck of the filter holder with a small amount of cotton batting. Turn the filter holder so that the neck is at the bottom, and place it into a beaker to support it. Add a layer of sand about 4 cm deep. On top of the sand, add a 4-cm layer of charcoal, then add a 4-cm layer of gravel on top of the charcoal.

Caution!
Do *not* taste any of the water at any time during this activity.

continued on next page ┈┈┈➤

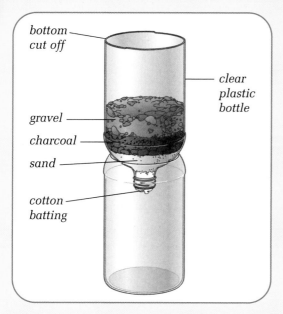

bottom cut off

clear plastic bottle

gravel

charcoal

sand

cotton batting

5 Place the assembled filter, neck down, on the empty bottle with the top cut off. Make sure it is exactly vertical, and doesn't fall over. Have a partner hold the filter in place while you slowly and carefully pour the top two-thirds of the dirty water sample from the first bottle into the filter. Do not overflow your filter.

6 Wait until about half the water has drained through. Then use the measuring spoon to add 30 mL of bleach to the water in the beaker. Then let the rest of the water drain through the filter.

7 Observe and smell the filtered water. Compare it with the tap water. Record your observations.

Keeping Records

8 Record your observations before, during, and after treating the water. You might want to use a chart like the one below to help organize your data.

Water Sample Data	
Time	**Observations**
Beginning of experiment	
Add alum	
5 min after adding alum	
10 min after adding alum	
15 min after adding alum	

Analyzing and Interpreting

9 How did your final water sample compare with the original water sample?

10 What happened to the water when you added the potassium aluminum sulphate?

11 How did the filtered water compare with the unfiltered water that had been treated with potassium aluminum sulphate?

12 Did the bleach change the appearance of the water? Why do you think it was used?

Forming Conclusions

13 Describe the process you used to treat the water. Is the treated water clean enough to drink? Why or why not?

Steps in Water Processing

People, farms, businesses, and factories use millions of litres of water every day. Getting good quality water to all these users is a big effort. Water from a source such as a lake, river, or groundwater is pumped into a treatment plant. There, it passes through a series of stages that gradually make it cleaner and cleaner until it is safe to drink. Then, it is pumped through pipes throughout the community, where it is used in homes, schools, offices, stores, manufacturing plants, and anywhere else people live and work. The used water goes down the drains into a separate pipe system. This water may be released into the environment or it may be treated in a waste-water treatment plant, such as those you learned about in earlier studies.

natural water source   water treatment plant for purification   use in the community   waste-water treatment plant   natural environment

The illustrations show how water is usually treated to make it drinkable, and then how it can be treated after it is used. Most communities in Canada treat their used water before releasing it into the environment.

1 Water comes into the system through screens that filter out large solids, plants, and fish.

2 Water is pumped into a large holding tank where a chemical is added to make small solids clump together and fall to the bottom.

3 The water is passed through a special filter to take out any remaining tiny solids.

4 Chlorine is added to kill any microscopic organisms. Fluoride may also be added at this stage.

5 The drinkable water is pumped out to storage and distribution systems.

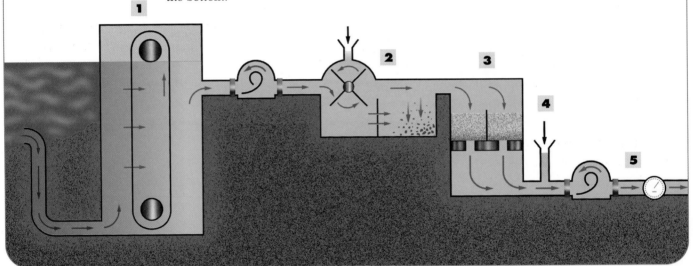

A diagram of a water treatment plant

Communicate

1 Earlier in this chapter, you learned how water constantly recycles itself naturally through the water cycle. Every community, though, also has its own water cycle. Your teacher will divide your class into groups so each group can take one part of your community water cycle: source protection, treatment, use, or waste-water treatment. Working with your group, prepare a presentation on your part of the community water cycle.

6.4 Natural-Resource Development and Water

Explore

In Canada, the natural-resource industries are an important part of our economy. These industries extract and process minerals, oil and natural gas, forest products, and fish. The natural-resource industries use water and affect the earth's water supply in a variety of ways. Logging and mine development may take place near streams, rivers, and lakes. Fish farming takes place in the ocean or lakes. Some oil and natural gas deposits are below the ocean floor. Natural-resource development can have both negative and positive effects on the earth's water supply.

What kind of effect do you think this fish farm might have on the water around it?

Develop

The Effect on Water

Natural resources are things in the natural environment that we use to meet our needs and wants. Without natural resources, you wouldn't have a house to live in, a bike to ride on, computer games to play with, or many other important products in your life. Like other industries, the natural-resource industries use water in their processes, such as in extracting oil from the ground, removing bark from logs, or making paper from wood pulp. They generally harvest or extract their raw materials, for example, mineral ores or logs, from remote areas. These materials must then be transported to places where they can be processed and used. Through all these phases of development, natural-resource industries can affect water in the natural environment.

Like manufacturing and other industries, natural-resource industries can harm waterways and water bodies. The following photos show some examples of these effects. How do you think some of these problems could be reduced or prevented?

Discharges of chemicals from pulp and paper mills can affect fish and other aquatic life.

Large amounts of rock are left over after the valuable metal is taken out of ore. This waste rock may contain substances that can pollute water supplies.

Large amounts of mud or rocks falling into a stream can change a stream's flow and affect the organisms that live there.

Dams for hydro-electric production can flood large areas and reduce the flow of water downstream.

Positive Effects

While we often hear about the negative effects of natural-resource development, this development can also have positive effects. Resources such as oil, natural gas, coal, and hydro-electricity provide the energy needed to purify water, dig wells, and process sewage. Some of the products used in these activities come from mines, such as the alum used in water purification and metals used to manufacture pumps.

• Can you think of other positive effects on water that natural-resource industries might have?

reSEARCH

Oil and gas development on land can change surface water and groundwater supplies. Offshore, oil and gas development can also affect the ocean environment as well as being affected by currents, high winds, and waves. Special technology is needed to drill below the ocean floor and to transport the oil and natural gas to shore. This technology is very expensive and the risks are great. Why do companies do it? Why do countries like Canada offer special programs to support it? Choose either Hibernia, off Newfoundland, or Sable Island, off Nova Scotia.

For the development you choose, find out:

• What are the economic benefits and costs of the project?
• What are the environmental effects of the project?
• How did the Canadian government support the project? Do you think the government should have given this much support? Why or why not?

1 In Canada, laws and regulations help to reduce the negative impacts of natural-resource industries on the environment. Companies use special equipment to control the release of pollutants. They monitor their activities to prevent accidental harm to the environment. Choose one of the following natural-resource industries. Make a poster showing how this industry uses or affects water and how companies in that industry try to reduce any negative effects on the water supply.

a) oil and natural gas

b) mining

c) fish farming

d) logging

6.5 Check Your Progress

1 Explain the following statement: *Drinkable water is not free.*

2 Earlier in this chapter, you learned that the amount of water on earth and in the atmosphere is the same as it was millions of years ago. Yet many people say that today we have a crisis in water supply in many places.

a) What do you think people mean by a "crisis in water supply"?

b) What has changed over the earth's history that could have caused this crisis?

3 Why would building on a flood plain affect the natural flow of a river?

4 Using a chart or other diagram, describe how water is processed to make it clean enough to drink.

5 In what ways might the following activities affect the local water supply if they are not done carefully? What could be done in each case to protect the water supply?

a) A large open-pit iron mine is developed. First, the soil is scraped away and the covering layers of rock are removed and piled to one side. Then, the iron ore is removed and trucked away.

b) Trees are cut down on a hillside. They are hauled away on a rough logging road that crosses several streams.

Holding Back the Water

The Question

Do dams have a positive or negative effect on water-system resources?

Background Information

Dams built across rivers are the oldest means of controlling water flow. Rainwater and water from melting snow that would otherwise be lost can be captured and stored in large **reservoirs** behind dams. It can then be released in a controlled manner as it's needed. Unfortunately, the damming of rivers, while providing many benefits, has wide-ranging environmental implications.

W.A.C. Bennett Dam, British Columbia, was built across the Peace River in 1968.

Advantages of Dams

The 362-km-long reservoir created by the Bennett Dam, Williston Lake, is the largest human-made lake in Canada.

Recreation. The large lake that forms behind a dam can provide many facilities for recreational activities.

Hydro-Electricity. The controlled release of water can be used to cleanly generate electricity.

Flood Protection. During times of high rainfall or heavy melting snow, water can be held back to eliminate or reduce costly flooding.

Irrigation. During periods of low rainfall, water can be released to irrigate crops.

Employment. The construction and operation of a dam provides many local jobs.

Shipping. Dams, in combination with locks, can make a once treacherous river safe for boats to travel on.

Disadvantages of Dams

The Peace-Athabasca River delta began to shrink when the Bennett Dam was built 1200 km upstream.

Water Flow. Dams decrease the flow of water which can shrink the size of lakes and wetlands downstream.

Salinity. As less fresh water flows downstream, more salt water from the ocean can enter the river's mouth. This harms species that cannot tolerate higher salt levels.

Habitat. Reservoirs displace people and wildlife. They also destroy natural habitat and valuable farmland.

Migration. Migrating and spawning fish need special fish ladders to swim upstream past dams.

Sedimentation. Sediment in the river is trapped behind the dam. This sediment normally collects in river deltas and flood plains, providing important plant nutrients.

Canadian Dam Facts

- Canada is one of the world's top ten dam builders.
- Most of the major river systems in Canada have been dammed.
- We have over 600 large dams and thousands of small dams.
- Most large dams in Canada are built to provide hydro-electricity.
- Most of Canada's dams are in Québec and British Columbia.
- If you combined all of the area flooded by dams in Canada, it would cover an area the size of Lake Ontario.

In Your Opinion

1 Imagine that a large electrical utility has proposed to build a dam at the site shown in the drawing at the bottom of the page. Draw a map to show what you think the area will look like *after* construction is complete.

2 a) What benefits will the dam provide?

b) What possible problems might it create? Can you think of ways to reduce the problems?

c) After you've examined the benefits versus the problems, state whether you think the dam should be built or not.

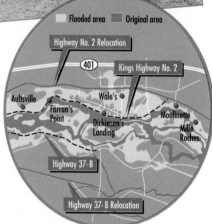

In the 1950s, a series of dams was built on the St. Lawrence River. The reservoir that was formed left the sites of six villages under water. The above photo shows a house being moved away from the area about to be flooded.

PROJECT

Getting Started

Where did the water you drank today come from before it got to your tap? The photo on this page suggests one of the places it might have been as it moved through the water cycle. Over and over, year after year, water cycles through the earth's atmosphere, oceans, lakes, rivers, glaciers, and groundwater. What stages of the water cycle can you identify in the photo?

Water is continuously on the move, not just from solid to liquid to gas, but in streams and rivers, and currents and waves. Sometimes it's salt water, and sometimes it's fresh. In large bodies, it can make a coastal area milder than an inland area at the same latitude. It supports life everywhere on the planet. But sometimes life, especially humans, can have a negative effect on the earth's water resources.

Lake Louise, Alberta—Many communities get their drinking water from lakes.

Humans use more water in more different ways than any other living things on earth. Although the total amount of water on earth does not change from year to year, our effect on it does. A rapidly increasing population means more demands on the water supply. It also means more pollution if efforts aren't made to protect our water supply.

Before You Start...

Look through your notes from the activities you did in this chapter. You learned about the water cycle. You also learned about the differences between salt and fresh water, and the diversity of organisms that live in each. You learned how waves, tides, and currents work, and how large bodies of water affect the environment. And you learned about the ways humans use water and the effect of this use. Now you have the chance to put all this knowledge together in a creative package.

Earlier in this chapter, you planned a water festival for your school to make other students aware of the many ways that water is used in your community and the importance of protecting and conserving it. Now you're going to design and present the festival's highlight: *Water's Journey.*

Water Festival
All Day, May 29

Tours - Talks - Displays
Games - Free Samples

See Water's Journey -
An Adventure In Travel

Don't Be All Wet!

Take The Plunge!

Drink It All In!

The criteria for your project are given below. Remember, you can use any information you have learned while studying this chapter or other science chapters in this grade or earlier grades. If you need additional information, you can use reference materials, including the Internet. Your presentation can take any form that you want, as approved by your teacher. It could be a video, a play, performance art, a computer presentation, readings, or a combination of these, along with written materials and posters or other visuals.

The Task

Create a presentation that shows the water cycle and how humans affect different parts of it.

Criteria for Your Water's Journey

Here are the criteria for your Water's Journey presentation.

☑ A raindrop is the starting point.

☑ The drop of water must be used at least once by humans.

☑ Points at which humans might affect the water drop should be shown.

☑ The water must pass through all three states—solid, liquid, and gas—naturally (without the help of humans).

☑ The water becomes part of a river, lake, or stream at one point and also enters the groundwater.

☑ The water joins at least one ocean and is moved by a current.

☑ The water drop can go through the different stages of the water cycle as many times as you need to have your presentation meet these criteria.

continued on next page ······►

Materials & Equipment

- *paper and pencils*
- *reference materials, Internet access*
- *materials for your presentation (these will depend on what form your presentation takes)*

Procedure

1 With your group, brainstorm the answers to the following questions:
a) Where will the raindrop fall?
b) What will happen to it after it falls?
c) What will be the human use?
d) How will you show the effects of human activities on the water drop at different stages?

2 Make a rough sketch of your water drop's journey through the water cycle. Think about how you will show these different steps in your presentation. Do you need any more information before you continue? If so, collect the information you need.

3 Design your presentation, and give the design to your teacher for approval before you begin preparing it. Include these items in your design package:
a) a brief description of the type of presentation you will do (play, computer presentation, etc.)
b) a sketch or outline of the water cycle that you will show
c) a diagram of any models or simulations you will use
d) a list of materials
e) a procedure for preparing your presentation
f) a schedule

4 Prepare your presentation according to the design and plan that your teacher approved.

5 Note any changes to your design or plan that you make as you're preparing your presentation. (If there are major changes, check with your teacher before making them.)

6 Rehearse your presentation. Make any necessary changes.

Share and Compare

7 Present your Water's Journey to your class. As you watch other groups, write down:
a) what you liked best about their presentations
b) any ideas or materials that you could have used in your presentation

Observations and Reflections

8 Look back at the criteria at the start of the project. How well does your presentation reflect all these criteria?

9 In your opinion, how well did your presentation explain the water cycle and human effects on it?

10 If you could revise your presentation, what would you do differently? Why?

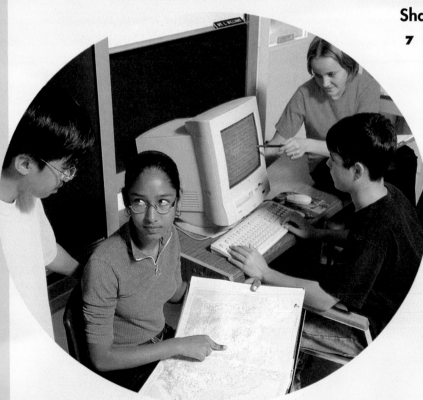

What steps will your water drop have to go through to meet all the criteria listed?

Project

CHAPTER REVIEW

Using Key Terms

1 Create a mind map that shows your understanding of the following terms.

water cycle
water table
groundwater
salinity
watershed
flood plain
wave
tide
current
glacier
water treatment

Reviewing the Big Ideas

2 a) In what states does water occur naturally on earth?

b) For each state, give an example of a place where you would find water in that state in the summer in Canada.

3 a) Where is most of the water on earth located?

b) Is this water useful to humans? Explain your answer.

4 Explain how the water table and groundwater are related.

5 What factors could cause the water table where you live to change?

6 What is the difference between a current and a tide?

7 Describe the differences between the water in a lake and the water in the ocean.

8 Which water environment would you go to if you wanted to study as many different types of aquatic organisms as possible? Why does this environment have so many different types of organisms?

9 Describe three types of human activities that can affect animals that live in the water.

10 a) What is the Continental Divide?

b) How does it affect the watershed that you live in?

11 How can scientists map the floor of the ocean without being able to see it?

12 How do waves affect a coastline?

13 What effects does a large body of water have on the climate of a city on its shore?

14 a) What is a glacier?

b) How do glaciers affect the environment?

c) How did glaciers shape our terrain in the past?

15 a) Describe three major ways that people use water worldwide.

b) For each one, give an example of how this use might affect water in the natural environment.

16 Draw and label a simple flowchart to show how water is treated for human use, from its source to when it's distributed to homes.

17 What positive effect can natural-resource development have on the water supply?

18 What are some environmental effects of flooding? Why are floods considered natural disasters?

Connecting the Big Ideas

19 With the help of diagrams, use your knowledge of the water cycle to explain why the earth's water supply will never run out.

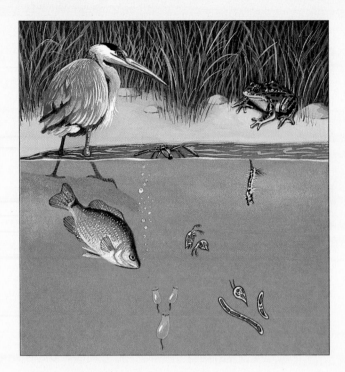

20 Whales are the largest animals in the world. Why are they found only in the oceans?

21 Agree or disagree with the following statements. Give evidence to support your decisions.

a) Because water is recycling itself all the time, we don't have to conserve it.

b) Only human activities can have negative effects on aquatic animals.

c) Ports on the east coast of North America have different tidal ranges from ports on the west coast because they are facing different directions.

22 Look around your community. What evidence do you see that human activities might be harming the earth's water supply? What evidence do you see that efforts are being made to conserve or protect water in your area?

Using the Big Ideas

23 In 1492, Christopher Columbus set sail from Spain. The first land he encountered after sailing across the Atlantic was in the Caribbean. If he had sailed straight west from Spain, he would have landed on the east coast of North America.

a) Why didn't he sail straight west? (He was an expert navigator.)

b) What route do you think he chose for his return to Spain?

24 A farmer applies fertilizer next to a lake. For the next few days, it rains heavily. In what ways do you think that the organisms in the lake's food web, shown here, might be affected by the run-off from the field? Why?

25 Imagine that you are a journalist who will be interviewing the head of a mining company that is about to develop a mine in a wilderness area of a province. Make a list of questions you will ask about how the development will affect water in that area.

26 Mexico City relies on groundwater for its millions of citizens. Now, the whole city is gradually sinking. This is happening elsewhere in the world as well, where large populations and agriculture use groundwater.

a) What causes the land to sink?

b) List some other effects that using a great deal of groundwater might cause.

Self Assessment

27 Look back on the work you did for this chapter. Identify the one piece of work that you are most proud of, one piece of work that you could do better if you were to do it again, and an assignment in which you learned something you didn't know before. For each piece of work, describe your thoughts about it in a few sentences.

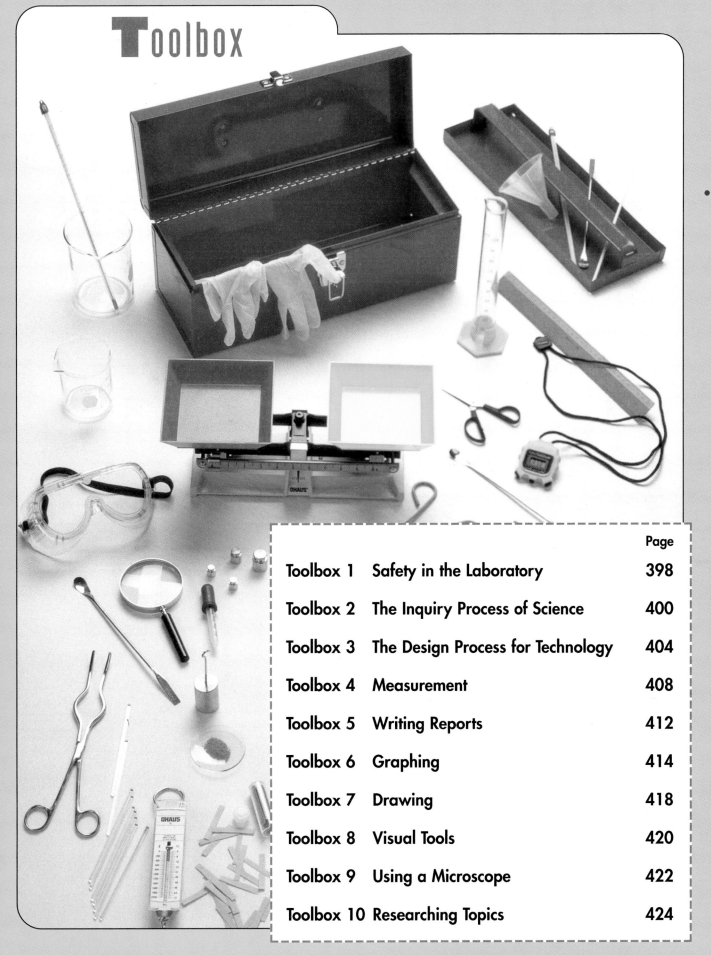

Toolbox

	Page
Toolbox 1 Safety in the Laboratory	**398**
Toolbox 2 The Inquiry Process of Science	**400**
Toolbox 3 The Design Process for Technology	**404**
Toolbox 4 Measurement	**408**
Toolbox 5 Writing Reports	**412**
Toolbox 6 Graphing	**414**
Toolbox 7 Drawing	**418**
Toolbox 8 Visual Tools	**420**
Toolbox 9 Using a Microscope	**422**
Toolbox 10 Researching Topics	**424**

Toolbox 1

Safety in the Laboratory

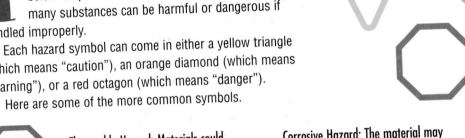

You have probably seen some of the hazard symbols below on products at home. They are a warning that many substances can be harmful or dangerous if handled improperly.

Each hazard symbol can come in either a yellow triangle (which means "caution"), an orange diamond (which means "warning"), or a red octagon (which means "danger").

Here are some of the more common symbols.

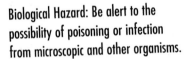

 Flammable Hazard: Materials could ignite (catch on fire) if exposed to flames, sparks, or friction.

Corrosive Hazard: The material may corrode ("eat away at") clothing, skin, or other materials.

 Explosive Hazard: The materials or equipment could explode.

Biological Hazard: Be alert to the possibility of poisoning or infection from microscopic and other organisms.

 Irritant Hazard: The material may cause irritation to eyes, nose, throat, skin, or lungs.

Electrical Hazard: Be alert to the possibility of an electric spark or shock.

Toxic Hazard: The material is very poisonous and could have immediate and serious effects.

Here are some other symbols you might see on the materials you use in your classroom. These symbols are called Workplace Hazardous Materials Information System (WHMIS) symbols. They are placed on hazardous materials used at job sites and school laboratories.

compressed gas

dangerously reactive material

oxidizing material

poisonous and infectious causing immediate and serious toxic effects

flammable and combustible material

biohazardous infectious material

corrosive material

poisonous and infectious causing other toxic effects

Can you identify the symbols that are similar to the household symbols above? Discuss with your teacher what some of the other symbols mean.

Common-Sense Safety Checklist

Your teacher may have safety instructions to add to the list below. Discuss or jot down your ideas about why each of these is an example of common-sense safety.

- Learn to recognize the warning symbols shown on the previous page.
- Keep your work area uncluttered and organized.
- Know the location of fire extinguishers and other safety equipment.
- Always wear safety goggles and any other safety clothing as requested by your teacher or this book.
- If you have long or loose hair, tie it back. Roll up long shirt sleeves.
- Don't wear any jewellery when doing laboratory activities.

- Inform your teacher if you have any allergies or medical conditions.
- Report any safety concerns you have, or hazards you see (such as spills) to your teacher.
- Handle all glassware carefully. If you see broken glass, ask your teacher how to dispose of it properly.
- Never smell any material or substance directly. Instead, gently wave your hand over it to bring its vapours toward your nose.
- Heat solids and liquids only in heat-resistant glass beakers and test tubes.
- When you heat test tubes, make sure that the open end is pointing away from you and anyone else in the room.
- If heating a substance, make sure the container does not boil dry.
- Follow your teacher's instructions to safely dispose of all waste materials.
- Always wash your hands well with soap, preferably liquid soap, after handling chemicals or other materials.
- Make sure you close the containers of chemicals immediately after you use them.
- Make sure that any water or wet hands are kept away from electrical outlets or sockets.

- When you have finished an experiment, clean all the equipment before putting it away. Be careful with hot plates and equipment that have been heated as they may take a long time to cool down.

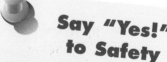

Say "Yes!" to Safety

Are you willing to:

✔ follow the safety instructions outlined by your teacher and this book?

✔ keep an eye open for possible hazards, and report them immediately?

✔ show respect and concern for your own safety and the safety of your classmates and teachers?

Toolbox 2

The Inquiry Process of Science

Scientists are always asking a lot of questions. They are always inquiring. They want to understand why the things they observe, and wonder about, happen. Experiments are important tools scientists use to help them answer their questions.

When scientists plan experiments, they usually follow a simple set of steps.

Step 1
Ask a cause-and-effect question.

Step 2
Restate the question in the form of a hypothesis.

Step 3
Develop a procedure to test the hypothesis.

Change procedure if there are flaws in the steps.

Step 4
Carry out the procedure and collect data.

Change procedure if data require it.

Step 5
Analyze and interpret the data.

Step 6
Form conclusions based on the data, and compare them with the hypothesis.

Step 7
Communicate the procedure and results of the experiment.

Hints

- Answers always lead to additional questions. New questions often lead to new hypotheses and experiments. Don't be afraid to ask questions, or to re-think the ones you've already asked.
- Science grows when scientists ask questions, answer them, and are willing to question those answers. Scientific knowledge is always growing and changing.

Step 1 **Ask a cause-and-effect question.**
Asking questions is easy. Asking questions that lead to reliable answers is more challenging. That's the reason scientists are especially fond of asking cause-and-effect questions. Here are a few examples.

- How does the concentration of laundry detergent in wash water affect the cleanliness of clothing?

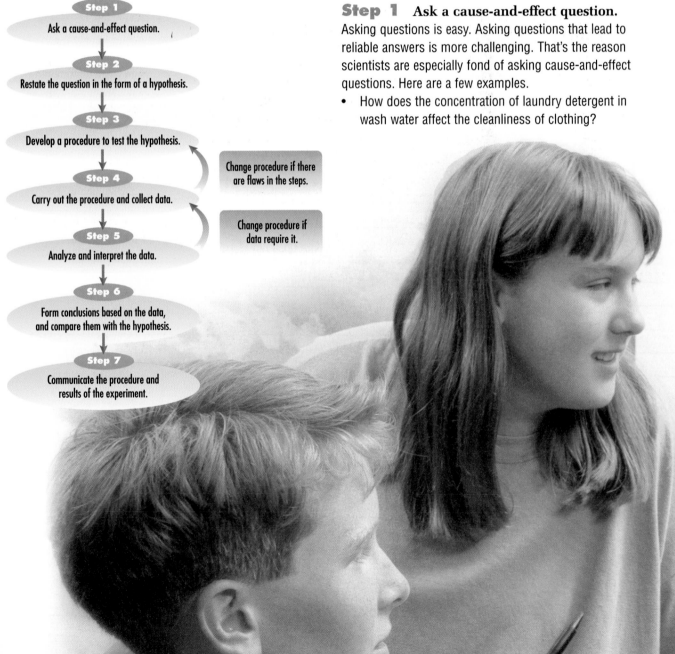

- How do different temperatures affect the growth of seedlings?
- How does the amount of moisture affect the growth of mould on bread?

Notice how the causes—the detergent, temperature, and moisture—are things that are changeable. For example, you can have different concentrations of detergent, different temperatures, and different amounts of moisture. Causes are *variables*. They are factors that can change.

The results are changeable, too. For example, some clothes may become cleaner than others, or not clean at all. Some seedlings may grow better than others, or some might not grow at all. Some bread samples may have lots of mould, some may have less, and some might not have any. Results are variables, too. They are factors that can change.

Step 2   Restate the question in the form of a hypothesis.

A hypothesis is a way of restating a cause-and-effect question so that it gives a reasonable, possible answer. Basically, a hypothesis is an intelligent guess at the solution to a problem or question.

Here are hypotheses for the questions outlined in Step 1.

- If the concentration of the detergent is high, then clothing will become cleaner.
- If the temperature is decreased, then the seedlings will not grow as well.
- If the amount of moisture is increased, then the bread will get mouldier.

Hints

A hypothesis is an early step in the experiment-planning process. Your hypothesis can turn out to be "right," but it doesn't always. That's what the experiment is for—to test the hypothesis.

Step 3   Develop a procedure to test the hypothesis fairly.

When you develop a procedure, you need to ask yourself some questions. Here are some questions you should think about. These questions are answered for the seedling example.

- **Which "cause" variable do you want to investigate?** For the seedling experiment, the "cause" variable is temperature.
- **How will you measure this variable (if it's measurable)?** You can measure temperature with a thermometer.
- **How will you keep all other variables constant (the same) so they don't affect your results?** In other words, how will you *control* your experiment so it is a fair test? To control the seedling experiment, these variables should be kept constant: the amount of light the seedlings receive; the amount and temperature of water applied to the seedlings; the kind of soil the seedlings are planted in.

- **What materials and equipment will you need for the experiment?** For the seedling experiment, the materials would include the seedlings, soil, growing pots or containers (same size), water and a watering can, a light source, a thermometer, and a ruler or other measuring device.
- **How will you conduct the experiment safely?** For the seedling experiment, some of the safety factors you should consider include putting the seedling pots in a place where they would not be disturbed, washing your hands after handling the materials, and making sure you don't have any allergies to the soil or seedlings you use.
- **How will you record the data you collect?** You could divide your seedlings into groups and grow each group at a certain temperature. You would keep track of how much each seedling in a group grew over a specified amount of time and calculate the average for the group.

Step 4 Carry out the procedure and collect data.

Depending on the kind of experiment you have planned, you may choose to record the data you collect in the form of a chart or table, a labelled sketch, notes, or a combination of these. For example, a good way to record the seedling data would be in tables like the one below.

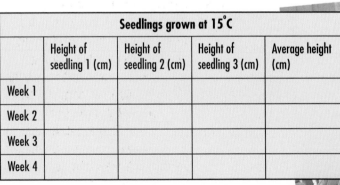

Seedlings grown at 15°C			
	Height of seedling 1 (cm)	Height of seedling 2 (cm)	Height of seedling 3 (cm)	Average height (cm)
Week 1				
Week 2				
Week 3				
Week 4				

Hints

Analyzing the data you collect is the only way you have to assess your hypothesis. It's important that your record keeping be organized and neat.

Step 5 Analyze and interpret the data.

Scientists look for patterns and relationships in their data. Often, making a graph can help them see patterns and relationships more easily. (Turn to Toolbox 6 for more about graphing.)

A graph of the seedling data would show you if there were any relation between temperature and growth rate.

Hints

If you have access to a computer, find out if it has the software to help you make charts or graphs.

Step 6 Form conclusions based on the data, and compare them with the hypothesis.

Usually, this is fairly straightforward. Either your data will support your hypothesis or they won't. Either way, however, you aren't finished answering your cause-and-effect question.

If your data support your hypothesis, you need to repeat your experiment several times to see if you get the same results over and over again. Doing your

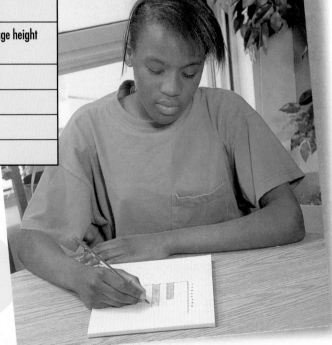

experiment successfully many times is the only way you and other scientists can have faith in your data and your conclusions.

If your data don't support your hypothesis, there are two possible reasons why.

- Perhaps your experimental plan was flawed and needs to be re-assessed and possibly planned again.
- Perhaps your hypothesis was incorrect and needs to be re-assessed and modified.

For example, if the seedlings did not grow as well in cooler temperatures, the hypothesis could be a good one. If the seedlings grew better in the lower temperatures, you would have to re-think your hypothesis, or look at your experiment for flaws. Do certain seedlings grow better at lower temperatures than others? Do different types of soil have more of an effect on growth than temperature? These are some of the questions that could be asked after doing the seedling experiment. Every experiment is different and will result in its own set of questions and conclusions.

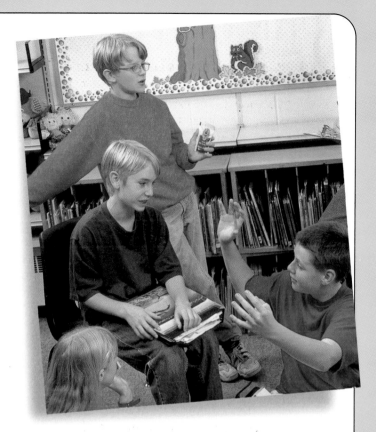

Hints

- If you don't have in-class time to repeat your experiment several times, you could ask your teacher about scheduling after-school time.
- You could also enlist the help of your classmates. If other scientists get the same results, the conclusions are usually reliable. If not, the hypothesis must be modified.

Step 7 Communicate the procedure and results of the experiment.

Scientists always share the results of their experiments with other people. They do this by summarizing how they performed the first 6 steps. Sometimes, they will write out a formal laboratory report stating their purpose, hypothesis, procedure, observations, and conclusions. Other times, they share their experimental results verbally, using drawings, charts, or graphs. (See Toolboxes 5, 6, and 7 for hints on how to prepare your results.)

When you have finished your experiment, ask your teacher how he or she would like you to prepare your results so you can share them with the other students in your class.

Toolbox 3

The Design Process for Technology

When you plan an experiment to answer a cause-and-effect question, you follow an orderly set of steps. The same is true for designing a product that solves a practical problem.

When designers try to solve practical problems, they usually follow a simple set of steps.

Step 1

Recognize a need or opportunity, or be willing to respond to a design challenge.

Step 2

Identify the specific problem to be solved.

Step 3

Set or consider the criteria that limit the nature of the solution.

Change ideas if criteria change.

Step 4

Generate a list of ideas, possible solutions, materials, and equipment.

Adjust ideas if model has design problems.

Step 5

Plan and construct a working model or prototype.

Modify model based on test results.

Step 6

Test, evaluate, and modify (if necessary) the model or prototype.

Step 7

Communicate the procedure and results of your design.

Step 1 Recognize a need or opportunity, or be willing to respond to a design challenge.

This involves recognizing what the problem is, or a need that exists, or a challenge that has been offered. For example, suppose you observe that a rope bridge across a ravine at a local park is very unstable and swings back and forth when crossed. This might be fine for people who want a thrill, but you find that most people are not comfortable crossing the bridge and don't get to enjoy one of the nicer areas of the park. You wish there were a way to make the bridge more stable so more people would use it. That is the situation or context of the problem.

Step 2 Identify the specific problem to be solved.

When you understand a situation, you can then define the problem more exactly. This means identifying a specific task to carry out. In the situation with the bridge, the task might be to build a new bridge or add support to the existing bridge.

Step 3 Set or consider the criteria that limit the nature of the solution.

Usually, there are factors that set limits on the possible solutions to a problem. For example, there may be limitations of time, of available materials, of the number of people needed, of cost, and of safety. If you are building a product for your own interests, you may set these criteria for yourself. Often in class, your teacher will outline these criteria.

For the bridge example, one factor might include cost. It might be too expensive to build a new bridge so the existing bridge would have to be modified.

Hints

Always consider safety. This includes safe handling and use of materials and equipment, as well as being aware of possible environmental impacts of your ideas. Discuss with your teacher and fellow students how your designs might affect the environment.

Step 4 Generate a list of ideas, possible solutions, materials, and equipment.

Brainstorming, conducting research, or both, are key components of this step. When you brainstorm, remember to relax and let your imagination go. Brainstorming is all about generating as many ideas as possible without judging them. Record your ideas in the form of words, mind maps, sketches—whatever helps you best.

Conducting research may involve reading books and magazines, searching the Internet, interviewing people, or visiting stores. It all depends on what you are going to design.

One idea for the rope bridge would be to anchor the bridge with strong rope or thick metal wire to large rocks or to the hillside at either end of the bridge. Sketches and diagrams would help to generate different ideas for the bridge design.

Hints

Humans have been inventors for tens of thousands of years—so take advantage of what's already been developed. When you're solving a problem, you don't have to "reinvent the wheel." See how others have solved the same problem before and use their efforts as inspiration. You can also look for ways to "build upon" or improve on their ideas.

Step 5 Plan and construct a working model or prototype.

Choose one possible solution to develop. Start by making a list of the materials and equipment you will use. Then make a working diagram, or series of diagrams, on paper. This lets you explore and troubleshoot your ideas early on. Your labels should be detailed enough so that other people could build your design. Show your plans to your teacher before you begin construction work.

A simple model of the bridge could be made to show how and where components such as stabilizing wires could be added.

Hints

If things aren't working as you planned or imagined, be prepared to modify your plans as you construct your model or prototype.

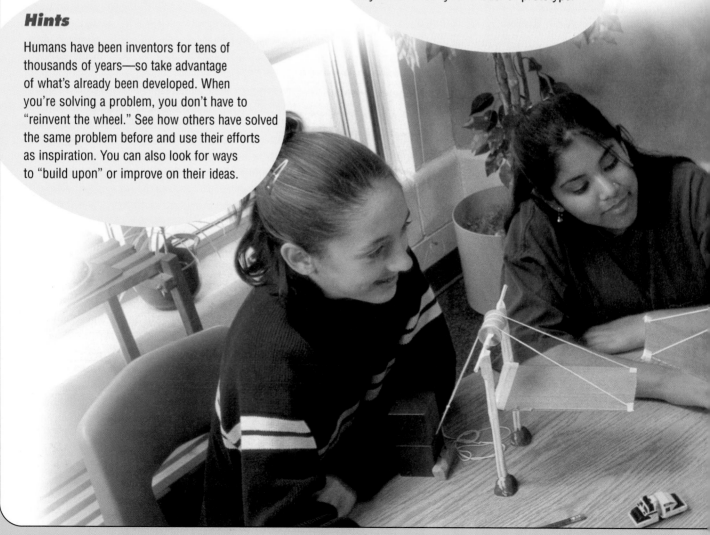

Step 6 Test, evaluate, and modify (if necessary) the model or prototype.

Testing lets you see how well your product solves the problem. Testing also lets you know if you need to make modifications. Does it meet all the established criteria? Does it solve the problem you designed it for?

Invite your classmates to try your product. Their feedback can help you decide what is and isn't working, and how to fix anything that needs fixing. Perhaps the stabilizing wires on the bridge model could be anchored elsewhere. Maybe more wires could be added.

Hints

For every successful invention or product, there are thousands of unsuccessful ones. Sometimes it's better to start over from scratch than to follow a design that doesn't meet its performance criteria.

Here's an old saying you've probably heard: "If at first you don't succeed, try, try again." Remember, there can be many possible solutions to a practical problem.

Step 7 Communicate the procedure and results of your design.

Inventors and engineers create things to meet people's needs. When they make something new, they like to show it to other people and explain to them how it works. Sometimes they will use a carefully drawn diagram of the new device and write about how they performed the first 6 steps. Other times, they will show the device to people and explain verbally how it works and how they built it. Your teacher will tell you how to prepare your results so you can exhibit the new device you make.

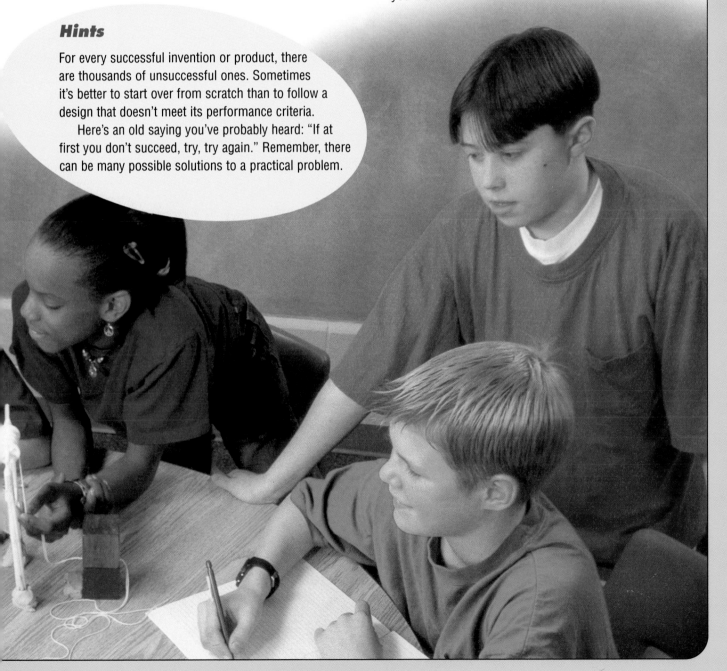

Toolbox 4

Measurement

Measuring helps everyone answer questions such as how far away something is, how massive it is, and how much space it takes up. Here are some types of measurements you might come across every day.

Length

Length tells you:

- how long or short something is
- how far or near something is
- how high or low something is
- how large or small something is.

Common units used to measure length include millimetres (mm), centimetres (cm), metres (m), and kilometres (km). All these units are based on a single standard: the metre.

CHECK IT YOURSELF

Which length unit would you use for each of the following? Why?

- the height of a table
- the depth of a lake
- the width of a dime
- the length of a skating rink
- the distance from Kitchener, Ontario, to Kamloops, British Columbia
- the distance from the earth's core to its surface

Hints

When you use a ruler, tape measure, or metre stick, always start from the 0 measurement point, not the edge of the measuring tool.

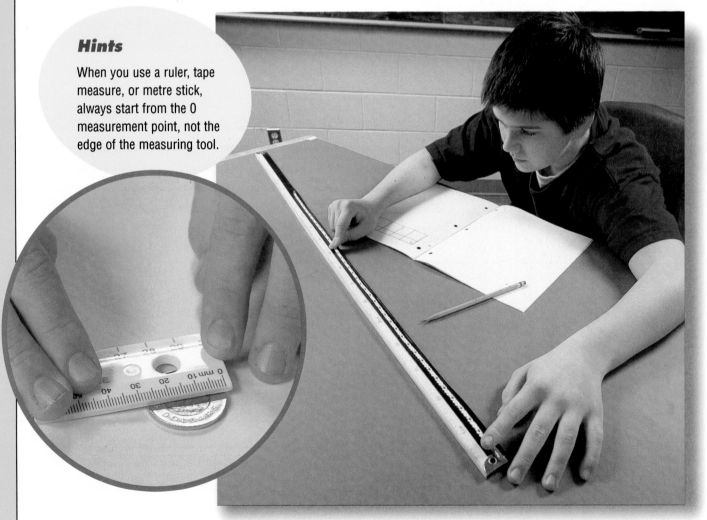

When you use a measuring tool such as a ruler, look directly in line with the measurement point, not from an angle.

Volume

The volume of something tells you the amount of space that it takes up (occupies). Common units used to measure volume include litres (L) and millilitres (mL). Remember, 1 mL equals 1 cm³.

At home, you often use a measuring cup to determine the volume of something. At school, you usually use a graduated cylinder. Here, "graduated" means a container that has been marked with regular intervals for measuring. For example, a measuring cup, a beaker, and a thermometer are all graduated.

CHECK IT YOURSELF

1 Which of the following tools could you use to measure volume? Why?
- a spoon
- a test tube
- a balance

2 How could you transform an empty can into a volume-measuring tool? Describe, step-by-step, how you would do it.

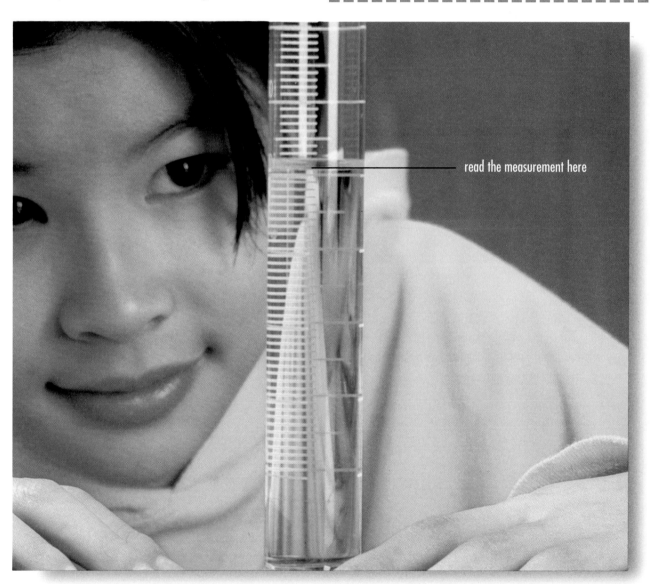

read the measurement here

When you add a liquid to a graduated cylinder, the top of the liquid is curved near the sides of the cylinder. This curve is called a *meniscus*. To measure the liquid's volume properly, you need to observe the liquid's surface at the flat, bottom portion of the curve and ignore the sides.

Mass and Weight

In science, the mass of an object and its weight mean different things. The mass of something tells you the amount of matter it has. The weight of an object is the measure of the force of gravity acting on it. We more often use mass in science. Common units used to measure mass include grams (g) and kilograms (kg).

You usually measure mass with a balance. Your classroom probably has an equal arm balance or a triple beam balance like the ones shown here.

The equal arm balance and triple beam balance basically work in the same way. You compare the mass of the object you are measuring with standard or known masses, or their mass equivalent values on the triple beam.

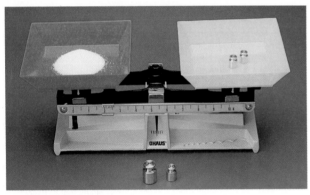

equal arm balance

An equal arm balance has two pans. You place the object whose mass you want to know on one pan. On the other pan, you place standard (known) masses until the two pans are balanced (level). Then, you just add up the values of the standard masses. The total is the mass of the object you are measuring.

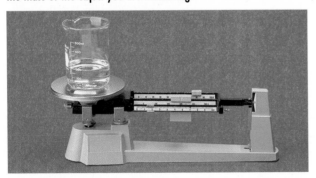

triple beam balance

A triple beam balance has a single pan. You place the object you are measuring on the pan. You adjust the masses on the beams until the beam assembly is level. Then, you add up the mass equivalent values of the beam masses from the scales on the beam.

Some businesses, such as grocery stores, use electronic balances to measure the weight of an item. When you place an object on top of the balance, it will calculate the weight of the object. The next time you're at the supermarket, ask the person at the deli or meat counter to show you how an electronic balance works.

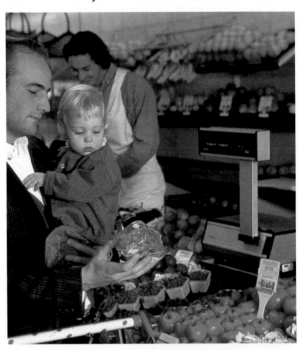

electronic balance

Before you use an electronic balance, you have to press the reset button so it starts at zero. Then, you place the object you are measuring on top of the balance. It will then produce an electronic display of the object's weight.

CHECK IT YOURSELF

1. The object on the triple beam balance is a water-filled beaker, so the balance is measuring the mass of the water plus the mass of the beaker. What if you wanted to measure just the mass of the water in the beaker? Describe, step-by-step, how you would do it.

2. How would you measure the mass of an apple? How would this be similar to and different from measuring the mass of a pile of salt?

Estimating

When you estimate, you use your imagination to guess the length, volume, or mass of an object. Sometimes, you can estimate by comparing one object with another object that has known measurements. For example, if you are asked to estimate the volume of your drink, you could estimate by comparing it with a large jar of mayonnaise in your fridge (which has its volume marked on the label).

Sometimes, it's useful to estimate the measurement of an object before you actually measure it. You might do this to help you decide which units of measurement and which measuring tool to use. In other cases, you might not be able to measure an object at all. In this case, an estimate of its length, volume, or mass might be the best you can do.

Try to estimate the measurements of the items listed below. Include the measurement units that you think should go with your estimates. Then, measure them to see how close your estimates were to the real values. Did you choose the correct measurement units? If you don't have some of these items in your classroom, check at home.

For a large object or distance, you might divide it up into portions in your imagination and guess the length, volume, or mass of one portion. You then multiply that guess by the number of imaginary portions to estimate the measurement of the whole.

Object	Length	
	estimate	actual value
pencil		
height of your teacher's desk		
length of your classroom		

Object	Mass	
	estimate	actual value
this textbook		
banana from someone's lunch		
piece of chalk		

Object	Volume	
	estimate	actual value
amount of water poured into an empty jar		
marker cap		
drink thermos		

Toolbox 5

Writing Reports

Toolbox 2 shows you how to plan a science experiment, and Toolbox 3 shows you how to do technological design. This toolbox will help you write a report so you can communicate the procedure and results of your work.

Here is a list of things you should try to do when writing your science reports.

- Give your report or project a title.
- Tell readers why you did the work.
- State your hypothesis or describe the design factors.
- List the equipment and materials you used.
- Describe the steps you took when you did your experiment or designed and made your product.
- Show and explain your experimental data or the results of testing your product.
- Make conclusions based on the outcome of the experiment or success of the product you designed.

Give your report or project a title

Write a brief title on the top of the first page of your report. Your title can be one or two words that describe a product you designed and made, or it can be a short sentence which summarizes an experiment you performed.

Tell readers why you did the work

Use a heading such as "Introduction" or "Purpose" for this section. Here, you give your reasons for doing a particular experiment or designing and making a particular product. If you are writing about an experiment, tell readers what your cause-and-effect question is. If you designed a product, explain why this product is needed, what it will do, who might use it, and who might benefit from its use.

State your hypothesis or describe the design factors

If you are writing about an experiment, use a heading such as "Hypothesis." Under this heading you will state your hypothesis. Remember, your hypothesis is your guess at the solution to a problem or question. Your hypothesis makes a prediction that your experiment will test.

If you are writing about a product you designed, use a heading such as "Design Challenge." Under this heading, you will describe why you decided to design your product the way you did. Explain how and why you chose your design over other possible designs.

List the materials and equipment you used

This section can come under a heading called "Materials and Equipment." List all the materials and equipment you used for your experiment or design project. Your list can be in point form or set up as a table or chart. Remember to include the exact amounts of materials used, when possible (for example, the number of nails used in building a model or the volumes and masses of substances tested in an experiment). Include the exact measurements and proper units for all materials used.

Also include diagrams to show how you set up your equipment or how you prepared your materials. Remember to label the important features on your diagrams. (See Toolbox 7 for drawing tips.)

Describe the steps you took when you did your experiment or designed and made your product

Under a heading called "Procedure" or "Method," describe, in detail, the steps you followed when doing your experiment or designing and making your product. If you made a product, describe how you tested it. If you had to alter your design, describe in detail how you did this.

Show and explain the data of your experiment or the results of testing your product

Give this section a heading such as "Data" or "Observations." In this section, you should show the data you collected while performing the experiment or testing your product. Use graphs, tables, diagrams, and any other visual aids that show the results of your tests. (See Toolbox 6 for graphing tips.) If you performed your experiment a few times, give results for each trial. If you tested different designs of your product, give results for each design.

Make conclusions based on the outcome of the experiment or success of the product you designed

This last section of your report can be called "Conclusions." In one or two paragraphs, explain what your tests and experiments showed. If you made a product, explain if your design did what it was supposed to do, or worked the way it was supposed to work. If you changed the design of your product, explain why one design is better than another.

If you did an experiment, explain if your results were predicted by the hypothesis. Describe how you might adjust the hypothesis because of what you learned from doing the experiment, and how you might test this new hypothesis.

Describe the practical applications your product or experiment might have for the world outside the classroom.

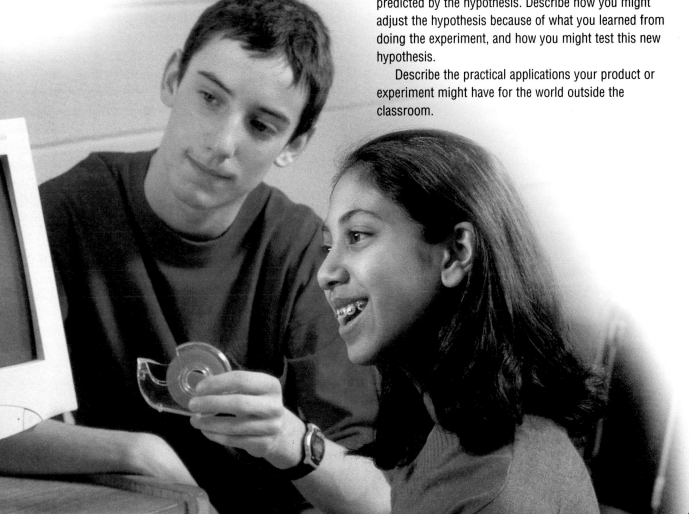

Graphing

Science and technology often involve collecting a lot of numerical data. This data may be recorded in tables or charts. Sometimes, however, it's difficult to see if there are any patterns in the numbers. That's when it's useful to reorganize the data into graphs.

A graph is similar to a picture or diagram that shows more easily how numbers are related to one another. You have probably drawn a lot of graphs over the years in your studies of mathematics, geography, and, of course, science and technology.

What Do You Recall about Line Graphs?

Line graphs are good for exploring data collected for many types of experiments. Using line graphs is a good way to analyze the data of an experiment that are continually changing. For example, here are some data collected by a group of students investigating temperature changes. They poured hot water into a large container (container A) and cold water into a smaller container (container B). After recording the starting temperatures in each container, they placed Container B inside Container A and took measurements every 30 s until there were no more temperature changes.

Here are the data they collected shown as a chart and as a line graph. How are they similar? Which one can you interpret more easily and more quickly?

Temperatures of Container A and Container B		
Time (s)	Temperature (°C) of water in Container A	Temperature (°C) of water in Container B
0	51	0
30	45	7
60	38	14
90	33	20
120	30	22
150	29	23
180	28	24
210	27	25
240	26	26
270	26	26
300	26	26

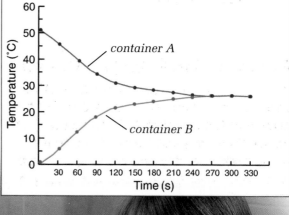

What Do You Recall about Bar Graphs?

Bar graphs are useful for displaying comparisons. For example, the chart in the next column shows the total average monthly precipitation (both snow and rain) for a city in Ontario. Compare the data in this chart with how they "look" when they are reorganized in the form of a bar graph. Which can you interpret more easily and more quickly?

Month	Total Average Precipitation (mm)
January	50.4
February	46.0
March	61.1
April	70.0
May	66.0
June	67.1
July	71.4
August	76.8
September	63.5
October	61.8
November	62.7
December	64.7

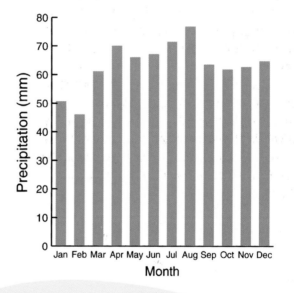

Hints

Scales for bar graphs are often rounded off to the nearest whole number.

What Do You Recall about Circle (Pie) Graphs?

A circle graph is useful when you want to display data that are part of a whole.
For example, in this circle graph, the "whole" is the total land area on the earth.
The "parts" are the approximate percentages of land made up by each continent.

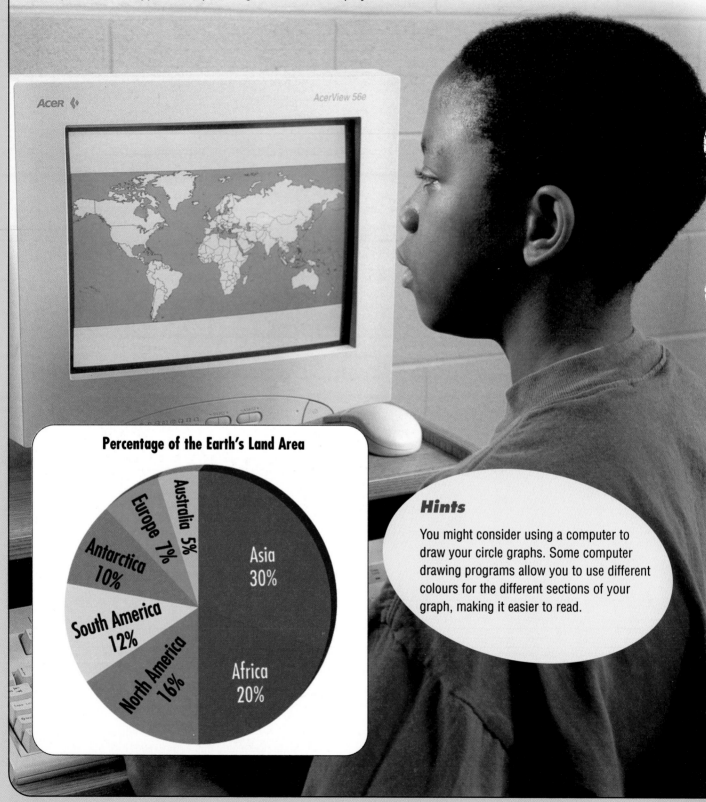

Percentage of the Earth's Land Area

Asia 30%
Africa 20%
North America 16%
South America 12%
Antarctica 10%
Europe 7%
Australia 5%

Hints

You might consider using a computer to draw your circle graphs. Some computer drawing programs allow you to use different colours for the different sections of your graph, making it easier to read.

Compare the data in this chart with how they "looked" when they were organized in the form of a circle graph on the previous page. Which can you interpret more easily and more quickly?

Continent	Percentage of the Earth's Land Area
Asia	30%
Africa	20%
North America	16%
South America	12%
Antarctica	10%
Europe	7%
Australia	5%

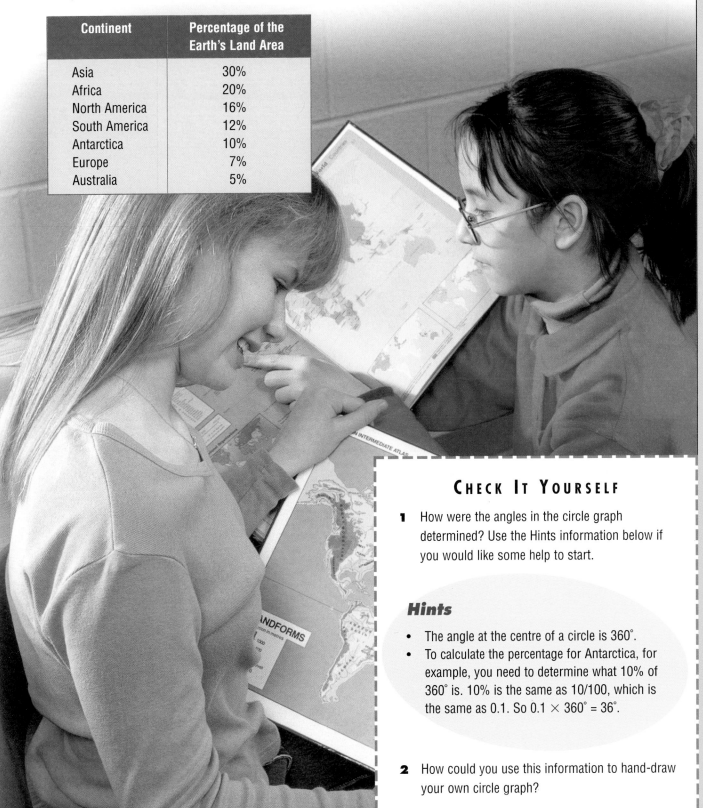

CHECK IT YOURSELF

1 How were the angles in the circle graph determined? Use the Hints information below if you would like some help to start.

Hints

- The angle at the centre of a circle is 360°.
- To calculate the percentage for Antarctica, for example, you need to determine what 10% of 360° is. 10% is the same as 10/100, which is the same as 0.1. So $0.1 \times 360° = 36°$.

2 How could you use this information to hand-draw your own circle graph?

Toolbox 7

Drawing

Have you heard the saying, "a picture's worth a thousand words"? In science, a picture can be worth even more. A carefully done drawing can help you express your ideas, record important information, and experiment with designs.

Four types of drawings you can use include: a Simple Sketch, a Technical or Scientific Drawing, an Orthographic (Perspective) Drawing, and a Computer-Assisted Drawing (CAD). Examples of each type of drawing are shown. A side view and a top view for a simple sketch are also shown. These different views can be made for each type of drawing.

Practise the four types of drawings on your own.

This photo appears in *Addison Wesley Science & Technology, Grade 7.* Practise drawing it using one or several of the drawing styles presented here. What labels would you include? Would your labelling choices change depending on the style of drawing you make?

A Simple Sketch

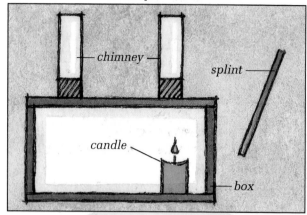

TOOLS OF THE TRADE

You will need the following equipment for each type of drawing.

Hand-drawing tools
- a sharp pencil or mechanical pencil
- a pencil sharpener or extra leads
- an eraser
- a ruler

For simple drawings
- blank, white paper

For technical and orthographic drawing
- blank graph paper

For computer-assisted drawing
- blank diskette
- access to computer and software

A Simple Sketch (Side View)

Hints

If you're going to use your drawing to help you design a structure, include a top, side, and front view.

REMEMBER!

- Give your drawing a title at the top of the page.
- Use the whole page for your drawing.
- Include only those details that are necessary, keep them simple, and identify them by name.
- If you need labels, use lines, not arrows. Place your labels in line with the feature being labelled, and use a ruler to keep your lines straight.
- Don't use colour or shading unless your teacher asks you to.
- Include notes and ideas if the sketch is a design for a structure or an invention.

An Orthographic Drawing

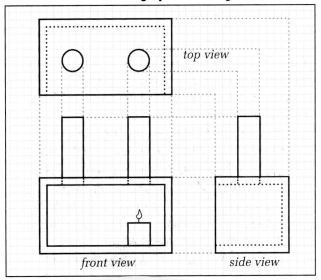

top view

front view   side view

Hints

You can use the squares of graph paper to make the scale of your orthographic drawing accurate. For example, suppose that each square stood for 1 cm. If what you're drawing is 14 cm long, you would use 14 squares to represent its length.

A Simple Sketch (Top View)

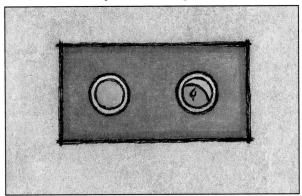

A Computer-Aided Drawing (CAD)

Hints

One advantage of using a computer is that you can easily change your work. After saving your original, practise making changes and moving the image around.

Isometric Drawing

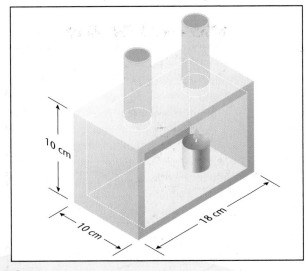

10 cm

10 cm

18 cm

Hints

Isometric drawings use actual measurements to produce 3-D scale drawings.

Toolbox 8

Visual Tools

Many people find it helpful to view, share, gather, and explore information in the form of pictures or diagrams. You have probably learned and used several of the techniques shown here. Try out the ones that are less familiar to you. You may find that some help you open up your thinking to new and creative ways.

Comparison Matrix

Comparison Matrix Chart

		Characteristics		
Things to compare		walk	use food	talk	swim
goat	X	X	X	
tree		X		
rock				
person	X	X	X	X

This is often used to compare the characteristics or properties of a number of things. To use a comparison matrix, ask yourself questions such as:
- What things do I want to compare?
- What characteristics will I choose to compare?
- How are the things I'm comparing similar and how are they different?

Hints

This technique can be useful for brainstorming.

Venn Diagram

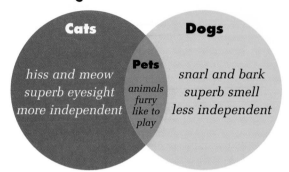

Cats hiss and meow superb eyesight more independent

Pets animals furry like to play

Dogs snarl and bark superb smell less independent

This is often used to compare two things. To use a Venn diagram, ask yourself questions such as:
- What things do I want to compare?
- What do they have in common?
- In what ways are they different?

Hints

You can use Venn diagrams to compare more than two things. Try it and see!

Concept Map

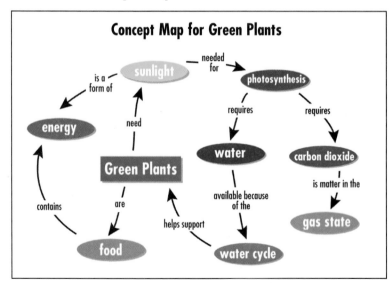

Concept Map for Green Plants

sunlight — is a form of → energy; sunlight — needed for → photosynthesis; energy — contains; photosynthesis — requires → water; photosynthesis — requires → carbon dioxide; Green Plants — need → sunlight; Green Plants — are → food; water — available because of the → water cycle; carbon dioxide — is matter in the → gas state; water cycle — helps support → Green Plants

A concept map, or a mind map, is a kind of web diagram with many uses. For example, you can use it to:
- review something you already know
- gather information about something you don't know

- explore new ways of thinking about something
- outline plans for an essay, a song, an experiment, a design challenge, a science project, and multimedia presentations

To use a concept map, ask yourself questions such as:
- What is the key idea, word, question, problem, or issue to build the map around?
- What words, ideas, objects, or questions come to mind when I think about the item at the centre of my map?

Tree Diagram

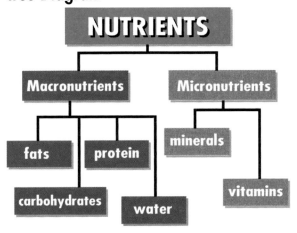

Tree diagrams allow you to see how things originate or how larger things can be broken down into their smaller components. Tree diagrams also allow you to organize or group concepts and things. Knowing about the parts of something helps you to better understand the concept or thing you are studying.

Stem-and-Leaf Plots

Are they graph-like charts, or are they chart-like graphs? Either way, a stem-and-leaf plot helps you summarize numerical information. For example, these numbers are the marks a group of students got on a recent science test.

97 75 69 80 61 69 67 75 81 72
70 58 94 77 66 87 72 80 75 55

To summarize this information with a stem-and-leaf plot, you do this.

1 Ignore the last digit of each number, and list the first digits in order in a vertical column.

Stem	Leaf
5	
6	
7	
8	
9	

2 The first number is 97. Since the last digit is 7, write a 7 beside the 9. The second number is 75. Write a 5 beside the 7.

Stem	Leaf
5	
6	
7	5
8	
9	7

3 Repeat step 2 for the remaining numbers.

CHECK IT YOURSELF

1 Based on the stem-and-leaf plot you just made, how many students got a mark of 75? How many got a mark of 80 or more? Which mark occurred most often?

2 Could you have answered these questions as quickly or as easily without a stem-and-leaf plot?

Toolbox 9

Using a Microscope

Classroom microscopes are compound microscopes. They are called "compound" because they have two or more lenses for viewing and magnifying objects. To view an object with a microscope, light must travel through the object. For this reason, the full name for your microscope is *compound light microscope*. Usually, it's shortened by leaving the word "light" out.

Before using a microscope, make sure you are familiar with its different parts and their uses. Take a look at the diagram below to remind yourself. Notice the path that light takes through a microscope to your eye.

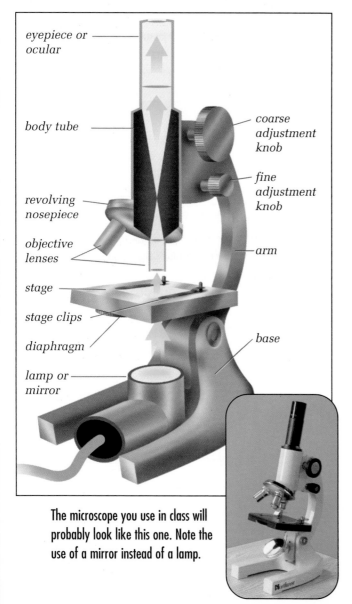

The microscope you use in class will probably look like this one. Note the use of a mirror instead of a lamp.

How to Use the Microscope

1 Plug in the microscope and turn on the light source. If your microscope uses a mirror instead of a lamp, be very careful *not* to reflect direct sunlight into the microscope. You could badly damage your eyes.

2 Rotate the objective lenses until the low-power objective lens (the smallest one) is pointing at the stage.

3 Place your slide on the stage. Use the stage clips to hold your slide in place.

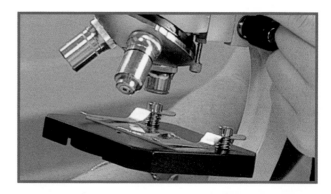

4 Watch the stage from one side of the microscope. Carefully turn the coarse adjustment knob until the lens is as close to the slide as possible without touching it. Make sure you don't hit the slide with the lens.

5 Look through the eyepiece. Slowly turn the coarse adjustment knob to move the lens away from the stage. This will focus the image.

6 Use the fine adjustment knob to sharpen the focus of the image.

7 When your slide is in focus, try using the medium-power objective lens. Watch from the side of the microscope. Carefully rotate the nosepiece  to move the medium-power lens so that it points at the stage. You should hear a "click" when it is in place. Use the fine adjustment knob to focus the image.

> **Caution!**
> **Never use the coarse adjustment knob with the medium- and high-power objective lenses.**

8 When your slide is once more in focus, try using the high-power objective lens. Repeat step 7 to change the lens from medium to high power. Make sure you watch from the side of the microscope to avoid hitting the slide with the lens.

Handling Hints

When using and handling a microscope, be sure to follow these rules:

- Always use both hands to hold and carry a microscope. Support its base with one hand and hold it by the arm with your other hand.
- Place your microscope away from the edge of your desk or work area. Except for your Science Journal, writing tools, and microscope-related equipment such as glass slides, keep your desk or work area clear and neat.
- When you aren't using your microscope, always keep it in an upright position.
- Always hold glass slides by their edges, between your thumb and forefinger.
- Try keeping both eyes open when you look through the microscope. You'll be able to observe longer without tiring the muscles around your eyes.

- When you are finished using your microscope, switch back to the low-power objective, put its plastic cover on, and return it to the place where you got it.

Drawing Hints

Here are some basic guidelines for drawing what you see through the microscope. Your teacher may have other suggestions as well.

1 Start with a sharp pencil and a blank, unlined piece of paper (or a clean page in your Science Journal). Use the whole page for your drawing.

2 Using a mathematical compass, draw a circle with a diameter of 10 cm to 12 cm. This represents the view you see through the eyepiece. Scientists call it a *field of view*, or just *field* for short.

3 Draw only what you see. Keep your details simple and straightforward. (You don't need to add colouring or shading.)

4 Add labels that identify features by name (if you know them) or with brief notes. Always draw your label lines with a ruler. Arrange your labels and label lines clearly and neatly on the page. Record which objective lens you used to observe the image.

5 Give your drawing a title at the top of the page.

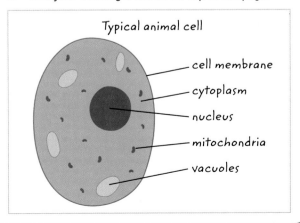

Typical animal cell
— cell membrane
— cytoplasm
— nucleus
— mitochondria
— vacuoles

TOOLBOX

Researching Topics

Research involves finding out something about a topic or subject. That means going to certain resources that will give you *accurate* information. And where can you find these resources? Well, information can be found just about anywhere: from your home bookshelves to the public library, from asking experts to looking on the Internet. Here are the steps you need to follow when you do your research.

Choosing a Topic

In some situations your teacher may give you the topic to research. Other times, you will have to select one of your own. If you have trouble coming up with a topic, try brainstorming ideas either by yourself or with a group. Remember, when you brainstorm, there are no right or wrong answers, just "ideas." Here are some brainstorming suggestions to get you started:

- List two or three general topics about science that interest you.
- For each topic, write down as many words or ideas that relate to that topic. They don't have to be directly connected to science. (Just spend a few minutes.)
- Share your list with others and ask them to suggest other possibilities.
- Now you have to "filter" your idea list to find a topic to research. In other words, go through your ideas until you find two or three that interest you. To help

you narrow your idea list, try grouping similar words or ideas, modifying what you've written, or even writing down a new idea. Sometimes, too, working with other people will help to focus your thoughts.

- When you settle on an idea for your topic, write it down. Try to explain it in a couple of sentences or a short paragraph. Do that for each of your two or three topic ideas.
- Have your teacher approve your topics. Now you're ready to go!

The next thing you have to do is settle on one topic. (Remember, you should start your research with two or three topic ideas.) One way to help you decide is to determine how easy it will be to find information on your topic.

- Use some of the resources listed on the next page to do your research.
- If you can't easily find at least *four* references for a topic, consider dropping it and going on to the next idea.

Hint

Sometimes topics are too broad in scope or too general to make good research reports (for example, "transportation" instead of just "bicycles"). Try rewriting your topic to narrow its focus.

Which Topic Should I Choose?

"How does product design help sell a product?"

"How do gears improve the performance of a bicycle?"

How Hard Will It be to Find Information?

How Camera Lenses Are Manufactured

How Mirrors Are Used in Some Optical Devices

If all the topics are easy to research, then you'll need some other criteria to help you decide.

- Which of your topics interest you the most?
- Which topic is *not* being researched by many students in your class?
- Which topics interest you the least? (eliminate them)

Once you've finally chosen your topic, you might want to work with other students and your teacher to:

- finalize its wording
- make sure it matches the project or assignment you are doing

Finding Information

There are many resources that you can use to look up information. Here is a suggested list. You'll find some of these resources:

- in your school
- in your community (such as your public library)
- on the Internet
- in CD-ROM encyclopedias and databases

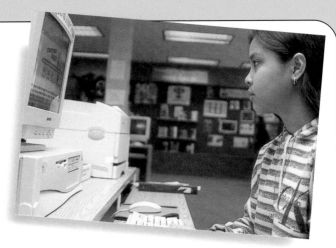

Resource	✓	Details
Books		
Library Catalogue		
CD ROMs		
Community Professionals or Experts		
Encyclopedias		
Films		
Government Agencies (local, provincial, and federal)		
Internet Sites		
Journals		
Laser Disks		
Newspapers		
Non-profit Organizations		
Posters		
Videos		

Searching Tips

Finding Information at Your Library

Library computer catalogues are a fast way to find books on the subjects you are researching. Most of these electronic catalogues have four ways to search: *subject, author, title,* and *key words*. If you know the *author* or *title* of a book, just type it in. Otherwise, use the *subject* and *key words* searches to find books on your topic.

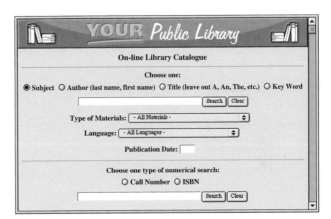

- If you're doing a *subject* search, type in the main topic you are researching. For example, if you're searching for information on solar energy, type in "solar energy." If there are no books on that topic, try again using a more general category, like "renewable resources," or just "energy."
- If you're doing a *key words* search, type in any combination of words that have to do with your topic. For the solar energy example, you could type in words such as: "renewable energy sun solar panels." Using several key words will give you a more specific search. Using only one or two key words, like "sun" and "energy," will give you a more general search.

Hint

The library may also have a way to search for magazine articles. This is called a *periodical search*. It's especially useful for searching for information on events and/or discoveries that have taken place recently. Ask your librarian how to do a periodical search.

Also, your library will probably have a reference section where all the encyclopedias are kept. There you may find science and technology, environmental, or even animal encyclopedias, as well as other reference books.

Finding Information on the Internet

On the Internet, you can use searching programs, called *search engines*, to search the Internet on just about any subject. To find a search engine, ask your teacher or click on the search icon found at the top of your Internet browser. Here are some suggestions on how to search the Internet:

- Once you reach a search engine Web page, type in key words or phrases that have to do with your topic, then press enter. For solar energy, you could type in "solar energy," "solar panels," "renewable resources," or any combination of these and other similar words.

- The search engine will display a list of Web pages it has found that have these words or phrases somewhere in them. Click on any Web page on the list that looks interesting.

- Quite often you will get a long list of possible Web pages to look at. You may need to make your search more specific. This can be done by adding other key words to your search. For example, if you were looking for solar energy examples in Canada and used the key word "solar energy," you may want to do a second search of these results with the key word "Canada" added.

- Don't forget to record the addresses of any interesting Web pages you find. Why not work with a friend? One person can record the addresses of Web pages while the other person searches on the computer. Or you can save it as a *bookmark*. Your Internet browser allows you to save Web pages for easy future access. Check with your teacher or librarian to find out how to save and organize your bookmarks.

You are here: <u>Home</u> > Search

Search the Web: Advanced Search

`solar energy`   **Search**

<u>Automotive</u>   <u>Computers</u>   <u>Health</u>
<u>Business</u>   <u>Education</u>   <u>Internet</u>
<u>Careers</u>   <u>Entertainment</u>   <u>Kids & Family</u>
<u>Communications</u>   <u>The Good Life</u>   <u>News</u>
                                       <u>Personal Finance</u>
                                       <u>Shopping</u>
                                       <u>Sports</u>
                                       <u>Travel</u>
                                       <u>What's New</u>

Searching THE WEB

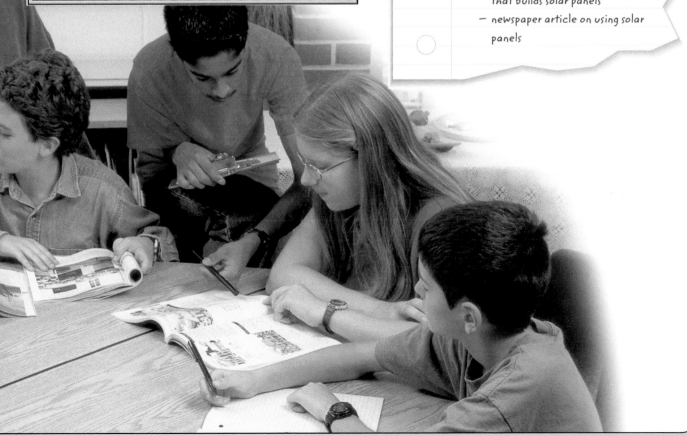

Web search results

1 - 10 of 478 results most relevant to solar energy > Canada

Next 10 > | Hide Summaries | Sort by date | Ungroup results

Contacting Any Company Inc. (Solar Energy Cell, Module, and Off-Grid, renewable...
Any Company Inc. is a Canadian company based in _____,
Alberta, which develops world class solar cells, solar modules,
and complete solar...
100% **Date: 7 Sep____**, Size 10.0K,
http://www.anycompany/contact/contactus.htm
Find similar pages | Grouped results from www.anycompany.com

SESCI Home Page
A Voice for Conservation and Renewable Energy in Canada. Pour
promouvoir l'usage optimal des nergie renouvelables. The new
sites may be incomplete and inconsistent. We would appreciate
any suggestions you might...
90% **Date: 3 Dec____**, Size 3.1K,
http://www.web.net/sustenergy/sesci.html
Find similar pages

Other Resources
Here are a few addresses and links where you can get more information about renewable energies. The following list is provided for
information only. Please e-mail if you notice inaccuracies.
Their main web...
87% **Date: 10 Nov____**, Size 3.1K,
http://dial.uwaterloo.ca/~watsun/res.htm
Find similar pages

GBIC - International Organizations - Links
Organizations listed below are generally related to environmental,
energy and advanced technology issues in the building sector -
for advanced small residential houses - British Columbia Building
Corporation R & D arm of Canada Mortgage and Housing
Corporation Canada Institute for....
81% **Date: 23 Sep____**, Size 23.2K,
http://greenbuilding.ca/abc-org.html
Find similar pages

Next 10 >

Organizing Information

Once you've collected your information, you need to
organize it before you start writing your report. Make an
outline of what you will say in your report. Identify for
each section of the outline how you will use the
information you have collected. For example, your solar
energy outline might look like this:

> Solar Energy Report Outline
> 1. What is solar energy?
>   – information from encyclopedia on
>   solar energy
>   – print out from energy CD-ROM
>   – textbook
> 2. Impact on the environment of using
>   solar energy
>   – phone call notes from Ministry of
>   Environment
>   – magazine article on solar energy
> 3. Canadian examples
>   – internet examples from company
>   that builds solar panels
>   – newspaper article on using solar
>   panels

TOOLBOX

A

alveoli tiny air-filled sacs in the lungs surrounded by blood vessels

amplitude height of the wave from its middle rest position to its highest point

angle of incidence angle between the incoming ray and the normal

angle of reflection angle between the reflected ray and the normal

antibiotic substance made from micro-organisms that can be used to kill other micro-organisms; e.g., penicillin

aperture hole or opening that lets in light in a camera

Archimedes' Principle buoyant force acting on an object equals the weight, or force of gravity, of the fluid displaced by the object

Archimedes screw spiral-shaped pump supposedly invented by Archimedes to remove water from the hold of a ship

area measurement of a surface in square units (cm^2, m^2, etc.)

arteries tube-like blood vessels that take blood away from the heart, transporting it to other parts of the body

average density average of all the densities of the different substances that exist within a given volume; a measure of the density of an object made of different substances

B

balanced forces opposite and equal forces acting on an object; when an object is at rest, the forces acting on it are balanced

bathyscaph a diving vessel used for deep-sea exploration

binoculars device for viewing distant objects; made up of two short refracting telescopes fitted together

brackish water fresh water mixed with salt water; the salinity here is higher than in fresh water, but lower than in the open ocean

breeze convection current caused by warmed air rising and cooler air moving in to take its place

bubble chart organizer with a key word or idea in the centre of a bubble; around this centre bubble are additional bubbles labelled: *Who? What? Where? When?* and *Why?*

bubble method determines viscosity of a liquid; a measurement of how long it takes an air bubble to rise through a tube of fluid

buoyant force (buoyancy) upward force that a liquid exerts on an object; opposite to the pull of gravity on an object in a liquid

C

capillaries thin, hair-like vessels connecting arteries and veins; capillary tissue is only one cell thick

cell membrane layer of a plant or animal cell that surrounds the cell contents; it allows substances to pass in and out of the cell

cells basic unit of a living organism that can perform all the processes associated with life

cell specialization cells in different parts of the body having special features that enable them to perform specific functions

cholesterol fatty substance; if there is too much in the body, it can form deposits in arteries

climate average weather measured over a long period of time

cold surface currents currents that move from polar or temperate areas to tropical areas

compound light microscope microscope that has two or more lenses and uses a lamp or mirror to provide light for viewing the object

compound machine tool or device made up of two or more simple machines

compression result when a force pushes on an object

compressor device that compresses the gases in a pneumatic system

concave lens piece of transparent material that is thinner in the middle than at the edges; it diverges or spreads out light rays passing through it

concave mirror reflecting surface that is curved inward like the inside of a bowl or a spoon; light rays reflected from it converge or come together

condensation change of state from a gas to a liquid

cones specialized cells in the retina that help us see; there are three types of cones, each sensitive to different ranges of colours: red, green, and blue

Continental Divide highest point of land on a continent; rivers flow into different oceans depending on where they are located relative to this point

continental glaciers glaciers that cover vast areas of land

continental shelf land that extends out from the edge of a continent below the ocean's surface

convection currents movement of a fluid, such as air or water, that occurs due to temperature differences in the fluid

convex lens piece of transparent material that is thicker in the middle than at the edges; it converges or brings together light rays passing through it

convex mirror reflecting surface that bulges out like the back of a spoon; light rays reflected from it diverge or spread out

cover slip small piece of glass or plastic that covers a specimen on a slide

currents streams of water that move within a larger body of water

cut-away view shows hidden details of an object or device

density mass per unit of volume; measured by dividing the mass of a substance by its volume

diaphragm part that changes the size of a camera's aperture; it varies the amount of light that reaches the film

diaphragm pump uses a flexible membrane to pump liquids or gases

diffusion movement of particles from an area where there are more of these particles to an area where there are fewer of them

downwelling surface water moving toward an ocean coast "piles up" and then sinks; downwelling brings warm, oxygen-rich water into the deeper layers of the ocean

drumlins small hills with a distinctive tapering shape that form when a glacier moves over moraines that had formed earlier; the tip of the drumlin points in the direction that the glacier was moving

efficiency comparison (usually in percent) that describes how much easier it is to do something with a mechanism or device compared with not using that mechanism or device; the more energy that is lost in a machine, the less efficient the mechanism is; expressed as a percentage less than 100%, which represents a machine with no friction

electromagnetic radiation all forms of radiant energy: visible light, infrared radiation, ultraviolet radiation, radio waves, X-rays, etc.

ergonomics study of how people use devices in their environment in order to make these devices more efficient

eskers deposits of sand and gravel in the pattern of a winding river that form when parts of a glacier melt

estuary where fresh water from rivers and streams mixes with the salt water of the ocean; many different kinds of plants, animals, and insects that can tolerate the brackish water live here

evaporation change of state from a liquid to a gas

exploded view shows all the parts of the device pulled or exploded apart

eyepiece lens or set of lenses in a microscope or telescope that is closest to the user's eye

feedback information that changes the output of a system

fibre optics thin, flexible tubing with an inner surface that reflects light; used in optical devices

field of view entire area of a specimen you can see through a microscope

film material that is sensitive to light; used in optical devices to record an image

fiords long, narrow bays that have high banks on either side

flood plain area flooded when a river overflows its banks; flood plains are a natural part of a river system

flow rate how fast a liquid moves through a tube; used to measure viscosity of a liquid

fluid any matter that has no fixed shape, can flow, and takes the shape of its container; any substance in a gas or liquid state

fluorescent form of artificial light; uses ultraviolet light waves to make the coating inside an opaque tube glow white

force push or pull that tends to cause an object to move; measured in newtons (N)

freezing change of state from a liquid to a solid

frequency number of times a wave source or medium vibrates in a given unit of time

friction force that opposes motion

gamma rays high-energy electromagnetic radiation; used to treat some types of cancer

gas physical state of matter where a substance has no definite shape or volume

glaciers large moving bodies of ice that form part of the water cycle; glaciers can be many metres or even kilometres thick

Grand Banks shallow ocean waters off the coast of Newfoundland that are warmed by the Gulf Stream; it is rich in marine life

gravity force trying to pull an object down to the centre of the earth

groundwater water that soaks into the ground, collecting in the spaces between grains of soil and in cracks in underground rocks

Gulf Stream an example of a warm surface current; warm Atlantic water from around the equator flows into the Gulf of Mexico and then up past the coast of eastern North America; it eventually flows past the west coasts of England and Scandinavia

heart organ that acts as a hydraulic pump for the circulatory system; pumps blood throughout the body; has a squeezing (contracting) action followed by a relaxing action

hidden details drawing shows what's inside an object; there are three ways to make a hidden details drawing; see-through drawings, sectional drawings, and drawings with dotted lines to outline the hidden details

high tide highest water level along the ocean coast

humidity measure of how much water is in the air

hydraulic system device that uses hydraulics to move or lift objects; uses liquids in a confined space to transfer forces; operates on Pascal's law

hydrometer device that measures the density of a liquid

hypothesis possible answer to a question or possible explanation for a situation or phenomenon

Ice Ages a time when large parts of the earth were covered with glaciers; much of Canada's geography was shaped by these huge sheets of ice

incandescent form of artificial light; uses electrical energy to heat a thin wire thread that glows a yellowish white

incident ray ray of light that arrives at a mirror or enters a substance

infrared rays electromagnetic waves that have less energy than visible light; a hot object gives off infrared waves as does the sun

innovation an improvement to an existing device

input information that goes into a system

input force force applied to a mechanism

interdependent depending on one another—here this refers to the concept that the body's organ systems depend on one another to function

intertidal zone shoreline along the ocean coast; it is rich in animal and plant life

invention new device or item that someone has created

invisible spectrum portion of the electromagnetic spectrum that the human eye cannot see

iris band of muscle in your eye that controls the size of the pupil and the amount of light entering your eye

kettle lake small round lake formed when large chunks of ice left behind by the glacier melted away

Labrador Current cold water current that flows southward between Greenland and Baffin Island and Labrador; it affects eastern Canada and the United States

lake-effect snow large snowfalls caused by dry, cold arctic air passing over the warmer water of the lakes

land breeze convection current that blows off the land and onto the water

laser light acronym for **l**ight **a**mplification by the **s**timulated **e**mission of **r**adiation; beam of light whose waves all have the same frequency and move in step and in the same direction; able to travel long distances without spreading out

law of reflection angle of incidence of a wave hitting a surface equals the angle of reflection

leaves plant organs where photosynthesis occurs

lens piece of glass or other transparent material that either brings together or spreads light rays passing through it; has two opposite surfaces, either both curved or one plane and one curved

light intensity amount of light arriving per unit area at a place

limnetic zone deeper open water area of a lake that still has light penetration; phytoplankton are food for the fish that live there

liquid physical state of matter where a substance has a definite volume but no definite shape

lithosphere hard outer layer of the earth that is made of solid rock broken into huge plates

littoral zone the shore of a lake to the location where aquatic plants stop growing

low tide lowest water level along the ocean coast

luminous objects that give out light; for example, the sun, light bulb, fire, etc.

magnified drawing shows details that would be too small to see

marine description of anything related to the ocean

marrow tissue in bones that makes red blood cells

mass measurement of the amount of matter or number of particles that are in an object

mechanical advantage comparison of the amount of force needed when a device is used for a task with the amount of force needed without using the device; *output force* divided by the *input force*

melanin dark substance in skin that helps block ultraviolet light

melting change of state from a solid to a liquid

microscope optical device that magnifies (enlarges) the image of small objects; has at least two lenses: the objective lens and the eyepiece lens

microwaves electromagnetic radiation that has a shorter wavelength than radio waves but carries more energy; used to cook food and transmit audio and video signals

mirage optical illusion of floating images in the distance produced by refraction of light in different layers of air

moraines land formation that forms from rocks and gravel that build up along the sides and at the end of the glacier

model small-scale version of an object, device, building, etc.; used to clarify and test a design

multicellular having or being made up of two or more cells; most plants and animals are examples

mycoplasma group of smallest organisms that scientists have discovered so far

natural resources things in the natural environment that we use to meet our needs and wants

non-luminous objects that do not give out light but may reflect it (for example, the moon); most objects on earth are non-luminous

normal line perpendicular to a surface (that is, forms a 90° angle with the surface)

objective lens lens in an optical device, such as a microscope or telescope, that gathers light from an object to form an image

oceanic zone deepest parts of the ocean beyond the continental shelves; much of this water receives no light at all, and since it is also far from shore, not as many nutrients are available for plants

opaque describes materials that do not allow light to pass through; for example, wood, metal, cardboard, etc.

organ group of different types of tissues that work together to perform a function

organelles small structures that work within a cell performing specific functions for the cell

organ system group of organs that work together to perform a function

osmosis movement of water particles through a selectively permeable membrane from an area of higher concentration to an area of lower concentration

output results or end product of a system

output force force produced from using a mechanism

ozone form of oxygen; a layer of ozone gas high up in the atmosphere protects the earth from too much ultraviolet radiation from outer space

paramecium type of one-celled animal; easy to see with a compound microscope; plural is *paramecia*

Particle Theory of Matter theory that explains the behaviour of solids, liquids, and gases; it states that all matter is made up of tiny moving particles that attract each other and have spaces between them

Pascal's law when pressure is applied to a liquid in a container, the pressure and force is transmitted equally and undiminished throughout the liquid; an enclosed liquid transmits pressure equally in all directions; as an equation: $p = F/A$, where p is pressure, F is force, and A is area

pasteurization process of slightly heating a food to kill harmful micro-organisms; named after its inventor, Louis Pasteur

penicillin germ-killing substance developed from the mould *Penicillium notatum*; it is the world's first known antibiotic

photosynthesis process by which plants use light energy, carbon dioxide, and water to make their own food

phytoplankton microscopic plants that live in the upper part of the ocean; many marine animals feed on these plants

piston pump uses a cylinder, called a piston, to pump liquids or gases

plane mirror flat mirror; reflecting surface has no curvature

plate tectonics theory that explains the formation of the major surface features of the earth

pneumatic system uses a gas in a confined space to transmit forces; operates on Pascal's law

point of incidence point where a light ray arrives at a mirror or enters a substance

precipitation solid (ice, snow) or liquid water that falls from clouds

pressure a measure of the amount of force applied to a particular area; measured in Pascals (Pa)

prevailing winds strong, steady winds that always blow in the same direction around the world

primary colours of light red, green, and blue light; adding these three colours of light produces white light

prism a block of transparent material that has triangular bases and rectangular sides; used to refract light, causing white light to split into the colours of the spectrum

profundal zone deepest water of a lake; no light penetrates this zone, so no plants grow here

pupil opening in the eye that lets in light

radio waves electromagnetic radiation used in communications around the world

rainbow band of colours across the sky that is produced by raindrops acting like prisms and splitting light into colours of the visible spectrum

ramp method determines viscosity of a liquid; a measurement of how long it takes a fluid to flow down a ramp

ray box device that produces one or more rays or beams of light

ray diagram diagram used to represent how light travels; each ray has an arrow to show the direction of travel

red blood cells cells that can carry oxygen to all the cells of the body

refracted ray ray that passes through a material having travelled through a different material

refraction bending of light as it travels from one material to another

reservoir part of a river that is dammed to form a lake

retina special lining on the back of your eye; when light hits the retina, receptor cells send messages to the brain, which are translated into an image

robot mechanical device that can do some of the work of humans

root portion of the plant that usually grows below the surface of the soil; keeps the plant in place and absorbs water and nutrients from the soil

rotary pump uses gears to pump liquids at a higher than normal pressure

salinity the amount of salt in water

sea breeze convection current that blows off the water and onto the land

secondary colours of light yellow, cyan, and magenta; colours made from adding any two primary colours of light

sectional drawing shows what you would see if you cut a slice through an object or device

see-through drawing shows what you would see if the outside casing of an object were transparent

selectively permeable allowing certain substances, but not others, to pass through; cell membranes are examples

shadow area of reduced light created whenever an opaque object blocks the path of light

shutter part that acts like a door to control the amount of light entering a camera

simple machine tool or device made up of one basic machine (lever, pulley, gear, etc.)

smallpox disease that produces a rash and high fever that can cause blindness and death; this is the first disease to be controlled by a vaccine

solid physical state of matter where a substance has a definite volume and a definite shape

specialized cells cells in different parts of the body having special features that enable them to perform specific functions

speed measurement of how fast something is moving

stability how reliable a system is

stem part of the plant that grows above the surface of the soil; provides support and transports water and nutrients to and from the leaves

stomata small, pocket-like openings on a leaf that allow water and gases to pass in and out; singular is *stoma*

swells waves in the open water far from shore

symmetry objects that have the same features on both sides of an imaginary centre line, as mirror images of one another

system set of parts or things that forms a complete unit; for example, a stage lighting system

telescope device for viewing distant objects; there are two types: reflecting and refracting telescopes

theory of colour addition theory that explains what happens when coloured lights are mixed together

theory of colour subtraction theory that explains what happens when coloured pigments (paints) are mixed together; each primary colour of pigment absorbs, or subtracts, a primary colour of light and reflects the other two

thermal pollution heated water from industries entering a river, lake, or ocean

thumbnail sketch rough, hand-drawn diagram

tidal basin major indentation in the coastline

tidal range difference between high and low ocean tide

tide change in the ocean water level

tissue group of the same type of cells that work together to perform a specific function

translucent describes materials that allow some light to pass through

transparent describes materials that allow light to pass through with little or no reflection; for example, glass

trenches deep ocean valleys

ultraviolet light electromagnetic waves that have more energy than visible light; most ultraviolet radiation is absorbed by the earth's ozone layer; too much ultraviolet radiation can increase the risk of skin cancer

unicellular having or being made up of only a single cell; most microscopic organisms are examples

upwelling deep, cold ocean water moving up to the surface; the cold water meeting warm air causes fog to form; areas of upwelling are important fishing areas because the cooler water is rich in nutrients

vaccine something that is taken by or injected into an animal or person to produce an immunity to a disease; usually prepared from a mild form of the disease

valley glaciers glaciers that spread down between the peaks of high valleys

valve device that controls the flow of fluids

veins *in animals*: tube-like blood vessels that transport blood from the organs back to the heart; *in plants*: bundles of tubes that transport water and nutrients

velocity measurement of how fast something is moving *and* in what direction it is travelling

velocity ratio represents the *Ideal Mechanical Advantage* of a machine if friction did not exist; equals the *input distance* divided by the *output distance*

viscosity a liquid's internal resistance or friction that keeps it from flowing

visible light spectrum colours of visible light; the colours in a rainbow or seen when light is split by a prism

warm surface currents currents that flow from tropical areas to cooler or temperate areas

water cycle movement of water through different states of matter

watershed area of land that drains into one main lake or river

water table underground boundary between the area where all the spaces between the soil are full of water and the area where there is a mixture of soil, air, and water

water vapour water in the atmosphere that is in the gas state

wavelength distance between the top or peak of one wave to the peak of the next

wave model of light model used to explain the characteristics and behaviour of light energy; it describes light as energy in the form of waves; the different colours of light have different wavelengths; waves with shorter wavelengths have higher energy

weight measure of the force of gravity on an object

well hole in the ground into which water from the soil drains

wet mount microscope slide that is made by placing a specimen in a drop of water and covering with a small piece of glass or plastic

X-rays high-energy electromagnetic radiation; can be used to make images of the interior of the body

zones layers of water in an ocean or lake that have distinct characteristics, such as temperature and the amount of oxygen and light

PHOTO CREDITS AND ACKNOWLEDGMENTS

The publisher wishes to thank the following sources for photographs, illustrations, and other materials used in this book. Care has been taken to determine and locate ownership of copyright material in this text. We will gladly receive information enabling us to rectify any errors or omissions in credits.

Photography

(Cover) J. Feingersh, First Image/ **p. 1** (top) Cabisco, Visuals Unlimited/ **p. 1** (centre) Mark Harmel, Tony Stone Images/ **p. 1** (bottom) Yorgas Nikas,Tony Stone Images/ **p. 2** (top) Corel Stock Photo Library/ **p. 2** (inset) F. Widdel, Visuals Unlimited/ **p. 2** (bottom) NASA/ **p. 3** NASA/ **p. 4** (left) Corbis-Bettmann/ **p. 4** (right) Corbis, Lester V. Bergman/ **p. 5** (top left) Andrew Syred, Tony Stone Images/ **p. 5** (top centre) George Lepp, Tony Stone Images/ **p. 5** (top right) Pete Turner, The Image Bank/ **p. 5** (bottom left) John Fowler, Valan Photos/ **p. 5** (bottom centre) Gary Morrison, Tony Stone Images/ **p. 5** (bottom right) Gavriel Jecan, Tony Stone Images/ **p. 6** (top) Alan Thornton, Tony Stone Images/ **p. 6** (bottom) Ray Boudreau/ **p. 7** Ray Boudreau/ **p. 8** Yorgos Nikas, Tony Stone Images/ **p. 9** Corel Stock Photo Library/ **p. 10** (top) Corel Stock Photo Library/ **p. 10** (bottom) Med. Illus. SBHA/Tony Stone Images/ **p. 11** Ray Boudreau/ **p. 12** Corel Stock Photo Library/ **p. 14** Baron Wolman, Tony Stone Images/ **p. 16** Corel Stock Photo Library/ **p. 17** (top) Cabisco, Visuals Unlimited/ **p. 17** (centre) Cabisco, Visuals Unlimited/ **p. 17** (bottom) Phototake, First Light/ **p. 18** Ray Boudreau/ **p. 19** Ray Boudreau/ **p. 20** Corbis/ **p. 21** (top row) Corel Stock Photo Library/ **p. 21** (bottom left) Corel Stock Photo Library/ **p. 21** (bottom centre) M. Abbey, Visuals Unlimited/ **p. 21** (bottom right) Corel Stock Photo Library/ **p. 22** (top) Dennis Kunkel, CNRI/Phototake/First Light/ **p. 22** (bottom) Ray Boudreau/ **p. 23** Corel Stock Photo Library/ **p. 24** Ray Boudreau/ **p. 25** Ottmar Bierwagen, Spectrum Stock/Ivy Images/ **p. 26** (left) David M. Phillips, Visuals Unlimited/ **p. 26** (right) Mark Carwardine, Spectrum Stock/Ivy Images/ **p. 27** (left) John Forsythe, Visuals Unlimited/ **p. 27** (right) M. Kage, Spectrum Stock/Ivy Images/ **p. 28** Ray Boudreau/ **p. 29** Ray Boudreau/ **p. 30** Robert Brons, BPS/Tony Stone Images/ **p. 31** (left) T.E. Adams, Visuals Unlimited/ **p. 31** (top right) Harold V. Green, Valan Photos/ **p. 31** (centre right) Spike Walker, Tony Stone Images/ **p. 31** (bottom right) Triarch, Visuals Unlimited/ **p. 34** Ray Boudreau/ **p. 35** (top) Corel Stock Photo Library/ **p. 35** (left centre) Mike Abbey, Visuals Unlimited/ **p. 35** (middle centre) Corel Stock Photo Library/ **p. 35** (right centre) Paul Johnson, BPS/Tony Stone Images/ **p. 35** (bottom) Bill Ivy/ **p. 36** V. Wilkinson, Valan Photos/ **p. 37** (left) Science Vu, Visuals Unlimited/ **p. 37** (right) S. Lowry, University of Ulster/Tony Stone Images/ **p. 38** Ray Boudreau/ **p. 39** Ray Boudreau/ **p. 40** Ray Boudreau/ **p. 41** Ray Boudreau/ **p. 42** Corbis-Bettmann/ **p. 44** Ray Boudreau/ **p. 45** Diane R. Nelson, Visuals Unlimited/ **p. 46** Ray Boudreau/ **p. 47** Ray Boudreau/ **p. 48** (inset) Bill Ivy/ **p. 48** (right) Ray Boudreau/ **p. 51** Phototake, First Light/ **p. 52** (top) David Becker, Tony Stone Images/ **p. 52** (bottom left) Ray Boudreau/ **p. 52** (bottom right) Visuals Unlimited/ **p. 54** (top) Mike Abbey, Visuals Unlimited/ **p. 54** (left centre) Robert Brons, BPS/Tony Stone Images/ **p. 54** (middle centre and right centre) G.W. Willis, BPS/Tony Stone Images/ **p. 54** (bottom left) Corel Stock Photo Library/ **p. 54** (bottom right) R.W. Van Norman, Visuals Unlimited/ **p. 55** (top) Samuel Lunenfeld Institute, Mount Sinai Hospital/ **p. 55** (bottom) Randy Bulmer, Samuel Lunenfeld Institute, Mount Sinai Hospital/ **p. 56** (top row) Corel Stock Photo Library/ **p. 56** (bottom left and bottom centre) Corel Stock Photo Library/ **p. 56** (bottom right) John Mitchell, Valan Photos/ **p. 57** Bill Ivy/ **p. 58** Ray Boudreau/ **p. 58** (inset) Kevin and Betty Collins, Visuals Unlimited/ **p. 59** Ray Boudreau/ **p. 61** (centre) David M. Phillips, Visuals Unlimited/ **p. 61** (top, bottom left, and bottom right) Ken Wagner, Visuals Unlimited/ **p. 63** Ray Boudreau/ **p. 64** Ray Boudreau/ **p. 65** (left) Alan Altair, The Image Bank/ **p. 65** (centre) Steve Satushek, The Image Bank/ **p. 65** (right) Cabisco, Visuals Unlimited/ **p. 66** S. Lowry, University of Ulster/Tony Stone Images/ **p. 67** Ray Boudreau/ **p. 68** Corel Stock Photo Library/ **p. 71** Dr. Dennis Kunkel, Phototake/First Light/ **p. 72** (top) Bill Ivy/ **p. 72** (centre) Corel Stock Photo Library/ **p. 72** (bottom) Robert Brons, BPS/Tony Stone Images/ **p. 73** (top) Stan Flegler, Visuals Unlimited/ **p. 73** (bottom left) David Becker, Tony Stone Images/ **p. 73** (bottom centre) Dr. Dennis Kunkel, Phototake/First Light/ **p. 73** (bottom right) John Cardmore, BPS/Tony Stone Images/ **p. 74** (top left) Tracy Frankel, The Image Bank/ **p. 74** (top right) "Canada's Food Guide to Healthy Eating, 1992," Health Canada. Reproduced with permission of the Minister of Public Works and Government Services Canada, 1999./ **p. 74** (bottom) Ray Boudreau/ **p. 76** Corbis-Bettmann/ **p. 77** (left) Archive Photos/ **p. 77** (centre) Bill Ivy/ **p. 77** (right) Bill Ivy/ **p. 77** (bottom) Ray Boudreau/ **p. 78** Ray Boudreau/ **p. 79** (top to bottom) Mike Abbey, Visuals Unlimited/ Mike Abbey, Visuals Unlimited/ Mike Abbey, Visuals Unlimited/ Jack Bostrack, Visuals Unlimited/ Luke A. Marshall, Helicobacter Foundation/ **p. 81** Keith Lennox/ **p. 83** Ray Boudreau/ **p. 86** Ray Boudreau/ **p. 87** (top left) Harold V. Green, Valan Photos/ **p. 87** (centre left) A.M. Siegelman, Visuals Unlimited/ **p. 87** (bottom left) Mike Abbey, Visuals Unlimited/ **p. 87** (right) Joe McDonald, Visuals Unlimited/ **p. 89** (top) Larry J. MacDougal, First Light/ **p. 89** (centre) Corel Stock Photo Library/ **p. 89** (bottom) Ray Boudreau/ **p. 90** Ray Boudreau/ **p. 91** Ray Boudreau/ **p. 92** Ray Boudreau/ **p. 93** (top) N. McKee, IDRC/ **p. 93** (bottom) Norman Piluke, Ivy Images/ **p. 94** (top) Larry J. MacDougal, First Light/ **p. 94** (bottom) N. McKee, IDRC/ **p. 95** (left) Alan Marsh, First Light/ **p. 95** (right) Tom Mareschal, Image Bank/ **p. 97** Ray Boudreau/ **p. 98** Ray Boudreau/ **p. 99** Ray

Museum/ **p. 392** Richard Hartmier, First Light/ **p. 394** Ray Boudreau/ **pp. 397–410** Ray Boudreau/ **p. 410** (right) David De Lossy, Image Bank/ **pp. 411–414** Ray Boudreau/ **p. 415** Greg Henkenhaf, CP Picture Archive/ **pp. 416–418** Ray Boudreau/ **p. 422–423** Ray Boudreau/ **p. 424–425** Dick Hemingway/ **p. 426–427** Ray Boudreau

The publisher wishes to thank the following teachers and schools and their students for their participation in photographic sessions:
Andrea Della Torre, Lincoln Alexander P.S., Ajax, Ontario
Karen Hume, E.A. Fairman P.S., Whitby, Ontario
Derek Totten, Parkland P.S., Markham, Ontario
Lynn Williams, Buchanan P.S., Scarborough, Ontario
Thanks are also owed to Paulette Hutchinson and Christine Pointer for their assistance.

Illustrations

Crowle Art **21, 23, 41, 43** (bottom), **51, 96, 103, 104, 130, 138, 164, 178** (margin), **187, 188, 194** (top and bottom), **203, 214, 245, 333, 347, 353, 369, 391** (both), **425, 426, 427**

John Fraser **15, 19, 32, 120, 129** (bottom), **153, 163, 217** (all), **267, 270**

Brian Hughes **all icons**

Bernadette Lau **8, 9, 10, 11, 12, 109, 322, 338, 349, 350, 355, 396**

Paul McCusker **50, 90, 91, 158, 177, 178** (bottom), **221, 283, 308**

Dave McKay **121** (top), **129** (top), **236, 243, 248, 250, 252, 253, 260, 261, 262, 263, 264, 271, 274, 282, 287, 343, 345, 356, 357, 361, 367, 368**

Allan Moon **16, 17, 33, 48, 55, 111, 118, 121** (bottom), **132, 134, 149** (top), **156, 180, 197** (bottom), **201, 206** (top and bottom), **207, 210** (bottom), **317, 324, 325, 328, 341, 342, 376, 377, 379, 385, 423** (right)

Josée Morin **72**

NSV Productions **13, 36, 60, 69, 70, 71, 80, 81, 99, 122, 125, 128, 139, 143, 144, 145, 146, 149** (bottom), **175, 179, 196, 197** (top), **210** (top), **215** (top and bottom), **216, 218, 219, 227, 228, 230, 242, 258, 272, 273, 276, 278, 286, 288, 290, 291, 294, 296, 298, 303, 319, 336, 346, 352, 354, 365** (top and bottom), **370, 371, 374** (both), **380, 386** (top and bottom), **393, 398, 414, 415, 416, 419** (top and bottom right), **420, 421, 422, 423** (left)

Dusan Petricic **42, 43** (top), **82, 224, 226, 269, 279**

Teco Rodrigues **62, 65, 66, 85, 170, 174, 234**

Angela Vaculik **57, 166, 330, 331, 332, 418, 419** (top and bottom left)